Precalculus
Mathematics for Calculus

SIXTH EDITION

James Stewart
McMaster University and University of Toronto

Lothar Redlin
The Pennsylvania State University

Saleem Watson
California State University, Long Beach

Prepared by

Douglas Shaw
University of Northern Iowa

BROOKS/COLE
CENGAGE Learning™

Australia • Brazil • Japan • Korea • Mexico • Singapore • Spain • United Kingdom • United States

ISBN-13: 978-0-8400-6883-5
ISBN-10: 0-8400-6883-2

Brooks/Cole
20 Davis Drive
Belmont, CA 94002-3098
USA

Cengage Learning is a leading provider of customized learning solutions with office locations around the globe, including Singapore, the United Kingdom, Australia, Mexico, Brazil, and Japan. Locate your local office at:
www.cengage.com/global

Cengage Learning products are represented in Canada by Nelson Education, Ltd.

To learn more about Brooks/Cole, visit
www.cengage.com/brookscole

Purchase any of our products at your local college store or at our preferred online store
www.cengagebrain.com

Printed in the United States of America
1 2 3 4 5 6 7 15 14 13 12 11

CONTENTS

Contents

PREFACE

The purpose of this *Instructor's Guide* is to save you time while helping you to teach a nice, honest, interesting, student-centered course. For each section, there are suggested additions to your lecture that can supplement (but not replace) things like the factoring of $x^2 + 3x + 2$. Lecturing is not your only option, of course. This guide provides group activities, ready for reproducing, that will allow your students to discover and explore the concepts of algebra. You may find that your classes become more "fun", but I assure you that this unfortunate by-product of an engaged student population can't always be avoided.

This guide was designed to be used with *Precalculus: Mathematics for Calculus, Sixth Edition* as a source of both supplementary and complementary material. Depending on your preference, you can either occasionally glance through the *Guide* for content ideas and alternate approaches, or you can use it as a major component in planning your day-to-day classes. In addition to lecture materials and group activities, each section has examples, sample homework assignments, and reading quizzes.

For many students, precalculus is the class where they decide whether or not they are good at math, and whether or not they like it. Therefore, teaching college algebra is an important, noble task. It is my hope that this book will make that task a little easier.

I very much value reactions from all my colleagues who are teaching from this guide, both to correct any errors and to suggest additional material for future editions. I am especially interested in which features of the guide are the most and the least useful. Please email any feedback to precalculus@dougshaw.com.

For giving me this opportunity, I thank Jim Stewart, Lothar Redlin, Saleem Watson, and Bob Pirtle. Cynthia Ashton has been a kind and patient editor, and I'm thankful for her work on this project. If you like the way this book looks, if you admire the clarity of the graphics and the smoothness of its design, join me in thanking Andy Bulman-Fleming, the best typesetter in the business.

This book is dedicated to Eric Giddens, the best math teacher in Cedar Falls, Iowa.

Douglas Shaw

HOW TO USE THE INSTRUCTOR'S GUIDE

For each section of *Precalculus: Mathematics for Calculus, Sixth Edition*, this *Instructor's Guide* provides information on the items listed below.

1. **Suggested Time and Emphasis**   These suggestions assume that the class is fifty minutes long. They also advise whether or not the material is essential to the rest of the course. If a section is labeled "optional", the time range given is the amount of time for the material in the event that it is covered.

2. **Points to Stress**   This is a short summary of the big ideas to be covered.

3. **Sample Questions**   Some instructors have reported that they like to open or close class by handing out a single question, either as a quiz or to start a discussion. Two types are included:

   - **Text Question:** This question is designed for students who have done the reading, but haven't yet seen the material in class. These questions can be used to help ensure that the students are reading the textbook carefully.

   - **Drill Question:** These questions are designed to be straightforward "right down the middle" questions for students who have tried, but not necessarily mastered, the material.

4. **In-Class Materials**   These suggestions are meant to work along with the text to create a classroom atmosphere of experimentation and inquiry.

5. **Examples**   These are routine examples with all the computations worked out, designed to save a bit of time in class preparation.

6. **Group Work**   One of the main difficulties instructors have in presenting group work to their classes is that of choosing an appropriate group task. Suggestions for implementation and answers to the group activities are provided first, followed by photocopy-ready handouts on separate pages. This guide's main philosophy of group work is that there should be a solid introduction to each exercise ("What are we supposed to do?") and good closure before class is dismissed ("Why did we just do that?")

7. **Homework Problems**   For each section, a set of essential **Core Exercises** (a bare minimum set of homework problems) is provided. Using this core set as a base, a **Sample Assignment** is suggested.

TIPS ON IN-CLASS GROUP WORK

This *Instructor's Guide* gives classroom-tested group work activities for every section of *Precalculus: Mathematics for Calculus, Sixth Edition.* One reason for the popularity of in-class group work is that *it is effective.* When students are engaged in doing mathematics, and talking about mathematics with others, they tend to learn better and retain the material longer. Think back to your own career: didn't you learn a lot of mathematics when you began teaching it to other people? Many skeptics experiment by trying group work for one semester, and then they get hooked. Pick a group activity from the guide that you like, make some photocopies, and dive in!

1. **Mechanics** Books and seminars on in-class group work abound. I have conducted many such seminars myself. What follows are some tips to give you a good start:

   (a) **Do it on the first day.**

   The sources all agree on this one. If you want your students to believe that group work is an important part of the course, you have to start them on the first day. My rule of thumb is "at least three times the first week, and then at least once a week thereafter." I mention this first because it is the most important.

   (b) **Make them move.**

   Ideally, students should be eye-to-eye and knee-to-knee. If this isn't possible, do the best you can. But it is important to have them move. If your groups are randomly selected, then they will have to get up and sit in a different chair. If your groups are organized by where they are seated in the classroom, make them move their chairs so they face each other. There needs to be a "break" between sitting-and-writing mode and talking-to-colleagues mode.

   (c) **Use the ideal group size.**

   Research has shown that the ideal group size is three students, with four-student groups next. I like to use groups of four: if one of them is absent (physically or otherwise), the group still has three participating members.

   (d) **Fixed versus random groups.**

   There is a lot of disagreement here. Fixed groups allow each student to find her or his niche, and allow you to be thoughtful when you assign groups or reassign them after exams. Random groups allow students to have the experience of working with a variety of people. I believe the best thing to do is to try both methods, and see which works best for you and your students.

   (e) **Should students hand in their work?**

   The advantage of handing in group works is accountability. My philosophy is that I want the group work to have obvious, intrinsic benefit. I try to make the experience such that it is obvious to the student that they get a lot out of participating, so I don't need the threat of "I'm grading this" to get them to focus. I sometimes have the students hand in the group work, but only as a last resort.

x

2. **Closure**   As stated above, I want my students to understand the value of working together actively in their groups. Once you win this battle, you will find that a lot of motivation and discipline problems simply go away. I've found the best way to ensure that the students understand why they've done an activity is to tell them. The students should leave the room having seen the solutions and knowing why they did that particular activity. You can have the students present answers or present them yourself, whatever suits your teaching style. I've had success with having groups write their results on transparencies and present them to the class (after I've checked their accuracy).

Here is another way to think about closure: Once in a while, give a future homework problem out as a group work. When the students realize that participating fully in the group work helps them in the homework, they get a very solid feeling about the whole process.

3. **Introduction**   The most important part of a group activity, in my opinion, is closure. The second most important is the introduction. A big killer of group work is that awful time between you telling your students they can start, and the first move of pencil on paper—the "what on earth do we do now?" moment. A good introduction should be focused on getting them past that moment. You don't want to give too much away, but you also don't want to throw them into the deep end of the swimming pool. In some classes, you will have to say very little, and in some you may have to do the first problem with them. Experiment with your introductions, but never neglect them.

4. **Help when you are needed**   Some group work methods involve giving absolutely no help when the students are working. Again, you will have to find what is best for you. If you give help too freely, the students have no incentive to talk to each other. If you are too stingy, the students can wind up frustrated. When a student asks me for help, I first ask the group what they think, and if it is clear they are all stuck at the same point, I give a hint.

5. **Make understanding a goal in itself**   Convey to the students (again, directness is a virtue here) that their goal is not just to get the answer written down, but to ensure that every student in their group understands the answer. Their work is not done until they are sure that every one of their colleagues can leave the room knowing how to do the problem. You don't have to sell every single student on this idea for it to work.

6. **Bring it back when you can**   Many of the group works in this guide foreshadow future material. When you are lecturing, try to make reference to past group works when it is appropriate. You will find that your students more easily recall a particular problem they discussed with their friends than a particular statement that you made during a lecture.

The above is just the tip of the iceberg. There are plenty of resources available, both online and in print. Don't be intimidated by the literature—start it on the first day of the next semester, and once you are into it, you may naturally want to read what other people have to say!

HOW TO IMPLEMENT THE DISCOVERY PROJECTS

One exciting yet intimidating aspect of teaching a course is projects. An extended assignment gives students the chance to take a focused problem or project and explore it in depth — making conjectures, discussing them, eventually drawing conclusions and writing them up in a clear, precise format. *Precalculus: Mathematics for Calculus, Sixth Edition* has links to many web-based Discovery Projects. They are excellent and well thought out, and should be explored if possible. Here are some tips on ensuring that your students have a successful experience.

Time Students should have two to three weeks to work on any extended out-of-class assignment. This is not because they will need all this time to complete it! But a fifteen-to-twenty-day deadline allows the students to be flexible in structuring their time wisely, and allows the instructors to apply fairly strict standards in grading the work.

Groups Students usually work in teams and are expected to have team meetings. The main problem students have in setting up these meetings is scheduling. Four randomly selected students will probably find it very hard to get together for more than a few hours, which may not be sufficient. One way to help your students is to clearly specify a minimum number of meetings, and have one or all group members turn in summaries of what was accomplished at each meeting. A good first grouping may be by location.

Studies have shown that the optimal group size is three people, followed by four, then two. I advocate groups of four whenever possible. That way, if someone doesn't show up to a team meeting, there are still three people there to discuss the problems.

Before the first project, students should discuss the different roles that are assumed in a team. Who will be responsible for keeping people informed of where and when they meet? Who will be responsible for making sure that the final copy of the report is all together when it is supposed to be? These types of jobs can be assigned within the team, or by the teacher at the outset.

Tell the students that you will be grading on both content and presentation. They should gear their work toward an audience that is bright, but not necessarily up-to-speed on this problem. For example, they can think of themselves as professional mathematicians writing for a manager, or as research assistants writing for a professor who is not necessarily a mathematician.

If the students are expected to put some effort into the project, it is important to let them know that some effort was put into the grading. Both form and content should be commented on, and recognition of good aspects of their work should be included along with criticism.

One way to help ensure cooperation is to let the students know that there will be an exam question based on the project. If every member of the group does well on that particular question, then they can all get a bonus, either on the exam or on the project grade.

Providing assistance Make sure that the students know when you are available to help them, and what kind of help you are willing to provide. Students may be required to hand in a rough draft ten days before the due date, to give them a little more structure and to make sure they have a solid week to write up the assignment.

Individual Accountability   It is important that the students are individually accountable for the output of their group. Giving each student a different grade is a dangerous solution, because it does not necessarily encourage the students to discuss the material, and may actually discourage their working together. A better alternative might be to create a feedback form If the students are given a copy of the feedback form ahead of time, and they know that their future group placement will be based on what they do in their present group, then they are given an incentive to work hard. One surprising result is that when a group consists of students who were previously slackers, that group often does quite well. The exam question idea discussed earlier also gives individuals an incentive to keep up with their colleagues.

HOW TO USE THE REVIEW SECTIONS AND CHAPTER TESTS

Review sections for chapters of a textbook are often assigned to students the weekend before a test, but never graded. Students realize they won't be evaluated on this work and often skip the exercises in place of studying previous quizzes and glancing at old homework. A more useful activity for students is to use the review sections in *Precalculus: Mathematics for Calculus, Sixth Edition* to discover their precise areas of difficulty. Implemented carefully, these are a useful resource for the students, particularly for helping them to retain the skills and concepts they've learned. To encourage more student usage, try the following alternatives:

1. Make notes of the types of exercises students have had difficulty with during the course. During a review session, assign students to work on similar exercises in the review sections and go over them at the end of class. Also assign exercises reminiscent of the ones you plan to have on the exam.

2. Use the review section problems to create a game. For instance, break students into groups and have a contest where the group that correctly answers the most randomly picked review questions "wins". One fun technique is to create a math "bingo" game. Give each group a 5×5 grid with answers to review problems. Randomly pick review problems, and write the questions on the board. Make sure that for a group to win, they must not only have the correct answers to the problems, but be able to give sound explanations as to how they got the answers.

3. A simple way to encourage students to look at the chapter tests is to use one of the problems, verbatim, as an exam question, making no secret of your intention to do so. It is important that students have an opportunity to get answers to any questions they have on the chapter tests before the exam is given; otherwise, this technique loses a great deal of its value.

1 FUNDAMENTALS

1.1 REAL NUMBERS

▼ Suggested Time and Emphasis

1–2 classes. Essential material.

▼ Points to Stress

1. The various subsets of the real number line.
2. The algebraic properties of real numbers.
3. Closed and open intervals of real numbers, and their unions and intersections.
4. Absolute value and distance.

▼ Sample Questions

- **Text Question:** Consider the figure below from the text.

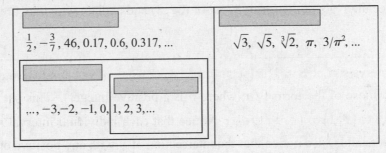

  Fill in each gray box with a label from the following list: integers, irrational numbers, natural numbers, and rational numbers.

  Answer:

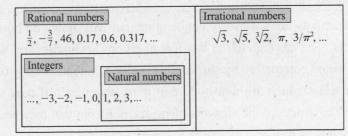

- **Drill Question: (a)** Find $(2, 5] \cup [3, 8)$.   **(b)** Find $(2, 5] \cap [3, 8)$.

  Answer: (a) $(2, 8)$ **(b)** $[3, 5]$

▼ In-Class Materials

- Point out that the set hierarchy in Figure 1 in the text isn't as simple as it may appear. For example, two irrational numbers can be added together to make a rational number ($a = 2 + \sqrt{3}$, $b = 3 - \sqrt{3}$), but two rational numbers, added together, are always rational (see Exercise 81). Similarly, mathematicians have long known that the numbers π and e ($\pi \approx 3.14159265\ldots$, $e \approx 2.718281828\ldots$) are irrational numbers, but it is unknown whether $\pi + e$ is rational or irrational. As people go further in mathematics, they break the real numbers down into other types of sets such as transcendentals, algebraics, normals, and computables, to name a few.

1

- Students probably already know how to multiply binomial expressions together; some of them already using the acronym FOIL to avoid thinking about the process altogether. Use the properties in this section to demonstrate why FOIL works:

$$\begin{aligned}(a+b)(c+d) &= a(c+d) + b(c+d) && \text{Distributive Property} \\ &= ac + ad + b(c+d) && \text{Distributive Property on the first term} \\ &= ac + ad + bc + bd && \text{Distributive Property on the second term}\end{aligned}$$

- Warn students that certain things cannot be rewritten. For example, an expression like $\dfrac{u}{u+1}$ cannot be simplified, while $\dfrac{u+1}{u}$ can be expressed as $1 + \dfrac{1}{u}$. Similarly, there is no way to simplify $a + bc$. Another common pitfall can be pointed out by asking the question: "Is $-a$ a positive or negative number?" and having students write their answer down before you go on to explain.

- Example 7(e) should be discussed: $|3 - \pi| = \pi - 3$. It touches on the ideas of distance, the absolute value of a negative number, and that we don't need to write out π to infinite precision to deduce that it is larger than three.

- Note that we never see intervals of the form $[3, \infty]$ or $(52, 3)$ and explain why they are not well formed.

▼ Examples

A nontrivial union of intervals: Let $S = \{x \mid x > 0, x \neq 1/n, \text{ where } n \text{ is a positive integer}\}$ (the set of all positive numbers except those of the form $1/n$, where n is a positive integer). This set is an infinite union of open intervals: $(1, \infty) \cup \left(\frac{1}{2}, 1\right) \cup \left(\frac{1}{3}, \frac{1}{2}\right) \cup \cdots$. Notice that each individual interval in the union is well behaved and easy to understand. Also notice that the intersection of S with any positive open interval such as $(0.1, 5)$ becomes a finite union.

▼ Group Work 1: What are the Possibilities?

Many questions in this activity are not overly challenging, but will show you how well the class understands unions and intersections. The answers to the last few questions are subtle, and while fun to think about, are not expected to be answered completely by students. It is nice to establish early on that students can be given questions to discuss in class which are worthwhile to think about even if they won't be on the exam. If a group finishes early and has some of the answers incorrect, point out that they need to fix something, without telling them which problem to fix.

Answers:

1. $(1, 3) \cup (2, 4)$ is one interval. $(1, 3) \cup (4, 5)$ is two intervals. It is not possible to choose values to make zero intervals or a single point.

2. $[1, 3] \cap [2, 4]$ is one interval. It is not possible to choose values to make two intervals. $[1, 3] \cap [4, 6]$ does not consist of any intervals. $[1, 3] \cap [3, 5]$ is the single number 3.

3. Yes

4. No. Choose $(0, \infty)$ and $(-\infty, 2)$.

5. No

6. No

7. No

8. Surprisingly, yes! Consider the union of all intervals of the form $\left[\frac{1}{n}, 2 - \frac{1}{n}\right]$ where n is a positive integer. The union of all such closed intervals is $(0, 2)$. Every number between zero and two is in infinitely many of the intervals, yet zero and two themselves are not in any of them.

▼ Group Work 2: Real-World Examples

Reinforce the distinction between closed and open intervals by trying to get the class to come up with real-world examples where each kind of interval is appropriate. Open the activity by referring to or copying the table above Example 5 from the text onto the board. Perhaps give them an example such as the following: "If the speed limit on a highway is 55 miles per hour and the minimum speed is 45 miles per hour, then the set of allowable speeds $[45, 55]$ is a closed interval." Gauge your class—don't let them start until they are clear as to what they will be trying to do. As the activity goes on, you can stop them halfway and let groups share one or two of their answers with the whole class to prevent groups from getting into mental ruts. Make sure to leave enough time for students to discuss their answers. If you can foster an atmosphere of pride and kudos this early in the semester, it will make the group work easier later on.

Answers:

These will vary. Some typical answers follow.

- Given that water freezes at $32\,°\text{F}$ and boils at $212\,°\text{F}$ ($0\,°\text{C}$ and $100\,°\text{C}$ respectively), the set of temperatures at which water is a liquid is then $(32, 212)$, an open interval.
- If an apple-flavored product advertises that it contains real apple juice then the percentage of apple juice it contains is in $(0, 100]$, a half-open interval.
- The set of all possible temperatures (in $°\text{C}$) that can be achieved in the universe is $[-273.16\ldots, \infty)$, a half-open infinite interval.

▼ Group Work 3: Foil the Happy Dolphin

If a group finishes early, ask them this surprisingly difficult follow-up question: "Write a paragraph explaining the answer to Problem 1 in such a way that a fourth-grader could understand it." Students may not succeed here, but the process of trying will help them to understand the concepts.

Answer: It is easiest to explain by allowing the number to be x:

We start with	x
Adding 4 gives	$x + 4$
Multiplying by 2 gives	$2(x + 4) = 2x + 8$
Subtracting 6 gives	$2x + 2$
Dividing by 2 gives	$\frac{1}{2}(2x + 2) = x + 1$
Subtracting the original number gives	$x + 1 - x = 1$

▼ Homework Problems

Core Exercises: 2, 5, 8, 23, 26, 37, 39, 47, 58, 65

Sample Assignment: 2, 5, 8, 9, 18, 23, 26, 30, 32, 37, 39, 42, 43, 47, 58, 65, 67, 72, 80

GROUP WORK 1, SECTION 1.1

What are the Possibilities?

1. Assume we have two intervals (a, b) and (c, d). Is it possible to choose a, b, c, and d so that $(a, b) \cup (c, d)$ can be expressed as a single interval? If so, how? Can it consist of two intervals? Zero intervals? Can it consist of a single point?

2. Assume we have two intervals $[a, b]$ and $[c, d]$. Is it possible to choose a, b, c, and d so that $[a, b] \cap [c, d]$ can be expressed as a single interval? If so, how? Can it consist of two intervals? Zero intervals? Can it consist of a single point?

3. Is the union of two infinite intervals always infinite?

4. Is the intersection of two infinite intervals always infinite?

5. Is it possible to take the union of two open intervals and get a closed interval? If so, how?

6. Is it possible to take the union of two closed intervals and get an open interval? If so, how?

7. Is it possible to take the union of infinitely many open intervals and get a closed interval? If so, how?

8. Is it possible to take the union of infinitely many closed intervals and get an open interval? If so, how?

GROUP WORK 2, SECTION 1.1

Real-World Examples

Your textbook describes nine types of intervals. These are not just mathematical abstractions; there are real-world phenomena that represent each type of interval. Your task is to find quality examples of each type in the real world. For instance, if you have to be at least $5'\,10''$ to ride a roller coaster, then the set of allowable heights in inches (according to the policy) is $[70, \infty)$, which is of the third type. (In practice, of course, a twenty foot tall person would be unable to ride the roller coaster, but the rule does not specifically prohibit it.)

1. (a, b)

2. $[a, b]$

3. $[a, b)$

4. $(a, b]$

5. (a, ∞)

6. $[a, \infty)$

7. $(-\infty, b)$

8. $(-\infty, b]$

9. $(-\infty, \infty)$

5

GROUP WORK 3, SECTION 1.1

Foil the Happy Dolphin

When I was in fourth grade, the following was written in a sidebar in my textbook, in a friendly font next to a picture of a happy dolphin:

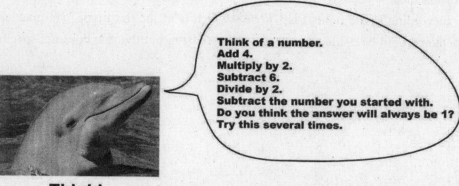

Think!

Think of a number.
Add 4.
Multiply by 2.
Subtract 6.
Divide by 2.
Subtract the number you started with.
Do you think the answer will always be 1?
Try this several times.

I tried it several times, and (can you believe it?) the answer was always 1. I was fascinated, because I had no idea why this was true. Later, when I learned about fractions, I tried it with $\frac{1}{2}$ and $\frac{2}{3}$ and it worked again. Much later, I learned about negative numbers and thought that surely this wondrous machine would break if I put in -2. But no, I still wound up with 1.

1. Does the Happy Dolphin Procedure (HDP) always yield 1? Show why it must be true, or find a number for which the HDP fails.

2. Come up with your own, more complicated, procedure that always gives the answer 1.

1.2 EXPONENTS AND RADICALS

▼ Suggested Time and Emphasis

1–2 classes. Essential material.

▼ Points to Stress

1. Definition of a^n in the cases where n is a positive integer, where n is zero, where n is rational, and where n is negative.
2. Algebraic properties of exponents.
3. Scientific notation and its relationship to significant digits.
4. Rationalizing denominators.

▼ Sample Questions

- **Text Questions:**

    1. What is the definition of $a^{3/4}$?

    2. Write 125,000,000 in scientific notation.

    3. Why is scientific notation useful?

    Answers:

    1. $a^{3/4} = \sqrt[4]{a^3}$

    2. $125{,}000{,}000 = 1.25 \times 10^8$

    3. It provides a compact way of writing very large numbers and very small numbers.

- **Drill Questions:**

    1. Simplify $\left(\dfrac{a}{3}\right)^{-3} a^5$.

    2. Simplify $\dfrac{\sqrt[3]{a^2}}{\sqrt[3]{a}} a^5$.

    Answers:

    1. $27a^2$

    2. $a^{16/3}$

▼ In-Class Materials

- One non-rigorous way to justify the way negative exponents work is to start a table such as this:

$$
\begin{array}{ll}
2^5 & 32 \\
2^4 & 16 \\
2^3 & 8 \\
2^2 & 4 \\
2^1 & 2
\end{array}
$$

    Note that every step we are dividing by two, and continuing the pattern we get $2^0 = 1$ and $2^{-1} = \frac{1}{2}$. After explaining this concept, take a minute to do 2^{-2} and 2^{-3}.

- Write "$\sqrt{ab} = \sqrt{a}\sqrt{b}$" on the board, and ask the students if this statement is always true. Point out (or have them discover) that this is a false statement when a and b are negative.

7

- When Andrew Waugh measured Mount Everest, he used the techniques that were state-of-the-art at the time. According to his measurements, Mount Everest was exactly 29,000 ft tall (to the nearest foot). He was afraid that people would think that it was an estimate: that he was merely saying that the mountain was between 28,500 ft and 29,500 ft tall. He was proud of his work. Discuss how he could have reported his results in such a way that people would know he was not estimating the height of the mountain. (Historically, he lied and said it was 29,002 ft tall, so people would know there were five significant figures. The accepted figure today is 29,029 ft, although some scientists think it is a few feet higher.)

- When people talk about groups of objects, they often use the word "dozen" for convenience. It is easier to think about 3 dozen eggs than it is to think about 36 eggs. Chemists use a similar word for atoms: a "mole". There are a mole of atoms in 22.4 L of gas. (You can bring an empty 1 L bottle to help the class picture it) and a mole of atoms in 18 mL of water. (Bring in a graduated cylinder to demonstrate.) A mole of atoms is 6.02×10^{23} atoms. Ask the students which is bigger:

  1. A mole or the number of inches along the Mississippi River

  2. A mole or a trillion

  3. A mole or the number of stars visible from Earth

  4. A mole or the number of grains of sand on Earth

  5. A mole or the number of sun-like stars in the universe

  The answer for all five is "a mole".

- There is a cube root magic trick that illustrates an interesting property of the cube function. A student takes a two-digit integer, cubes it, and gives you the answer (for example, 274,625). You knit your brow, think, and give the cube root (65) using the power of your mind. If the students are not impressed, stop there. If they are, do it a second time, getting the answer wrong by 1. Try it a third time, and again get the correct answer. Have them try to figure the trick out, and promise to reveal the secret if they do well on a future quiz or test.

  The trick is as follows. Memorize the first ten cubes:

x	0	1	2	3	4	5	6	7	8	9
x^3	0	1	8	27	64	125	216	343	612	729

Notice that the last digit of each cube is unique, and that they aren't very well scrambled (2's cube ends in 8 and vice versa; 3's ends in 7 and vice versa). So the last digit of the cube root is easily obtained (274,625 ends in 5, so the number you were given is of the form ?5). Now the first digit can be obtained by looking at the first three digits of the cube, and seeing in which range they are. (274 is between 6^3 and 7^3, so the number you were given is 65). Make sure to tell the students that if they do this trick for other people, they should not get the answer too fast, and they should get it wrong in the last digit occasionally. This will make it seem like they really can do cube roots in their heads.

▼ Examples

- A product whose answer will be given by a calculator in scientific notation:

$$(4{,}678{,}200{,}000)\,(6{,}006{,}200{,}000) = 28{,}098{,}204{,}840{,}000{,}000{,}000$$

- A product whose answer contains too many significant figures for many calculators to compute accurately:

$$(415,210,709)\,(519,080,123) = 215,527,625,898,637,207$$

- A fractional exponent simplification that works out nicely: $\dfrac{\sqrt[3]{8^5}}{\sqrt[3]{8^4}} = \sqrt[3]{\dfrac{8^5}{8^4}} = \sqrt[3]{8} = 2$.

▼ Group Work 1: Water Bears

This is a good time to teach students how to find numbers such as $\sqrt[5]{12}$ on their calculators

Answers:

1. a
2. $\sqrt[5]{12} \approx 1.64375$
3. $a = 3$, $B = 40$
4. Answers will vary, given the fuzziness of real-world data. B is approximately 38 and a is approximately 2.5.

▼ Group Work 2: Guess the Exponent

This exercise will give students a feel for orders of magnitude. Put them into groups of three or four, and have them discuss the questions. Some are easy, some are tricky. When the groups seem to have achieved consensus, scramble them up, trying to make sure everybody is with two or three new people. Have the new groups try to achieve agreement. If they disagree, allow the groups to vote. For each problem, poll the groups, and then give the answer.

Answers: 1. 2   **2.** 8   **3.** 3   **4.** 6   **5.** 0   **6.** 7   **7.** 4   **8.** 1   **9.** 3   **10.** 1   **11.** 5
       12. 7   **13.** 8   **14.** 21   **15.** 5   **16.** 10   **17.** 5   **18.** 4   **19.** 2   **20.** 4   **21.** 3   **22.** 3

23. The answer, my friend, is blowing in the wind. Forty-two is an acceptable answer, as is "seven" if written in confident handwriting.

▼ Group Work 3: Find the Error

Students are invited to pick a hole in someone else's reasoning. Many students do not understand, at first, what they are trying to do — they will tend to point at the conclusion and say words to the effect of "$-1 \neq 1$, so that is the error," or they will start at a given step, proceed differently, and not wind up with a paradox. They will have to be guided to the idea that they must actually analyze *someone else's* reasoning, and find where that other person made the mistake.

Answer: The definition $a^{m/n} = \sqrt[n]{a^m}$ is valid only if m/n is in lowest terms.

▼ Homework Problems

Core Exercises: 2, 7, 16, 19, 30, 36, 37, 49, 77, 80, 89

Sample Assignment: 2, 3, 7, 8, 16, 19, 23, 26, 30, 34, 36, 37, 46, 49, 55, 77, 80, 89, 92, 97

GROUP WORK 1, SECTION 1.2

Water Bears

The Warm-Up

1. Simplify the expression $\dfrac{Ba^{n+1}}{Ba^n}$.

2. If we know that $a^5 = 12$, find a.

Many types of populations grow this way: They start out growing slowly, then more quickly, then very, very quickly. For example, assume we put some water bears (a cute microscopic organism) in a petri dish. Here is a table showing their population over time:

Day	Population
1	120
2	360
3	1080
4	3240
5	9720
6	29,160
7	87,480
8	262,440
9	787,320
10	2,361,960

The Water Bears

3. This type of growth is called **exponential growth**. After n days, there are Ba^n water bears. B and a are constants that we have to figure out. (Oh, by the way: in this context the word "we" actually means "you".) Find B and a.

4. The previous table wasn't really accurate. A true table of exponential growth might look more like this:

Day	Population
1	95
2	238
3	594
4	1484
5	3711
6	9277
7	23,190
8	57,980
9	144,960
10	362,390

Now calculate the real values of B and a.

The Hint Sheet

1. Calculate this ratio: the water bear population on Day 3 over the population on Day 2.

2. Now calculate the ratio of the population on Day 4 over the population on Day 3.

3. One more: calculate the ratio of the population on Day 5 over the population on Day 4.

4. How about in general? What is the ratio of the population on Day $n + 1$ over the population on Day n?

5. Recall that the population at day n is given by Ba^n. (This is the definition of exponential growth.) Write an algebraic formula describing water bear populations. The left-hand side of the formula will be Ba^n.

6. Use the above to find a, and then find B.

Guess the Exponent

Most math problems ask you to figure out if the answer is 4, 5 or 6. Not these! We are going to give you the questions *and* the answers. For your comfort and convenience, the answers will be written in scientific notation. The only thing you have to do is supply the exponent. How hard can that be? How hard, indeed...

1. Approximately how many countries are there in the world?

   Answer: $1.9 \times 10^{\boxed{}}$

2. How many major credit cards are currently issued in the United States?

   Answer: $2.25 \times 10^{\boxed{}}$

3. How many crochet stitches are there in an adult-sized mitten?

   Answer: $1.73 \times 10^{\boxed{}}$

4. How many people lived in the United States in 1800?

   Answer: $5.08 \times 10^{\boxed{}}$

5. How many president's faces are on Mount Rushmore?

   Answer: $4 \times 10^{\boxed{}}$

6. Approximately how many species of insect are there in the world?

   Answer: $3.0 \times 10^{\boxed{}}$

7. According to the Internet Movie Database, how many different television series have been released in the world, as of 2003?

   Answer: $2.4 \times 10^{\boxed{}}$

8. How many breeds of domestic cat are there?

   Answer: $4.6 \times 10^{\boxed{}}$

9. What is the longest a Redwood tree can live?

   Answer: $2 \times 10^{\boxed{}}$ years

10. How many playing cards are there in a hand of bridge?

    Answer: $1.3 \times 10^{\boxed{}}$

11. The average human head has how many hairs?

    Answer: Between $0.8 \times 10^{\boxed{}}$ and $1.2 \times 10^{\boxed{}}$

12. How many books are there in the United States Library of Congress?

    Answer: $1.8 \times 10^{\boxed{}}$

13

13. How many documents are there in the United States Library of Congress (including books, manuscripts, recordings, photographs, etc.)?

    Answer: $1.2 \times 10^{\boxed{}}$

14. How many sun-like stars (stars that have planets) are there in the universe?

    Answer: $1 \times 10^{\boxed{}}$

15. How far is it from the earth to the moon (on average)?

    Answer: $2.5 \times 10^{\boxed{}}$ miles

16. Approximately how many neurons are there in a human brain?

    Answer: $1 \times 10^{\boxed{}}$

17. How many words are there in the English language?

    Answer: $8.16 \times 10^{\boxed{}}$

18. How many words are there in a typical novel?

    Answer: Between $4.5 \times 10^{\boxed{}}$ and $15 \times 10^{\boxed{}}$

19. How many paintings did the artist Van Gogh create?

    Answer: $8 \times 10^{\boxed{}}$

20. How many feet down is the deepest spot in the ocean (the Mariana Trench in the Pacific Ocean)?

    Answer: $3.60 \times 10^{\boxed{}}$

21. How many miles long is the Mississippi River?

    Answer: $2.350 \times 10^{\boxed{}}$

22. How many miles long is the Nile River?

    Answer: $4.15 \times 10^{\boxed{}}$

23. How many seas must the white dove sail before she sleeps in the sand?

    Answer:

GROUP WORK 3, SECTION 1.2

Find the Error

It is a beautiful Autumn day. Everyone around you is happy and excited because school has begun, and it is time to begin the joy of learning and hard work as opposed to the long summer of idle hooliganism. You are particularly happy because you are taking Precalculus. You sit at a picnic table, set up your peanut-butter and banana sandwich and a thermos of cold milk, and start reading where you had left off. Suddenly, you are aware of an odd odor, and turn around to see a wild-eyed ten-year old boy licking a giant lollipop. "What are you reading?" he asks.

"I am reading *Precalculus: Math for Calculus, Sixth Edition*," you say. "It is a bit advanced for you, but it is jam-packed with useful and important information. Worry not, lad, the day will come when you, too, are able to read this wonderful book."

"I've already read it," the boy says smugly, "and think it is full of LIES."

"What do you mean?" you ask incredulously. "James Stewart, Lothar Redlin and Saleem Watson have taken some of the greatest knowledge of our civilization, melted it down, mixed it with love, and put it into my textbook."

"Great knowledge, huh?" he asks. "Tell me, what is $(-1)^1$?"

"Why, that is equal to -1," you answer. "Any number to the first power is itself. I knew that even before taking Precalculus!"

"Okay then, what is $(-1)^{6/6}$?"

"Well, by the definition of rational roots, that would be $\sqrt[6]{(-1)^6} = \sqrt[6]{1} = 1$."

"I thought you said $(-1)^1 = -1$, and now you are saying that $(-1)^{6/6} = 1 \ldots$ In other words, you are saying that $-1 = 1$!"

You can't be saying that, can you? The rude stranger must have made a mistake!

What was his mistake? Find the error.

1.3 ALGEBRAIC EXPRESSIONS

▼ Suggested Time and Emphasis

$1-1\frac{1}{2}$ classes. Essential material.

▼ Points to Stress

1. Definition of and algebraic operations with polynomials.
2. Special product formulas.
3. Factoring expressions by finding common factors and recognition of special cases.
4. Factoring quadratics by trial and error.

▼ Sample Questions

- **Text Question:**

  (a) Give an example of an expression that is a polynomial.

  (b) Give an example of an expression that is not a polynomial.

- **Drill Question:** Factor the polynomial $12x^3 + 18x^2y$.

  Answer: $6x^2(2x + 3y)$

▼ In-Class Materials

- Remind students of the standard multiplication algorithm (some people don't learn it) by multiplying 352 by 65. Then multiply $3x^2 + 5x + 2$ by $6x + 5$ using the algorithm in the text. If your students are used to "lattice multiplication" this can also be done. One doesn't really need the "lattice" but the process can be put into the same form they are used to.

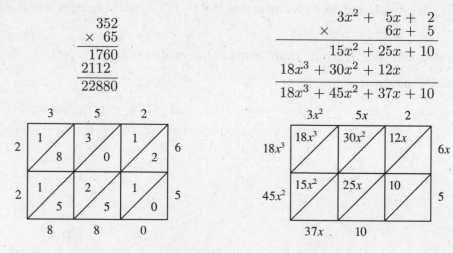

- This is an interesting product to look at with students:

$$(x - 1)\left(1 + x + x^2 + x^3 + x^4 + \cdots + x^n\right) = x^{n+1} - 1$$

Have them work it out for $n = 2, 3,$ and 4 and see the pattern. Once they see how it goes, you can derive

$$\left(1 + x + x^2 + x^3 + x^4 + \cdots + x^n\right) = \frac{x^{n+1} - 1}{x - 1}$$

16

and use it to estimate such things as $1 + \frac{1}{2} + \frac{1}{4} + \frac{1}{8} + \cdots$ or the sum of any geometric series.

- After doing some routine examples, show your students that grouping is not always obvious, as in examples like

$$2xa + 4y + ay + 8x = (2xa + ay) + (4y + 8x) = a(2x + y) + 4(y + 2x) = (2x + y)(a + 4)$$

Some of the standard formulas can also be awkward. For example, $x^2 - 2$ can be factored, even though we don't often refer to the number 2 as a "square".

- Most people would look at $x^4 + 324$ and think it cannot be factored. (Point out that we could use the difference of two squares formula if it were $x^4 - 324$). It can be factored, although the factorization is not obvious:

$$x^4 + 324 = x^4 + 36x^2 - 36x^2 + 324 = (x^2 + 18)^2 - 36x^2$$
$$= (x^2 + 18)^2 - (6x)^2 = (x^2 + 6x + 18)(x^2 - 6x + 18)$$

- This is a good opportunity to foreshadow polynomial division, which is covered in Section 3.3. Have students try to factor an expression such as $x^3 + 2x^2 - 21x + 18$. Now assume you have the hint that $x - 1$ is a factor. Show them how you can use the hint by dividing the polynomial by $x - 1$ to get a remaining quadratic, which is easy to break down.
  Answer: $(x - 3)(x + 6)(x - 1)$

▼ Examples

- A cubic product: $(3x^3 - 2x^2 + 4x - 5)(x^3 - 2x^2 - 4x + 1) = 3x^6 - 8x^5 - 4x^4 - 2x^3 - 8x^2 + 24x - 5$
- A fourth degree polynomial with integer factors:

$$(x - 1)(x - 1)(x + 2)(x - 3) = x^4 - 3x^3 - 3x^2 + 11x - 6$$

- A polynomial that can be factored nicely using the method of In-Class Materials Point 4:

$$x^4 + 64 = (x^2 - 4x + 8)(x^2 + 4x + 8)$$

▼ Group Work 1: Find the Error

This particular paradox was found carved in a cave-wall by Og the Neanderthal Algebra teacher. Even though it is an old chestnut, it is still wonderful for students to think about, if it is new to them. There is some value in tradition!

Answer: $b - a = 0$ and one cannot divide by zero.

▼ Group Work 2: Designing a Cylinder

This activity gives students an opportunity to experiment with an open-ended problem requiring approximations and the use of formulas. Answers will vary.

▼ Group Work 3: Back and Forth

While expansion and factoring are inverse processes, they are not perfectly symmetrical. It is generally easier to expand than to factor, as illustrated by this activity. Introduce this activity by pointing out that when writing tests, one can't just put up a random polynomial to factor, because the answer might be too hard to find, or too complex to write clearly.

Divide the room into two halves A and B and give each half the corresponding form of the activity. Students expand six expressions and write their answers in the space provided. Emphasize that they should write only their expanded answers, not the work leading up to them, in the blanks. As students finish, they will trade papers, finished As swapping with finished Bs. After the swap, they factor their partner's answer. The pair will then (hopefully) have obtained the original questions back; if not, they should get together and figure out their errors. If a pair finishes early, have them repeat the exercise, making up their own expressions. (If students are taking a long time, you can have them omit Question 6.)

When closing the activity, note that while it is theoretically possible to do all of them, some (such as Question 6) are extremely difficult to factor.

Answers:

Form A:
1. $x^2 - 3$
2. $x^2 + 5x + 6$
3. $8x^3 + 27$
4. $3rm + 9rn + sm + 3sn$
5. $4b^2x + 4b^2 - 12bx - 12b + 9x + 9$
6. $x^5 + 3x^4 - 5x^3 - 15x^2 + 4x + 12$

Form B:
1. $x^2 + 6x + 9$
2. $2x^2 + 3x - 2$
3. $x^3 - 8$
4. $m^2n - m^2 + 8mn - 8m + 16n - 16$
5. $2ar - 10as + br - 5bs$
6. $x^5 + x^4 - 13x^3 - 13x^2 + 36x + 36$

▼ Homework Problems

Core Exercises: 7, 12, 18, 24, 35, 47, 62, 67, 98, 101

Sample Assignment: 7, 8, 12, 18, 20, 24, 35, 43, 47, 52, 62, 63, 67, 86, 98, 101, 112, 131

Find the Error

It is a beautiful autumn day. You are collecting leaf samples for your biology class. Your friend Ed is with you, and every time you collect a leaf he says, "School sure is fun, isn't it?" and you say, "It truly is." After the tenth time, it starts getting old, but you continue to do it. Suddenly, you smell the sweet smell of sticky lollipop and a voice says, "Plenty of fun if you don't mind LIES!" You turn around and there is the wild-eyed boy you've seen before, with a grin on his face that is even stickier than his lolly.

"What are you talking about?" you ask. "Nobody has lied to me today. In chemistry we learned about chemicals, in music we learned about madrigals, in history we learned about radicals, and in mathematics we learned about..." You pause, trying to think of something that rhymes. And as you pause, he interrupts:

"You learned about LIES. Watch me, old-timer, and learn!"

You wince at being called "old-timer" and you wince again when you realize that the boy has snatched a particularly nice maple leaf from Ed's hand. Using a felt-tip pen, he writes:

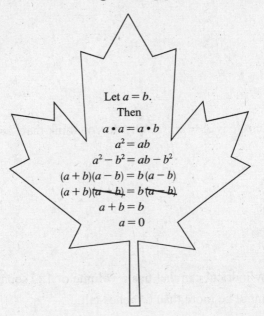

Let $a = b$.
Then
$$a \cdot a = a \cdot b$$
$$a^2 = ab$$
$$a^2 - b^2 = ab - b^2$$
$$(a + b)(a - b) = b(a - b)$$
$$(a + b)\cancel{(a - b)} = b\cancel{(a - b)}$$
$$a + b = b$$
$$a = 0$$

"See that? All those letters and variables bouncing around — it's a waste of time! Because I've just shown that $a = 0$ no matter what you want it to be. Zero. Always zero!"

Is the boy correct? Are all variables equal to zero? That doesn't seem very "variable" of them.

Save all of algebra! Find the error.

GROUP WORK 2, SECTION 1.3

Designing a Cylinder

The volume of a right circular cylinder with height h and radius r is given by $V = \pi r^2 h$.

1. Draw such a cylinder.

2. The equation for the area of a circle is $A = \pi r^2$. Why do you think that "πr^2" also appears in the formula for the volume of a cylinder?

3. Assume you are designing a cylindrical can that has a volume of 120 square inches. Find dimensions of such a can, assuming that it cannot be more than 6 inches tall.

4. Find different possible dimensions for a can with a volume of 120 square inches, again assuming it cannot be more than 6 inches tall.

5. Find dimensions of a can with a volume of 120 square inches that is long and skinny.

6. Find dimensions of a can with a volume of 120 square inches that is short and fat.

7. Assume that this is going to be a can of Vegetarian Baked Beans to be manufactured in great quantity and sold to grocery stores. Find the dimensions that would be best to use, in your opinion. Why did you pick those dimensions?

Expand the following expressions. Write your answers (the answers only — do not show your work) at the bottom of this sheet, where indicated.

When you are finished, fold the top of the page backward along the dotted line and trade with someone who has finished Form B. Your job will then be to factor the expressions you receive.

1. $(x + \sqrt{3})(x - \sqrt{3})$

2. $(x + 2)(x + 3)$

3. $(2x + 3)(4x^2 - 6x + 9)$

4. $(3r + s)(m + 3n)$

5. $(2b - 3)^2(x + 1)$

6. $(x + 1)(x - 1)(x + 2)(x - 2)(x + 3)$

- -

Answers:

1.

2.

3.

4.

5.

6.

Expand the following expressions. Write your answers (the answers only — do not show your work) at the bottom of this sheet, where indicated.

When you are finished, fold the top of the page backward along the dotted line and trade with someone who has finished Form A. Your job will then be to factor the expressions you receive.

1. $(x+3)(x+3)$

2. $(2x-1)(x+2)$

3. $(x-2)(x^2+2x+4)$

4. $(m+4)^2(n-1)$

5. $(2a+b)(r-5s)$

6. $(x+2)(x-2)(x+3)(x-3)(x+1)$

- -

Answers:

1.

2.

3.

4.

5.

6.

1.4   RATIONAL EXPRESSIONS

▼ Suggested Time and Emphasis

$\frac{1}{2}$–1 class. Review material.

▼ Points to Stress

1. Finding the domain of an algebraic expression.
2. Simplifying, adding, and subtracting rational expressions, including compound fractions.
3. Rationalizing numerators and denominators.

▼ Sample Questions

- **Text Question:** What is a rational expression?

  Answer: A rational expression is a fractional expression where both the numerator and the denominator are polynomials.

- **Drill Question:** Simplify $\dfrac{(x+2)/(x-3)}{x/(x-2)}$.

  Answer: $\dfrac{(x-2)(x+2)}{x(x-3)}$ or $\dfrac{x^2-4}{x^2-3x}$

▼ In-Class Materials

- One of the most persistent mistakes students make is confusing the following:

$$\frac{a+b}{c} = \frac{a}{c} + \frac{b}{c}$$

$$\frac{a}{b+c} = \frac{a}{b} + \frac{a}{c} \quad \longleftarrow \quad \mathfrak{Wrong!}$$

Make sure students understand the difference between these two cases. Perhaps give them the following to work with:

$$\frac{2+3}{5} = \frac{2}{5} + \frac{3}{5}$$

$$\frac{5}{2+3} = \frac{5}{2+3}$$

$$\frac{u+1}{u} = 1 + \frac{1}{u}$$

$$\frac{u}{u+1} = \frac{u}{u+1}$$

$$\frac{x^3+x+\sqrt[3]{x}}{x} = x^2 + 1 + x^{-2/3}$$

$$\frac{x}{x^3+x+\sqrt[3]{x}} = \frac{x}{x^3+x+\sqrt[3]{x}}$$

- Ask your students why we like to rationalize the denominator. Note that it is a matter of context; often it is a matter of taste. There is nothing inherently "simpler" about $\frac{\sqrt{2}}{2}$ as opposed to $\frac{1}{\sqrt{2}}$ if they are just sitting there as numbers. However, they would probably prefer to add $\frac{\sqrt{2}}{2} + \frac{\sqrt{3}}{3} + \frac{1}{6}$ than to add $\frac{1}{\sqrt{2}} + \frac{1}{\sqrt{3}} + \frac{1}{6}$. See if students can come up with other reasons or instances when it is convenient to rationalize a denominator.

- This is a good time to start talking about magnitudes. For example, look at $\dfrac{x+6}{x^2+4}$ and ask the question, "What happens to this fraction when x gets large? What happens when x gets close to zero? What happens when x is large and negative, such as $-1,000,000$?" The idea is not yet to be rigorous, but to give students a feel for the idea that a large denominator yields a small fraction, and vice versa. You can pursue this idea with fractions like $\dfrac{x^2+4}{x}$ and $\dfrac{6}{x+(3/x)}$.

▼ Examples

- A compound fraction to simplify: $\dfrac{x+(3/b)}{b+(2x/6)} = 3\dfrac{xb+3}{b\,(3b+x)}$

- A denominator to rationalize: $\dfrac{x}{\sqrt{x}+\sqrt{3}} = \dfrac{x\left(\sqrt{x}-\sqrt{3}\right)}{x-3}$

▼ Group Work: A Preview of Calculus

In the spirit of Exercises 69–74, this activity gives students practice in some of the types of calculations seen in calculus, and foreshadows the concept of a "difference quotient". They may not all finish. At any point after they are finished with Problem 5(a) you can close the activity by allowing students to present their answers.

After the answers are presented, if there is student interest, you can point out that in calculus, we want to see what happens when h gets close to 0. Before we have simplified the expressions, if you let $h = 0$ all of the expressions become the undefined $\dfrac{0}{0}$. After they are simplified, you obtain expressions in x when you allow $h = 0$. Note that technically we cannot allow $h = 0$ after we have factored the expressions, because we would have divided by zero; hence one reason for the existence of calculus.

Answers:

1. $\dfrac{\dfrac{1}{x+h}-\dfrac{1}{x}}{h} = -\dfrac{1}{(x+h)\,x}$ 2. $\dfrac{(x+h)^2 - x^2}{h} = 2x+h$ 3. $\dfrac{\sqrt{x+h}-\sqrt{x}}{h} = \dfrac{1}{\sqrt{x+h}+\sqrt{x}}$

4. (a) $\dfrac{(x+h)^3 - x^3}{h}$ (b) $\dfrac{2\,(x+h)-2x}{h}$ (c) $\dfrac{(x+h)^2 + (x+h) - \left(x^2+x\right)}{h}$

   (d) $\dfrac{5-5}{h}$ (e) $\dfrac{3^{x+h}-3^x}{h}$

5. (a) $3x^2 + 3xh + h^2$ (b) 2 (c) $2x+h+1$ (d) 0

   (e) $3^x\dfrac{3^h - 1}{h}$. We cannot simplify this further, nor could we substitute $h = 0$ even if we wanted to. You can't win 'em all!

▼ Homework Problems

Core Exercises: 7, 14, 24, 31, 40, 45, 60, 82, 83, 87

Sample Assignment: 2, 3, 4, 7, 11, 14, 24, 31, 36, 40, 45, 50, 60, 62, 82, 83, 87, 103, 105

Example 8 in the text involves simplifying an expression similar to this one:

$$\frac{\dfrac{1}{x+h} - \dfrac{1}{x}}{h}$$

1. Expressions of this kind occur often in calculus. Without looking at your book, simplify this expression.

2. Now simplify $\dfrac{(x+h)^2 - x^2}{h}$.

3. Now try $\dfrac{\sqrt{x+h} - \sqrt{x}}{h}$. (**Hint:** Rationalize the numerator, as done in Example 10 in the text.)

These types of expressions are called **difference quotients**. We could write the following abbreviations:

$$DQ\left(\frac{1}{x}\right) = \frac{\dfrac{1}{x+h} - \dfrac{1}{x}}{h}$$

$$DQ\left(x^2\right) = \frac{(x+h)^2 - x^2}{h}$$

$$DQ\left(\sqrt{x}\right) = \frac{\sqrt{x+h} - \sqrt{x}}{h}$$

In other words, given an expression with x as the variable, we can write its difference quotient. It isn't just a game that algebra teachers play; the difference quotient turns out to be an important concept in higher math: given information about a quantity, we can figure out how that quantity is changing over time.

4. Let's see if you've picked up on the pattern. Write out the following difference quotients:

(a) $DQ\left(x^3\right)$

(b) $DQ\left(2x\right)$

(c) $DQ\left(x^2 + x\right)$

(d) $DQ\left(5\right)$

(e) $DQ\left(3^x\right)$

5. Simplify the difference quotients you found above.

1.5 EQUATIONS

▼ Suggested Time and Emphasis

2 classes. Essential material.

▼ Points to Stress

1. Solving equations using the techniques of adding constants to both sides of the equation, multiplying both sides of the equation by a constant, and raising both sides of the equation to the same nonzero power.

2. Avoiding the pitfalls of accidentally multiplying or dividing by zero, or introducing extraneous solutions.

3. Solving quadratic equations using the techniques of factoring, completing the square, and the quadratic formula, and the use of the discriminant to determine the nature of the solutions to a quadratic equation.

4. Solving generalized quadratic equations.

5. Solving equations involving fractional expressions.

▼ Sample Questions

• Text Questions:

1. Give two reasons that it is important to check your answer after you have solved an equation such as $2 + \dfrac{5}{x-4} = \dfrac{x+1}{x-4}$.

2. Solve: $\dfrac{1}{x+4} = \dfrac{1}{2x}$.

Answers:

1. Firstly, we must make sure that our answer is not extraneous, and secondly, we should check that we have not made an error in calculation.

2. $x = 4$

• Drill Questions:

1. Solve $x^2 + 3x = -2$ for x.

2. Solve $(x+3)^2 + 2(x+3) = -1$ for x.

Answers:

1. $x = -2$ or $x = -1$

2. $x = -4$

▼ In-Class Materials

• There are two main anomalies that students may encounter when solving linear equations: $0 = 0$ and $1 = 0$. Although it is not a good idea to dwell on these situations, as opposed to focusing on the cases where the students will spend a majority of their time, it is good to address them, because they *do* come up, in math class and in real life. Have the students attempt to solve the following equations, and check their work:

$$3x + 4 = x + 6$$
$$3x + 4 = x + 6 + 2x - 2$$
$$3x + 4 = x + 6 + 2x + 2$$

By the time this example is presented, most students should be able to obtain $x = 1$ for the first equation, and to check this answer. The second one gives $0 = 0$. Point out that $0 = 0$ is always a true statement. (If you like, introduce the term "tautology".) It is a true statement if $x = 1$, it is a true statement if $x = 2$, it is a true statement if the author J. K. Rowling writes another book, it is a true statement if she does not write another book. Therefore, the students can test $x = 1$, $x = 2$, and $x = -\sqrt{2}$ in the second equation, and all of them will yield truth. The third statement gives $1 = 0$ (actually, it gives $0 = 4$, but we can multiply both sides of the equation by $\frac{1}{4}$). This is a false statement, no matter what value we assign to x. Point out "Currently, it is false to say that this piece of chalk is blue. Now, is there a value I can assign to x to change that?" Again, test various values of x in the third equation to see that, no matter what, we get that the LHS is always 4 less than the RHS.

- The zero-product property is the basis of various methods of solving quadratic equations. Many errors students make in solving these equations stem from misunderstanding the zero-product property. Students should see the difference between these two equations:

$$(x - 2)(x - 3)(x - 4) = 0$$
$$(x - 2)(x - 3)(x - 4) = -24$$

Note how the solution to the first is immediate, whereas the solution to the second requires some work. ($x = 0$ is the only real solution to the second.)

- Go through an example where the appearance of a quadratic equation may be unexpected. For example, assume that if we charge \$200 for a pair of handmade shoes, we can sell 100 pairs. For every five dollars we raise the price, we can sell one fewer pair. (Conversely, for every five dollars we lower the price, we can sell one more pair.) At what prices will our revenue be \$23,520? (Answer: \$280, \$420.) Point out that this is somewhat artificial—in practice we would be more interested in finding a maximum revenue, or (ideally) maximum profit. Later (in Chapter 10) students will be able to solve such problems.

- A resistor is an electrical device that resists the flow of electrical current in an electric circuit. It allows the circuit designer to control the current for a given voltage, among other applications. For two resistors in series, the total resistance is easy to find: $R = R_1 + R_2$. Have students solve the following straightforward problem: "Two resistors are in series. The total desired resistance is $100 \ \Omega$. The first resistor needs to have a resistance $45 \ \Omega$ greater than the second. What should their resistances be?"
Answer: The equation is $R_1 + (R_1 - 45) = 100$, so $R_1 = 72.5$ and $R_2 = 27.5$.

Things get more complicated if the resistors are in parallel. In that case we have $\frac{1}{R} = \frac{1}{R_1} + \frac{1}{R_2}$. Have the students try to set up and solve the same problem, only with the resistors in parallel.

Answer: $R_1 = 225$ and $R_2 = 180$. There is also an extraneous solution.

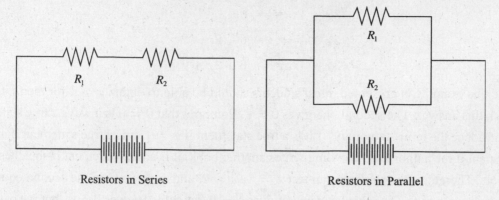

Resistors in Series   Resistors in Parallel

- One can demonstrate an equation involving two square roots. For example:

  The square root of a number, plus one more than that number, is exactly 5. Find the number.

  Answer: $\sqrt{x} + (x+1) = 5 \Leftrightarrow \sqrt{x} = 4 - x \Leftrightarrow x = 16 - 8x + x^2 \Leftrightarrow x^2 - 9x + 16 = 0$. The solutions to the quadratic are approximately 2.438 and 6.562. The latter proves to be extraneous, leaving 2.438 as the answer.

- It has been proved mathematically that any polynomial can be factored into the products of linear factors and irreducible quadratic factors. It has also been proved that if the degree of the polynomial is greater than four there is no formula (analogous to the quadratic formula) that will allow us to find those factors in general.

▼ Examples

- An equation with an extraneous solution:

$$\frac{x^2}{x+1} = \frac{x+2}{x+1}$$

This simplifies to $x^2 - x - 2 = 0$, either by multiplying by $x + 1$ directly or by first subtracting the RHS from the LHS and simplifying. The students can verify that $x = -2$ and $x = 2$ are solutions and that $x = -1$ is an extraneous solution.

- Quadratic equations with zero, one, and two solutions:

  $x^2 - 6x + 11 = 3$ has two solutions, $x = 2$ and $x = 4$.

  $x^2 - 6x + 12 = 3$ has one solution, $x = 3$.

  $x^2 - 5x + 13 = 3$ has no real solution.

- An equation in quadratic form: $\left(x^2 + 4x + 5\right)^2 - 3\left(x^2 + 4x + 5\right) + 2 = 0 \Rightarrow x = -3, x = -2,$ or $x = -1$.

▼ Group Work 1: Leaving the Nest

This lightly foreshadows the next section, in that students are asked to use an equation to solve a real-world problem. This problem can be modified to make the original savings a parameter instead of the constant 100. If students solve Problems 7 and 8 in different ways, make sure that the class sees the various methods used.

Answers:

1. $\dfrac{1200}{70} = 17.142857$ — about 18 months

2. Moving-out time $= \dfrac{1200}{x}$ $\left(\text{technically } \left\lceil \dfrac{1200}{x} \right\rceil\right)$

3. $3 = \dfrac{1200}{x}$ $\Rightarrow$ $x = \$400$ per month

4. $\dfrac{550}{70} \approx 7.86$; 8 months

5. $\dfrac{1300/3 - 100}{70} \approx 4.76$; 5 months

6. $\dfrac{1300/(n+1) - 100}{70} = \left[\dfrac{130}{7(n+1)} - \dfrac{10}{7}\right]$ months

7. $\dfrac{1300/(n+1) - 100}{70} = 3$, $n = \dfrac{99}{31}$; 4 roommates

8. $\dfrac{1300/(n+1) - 100}{70} = \dfrac{1}{4}$, $n = \dfrac{473}{47}$; 11 roommates

▼ Group Work 2: The Tour

Students may have questions about the setup of this problem. Don't answer them right away; part of the goal of this chapter is to teach students how to read a paragraph and figure out what it is asking. Conclude by pointing out that we did not answer an important question: What is the maximum possible profit? Questions like this are an important part of the study of calculus.

Answers:

1. The equation $-x^2 + 51x - 700 = 0$ has no solution, so it is not possible to make $700.

2. The solutions of $-x^2 + 51x - 494 = 0$ are 13 and 38, so 13 is the smallest number of people that will result in a profit of $700.

3. The solutions of $-x^2 + 47x - 544 = 0$ are approximately 20.6277 and 26.3723, so the answers are **(a)** 21 and **(b)** 26. Note that in part (a) we must round up because if we round down, we make slightly less than $700. Similarly, we must round down in part (b).

▼ Group Work 3: An Infinite Fraction

Open by writing the fraction from the group work on the board, and allowing a full minute of silence for students to start to play with it and think about it. Have them think about whether it makes sense, whether it works out to a single number, etc. Then group them and hand out the activity.

Answers:

1. $\frac{1}{2} = 0.500000$

2. $\frac{1}{3} = 0.333333$

3. $\frac{3}{7} = 0.428571$

4. $\frac{7}{17} = 0.411765$

5. $\frac{17}{41} = 0.414634$

6. Any well-stated answer should count as credit. The idea is the recursion, the self-similarity.

7. Solving $x^2 + 2x - 1 = 0$, we find that $x = -1 \pm \sqrt{2}$. The negative solution is extraneous, so $x \approx 0.414214$.

▼ Group Work 4: An Infinite Root

The positive answer to this question is called the golden ratio. One can spend many hours posing questions whose answer is the golden ratio. For example, the limit of the ratios of adjacent Fibonacci numbers is the golden ratio. Many artists have used rectangles in their work whose proportions approximate the golden ratio.

Answers:

1. (a) $\sqrt{1 + \sqrt{1}} \approx 1.41421$

   (b) $\sqrt{1 + \sqrt{1 + \sqrt{1}}} \approx 1.55377$

   (c) $\sqrt{1 + \sqrt{1 + \sqrt{1 + \sqrt{1}}}} \approx 1.59805$

   (d) $\sqrt{1 + \sqrt{1 + \sqrt{1 + \sqrt{1 + \sqrt{1}}}}} \approx 1.61185$

2. (a) $x^2 = 1 + x$

   (b) $x^2 - 1 = x$

   (c) We solve $x^2 - x - 1 = 0$ to find $x = \frac{1 \pm \sqrt{5}}{2}$.

▼ Homework Problems

Core Exercises: 8, 12, 30, 33, 45, 57, 68, 85, 88, 99, 105

Sample Assignment: 2, 8, 12, 18, 30, 33, 35, 45, 49, 57, 59, 68, 82, 85, 88, 99, 105, 108, 110, 121

GROUP WORK 1, SECTION 1.5

Leaving the Nest

1. I am a mathematics professor who lives in a town where an inexpensive apartment costs $650 per month. In order to rent an apartment here, I need the first month's rent up front, and a security deposit equal to the monthly rent. Assume that I have $100 saved up in the bank, and I can save $70 per month from my professorial salary. How long will it be before I can move out of my parent's basement?

2. Depressing thought, eh? Well, one way to move out sooner would be to save more money. How long will it be before I can move out, assuming I can save x dollars per month?

3. How much would I have to save per month if I wanted to move out in three months?

4. Realistically, I can't really save all that much more money. Math supplies do not come cheap. Let's go back to the situation where I am saving $70 per month. Another way I could move out sooner would be to get a roommate. How long would it be before I could move out, assuming a roommate would pay half of the first month's rent and the security deposit?

5. How long would it take if I had 2 roommates?

6. How about n roommates?

7. How many roommates would I have to have if I wanted to move out in three months?

8. For reasons best left to your imagination, it would make things a lot easier if I moved out next week. How many roommates will I need for this to happen?

There is increasing interest in touring the place of your birth — the places you played, the places you ate, the stores where your food was purchased, etc. And who better to give such tours than you? You decide to charge $50 per person. But that is a bit excessive, so you decide to give group discounts of $1 per person. In other words, if two people go on one tour, you will charge $49 per person (for a total of $98) and if three people go on the tour you will charge $48 per person (for a total of $144).

1. How many people have to go on the tour in order for you to make $700?

2. You are not satisfied with this measly amount of money. So you add a fee of $206 per tour group, regardless of size. Now what is the smallest number of people who have to go on the tour in order for you to make $700?

3. If you are going to charge that much for a tour, you should at least give everyone lunch. Assume that each person on the tour is going to eat a $4 lunch, the cost of which comes out of your pocket. Also assume that the caterer is going to charge you a flat fee of $50, regardless of how many people eat.

   (a) What is the smallest number of people who have to go on the tour in order for you to make $700, under these circumstances?

   (b) If too many people show up, of course, then you will actually be paying *them* to take the tour! You want to make sure to cap the number of people who are allowed to go on the tour. What is the largest number of people who can go on the tour without causing your profit to dip below $700?

Consider this odd fraction:

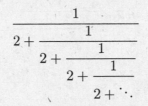

$$\cfrac{1}{2+\cfrac{1}{2+\cfrac{1}{2+\cfrac{1}{2+\ddots}}}}$$

Take a minute to think about it before going on. What does it mean? Do you think it is a number? Infinity? Is it even defined?

We can start to get a handle on this fraction by looking at approximations as follows. Write your answers as decimals with at least four significant figures.

1. $\dfrac{1}{2}$

2. $\dfrac{1}{2+1}$

3. $\cfrac{1}{2+\cfrac{1}{2+1}}$

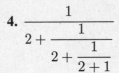

4. $\cfrac{1}{2+\cfrac{1}{2+\cfrac{1}{2+1}}}$

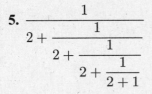

5. $\cfrac{1}{2+\cfrac{1}{2+\cfrac{1}{2+\cfrac{1}{2+1}}}}$

Notice that there is definitely a trend here: the answers you are getting are zeroing in on a particular number. Now let's try to find that number. We call that number x, so we can write

$$x = \cfrac{1}{2 + \cfrac{1}{2 + \cfrac{1}{2 + \cfrac{1}{2 + \cdots}}}}$$

6. Why is it correct to write $x = \dfrac{1}{2+x}$?

7. Find x. Is it close to what you approximated in Problem 5?

An Infinite Root

1. Compute the following:

   (a) $\sqrt{1 + \sqrt{1}}$

   (b) $\sqrt{1 + \sqrt{1 + \sqrt{1}}}$

   (c) $\sqrt{1 + \sqrt{1 + \sqrt{1 + \sqrt{1}}}}$

   (d) $\sqrt{1 + \sqrt{1 + \sqrt{1 + \sqrt{1 + \sqrt{1}}}}}$

2. You may notice that your answers in Problem 1 seemed to be getting closer and closer to some number. We are going to try to find out that number exactly, using algebra. In other words, we are going to attempt to discover

$$\sqrt{1 + \sqrt{1 + \sqrt{1 + \sqrt{1 + \sqrt{1 + \sqrt{1 + \cdots}}}}}}$$

   (a) We let $x = \sqrt{1 + \sqrt{1 + \sqrt{1 + \sqrt{1 + \sqrt{1 + \sqrt{1 + \cdots}}}}}}$. What is x^2 equal to?

   (b) What is $x^2 - 1$ equal to?

   (c) Find x.

1.6   MODELING WITH EQUATIONS

▼ Suggested Time and Emphasis

1 class. Essential material.

▼ Points to Stress

1. Solving applied problems described verbally.
2. Presenting the solution process in a clear, organized way.

▼ Sample Questions

- **Text Question:** Discuss one of the problems presented in this section. You don't have to use any specific numbers, but describe the problem and the method of solution.
- **Drill Question:** A car rental company charges $20 a day and 30 cents per mile for renting a car. Janice rents a car for three days and her bill comes to $72. How many miles did she drive?

  Answer: The total cost is $C = 20d + 0.30m$, where d is the number of days and m is the mileage. In this case we have $72 = 20\,(3) + 0.30m \;\Rightarrow\; m = 40$, so Janice drove 40 miles.

▼ In-Class Materials

- Some precalculus students will have seen this material at one point in their lives, and may have many different ideas and habits. It is important to make your requirements explicit: is it acceptable to present an answer with no work at all? With work shown but barely decipherable? Do you require students to explicitly go through the steps described in the text? Do you require them to write out a table (as in the examples in the text)? Much conflict can be avoided if your requirements are specified in a handout at the outset.

- Here is a simple-sounding problem: A person is currently making $25,000 a year (after taxes) working at a large company and has an opportunity to quit the job and make $35,000 independently. Is this a good deal financially? Elicit other considerations such as: Insurance tends to cost $400 per month for an individual — the company is no longer paying for that. Taxes will be roughly 30%. The large company probably pays some percentage (say 2%) toward a retirement account. Discuss this situation with your class, trying to come up with a linear equation that converts an annual gross income for an independent contractor to a net income, and then figure out how much the independent contractor would have to charge in order to net $25,000. Other hard-to-quantify considerations may come up such as paid vacations, sick leave, "being one's own boss", the tax benefits of having a home office, quality of life, and so forth. Acknowledge these considerations, and perhaps (for purposes of comparison) try to quantify them. Perhaps assume that the tax benefits for the home office add 5% to the gross income. Ask the class if the pleasure of not having a boss is worth, say, $2000 a year. (On the other hand, would they would get any work done at all without a boss standing over them?) This is a real-life modeling situation that, every year, more and more people find themselves thinking about.

- This section is particularly suited to having students come up with their own problems to solve, or have others solve. Once they understand the concept, with a little (or a lot of) thought, they should be able to come up with practical, relevant problems. If students need a little prompting, you can wonder how many

38

recordable CDs one would have to buy to store a hard drive full of music, how many people one could invite to a party that has a firm budget of $200 (have them list fixed costs and per-person costs), how many miles one could drive a car (paying all expenses) for $2000/year, etc.

▼ Examples

- A straightforward mixture problem: A child makes two quarts of chocolate milk consisting of 30% syrup and 70% milk. It is far too sweet. How much milk would you have to add to get a mixture that is 5% syrup?
  Answer: 10 quarts

- A straightforward job-sharing problem: If it takes Mike two hours to mow the lawn, and Al three hours to mow the lawn, how long does it take the two of them, working together?
  Answer: 1.2 hours

- A classic (i.e. very old) trick question: If it takes two people three hours to dig a hole, how long does it take one person to dig half a hole?
  Answer: You can't dig half a hole. Don't worry; my students did not laugh either.

▼ Group Work 1: How Many People?

This modeling problem has a lot of data, and is designed to teach students to distinguish between fixed and variable costs. As in the real world, some data are irrelevant (e.g. the maximum capacity of the hall) and some seem irrelevant, but are not (e.g. the length of the reception). The problems are deliberately not given in a standard order. Students would normally be asked to do Problem 3 before Problem 2; they are presented in this way to see if students realize that the easiest way to solve Problem 2 is to come up with an algebraic formula.

If a group finishes early, ask them how many people could be invited if the budget is $3000 and 70% of the people who have been invited attend. (Answer: 163)

Answers:

1. $2,225

2. 114. If a student answers 114.58, they must include an explanation of what they mean by that, given that 0.58 of a person doesn't make sense on the face of it. Note that if a student rounds up to 115, then they may go over budget. Given that there are approximations involved, it would be better to err on the side of caution, perhaps hosting 110 people rather than pushing it to the limit of 114.

3. $C = 12x + 1625$

▼ Group Work 2: Some Like it Hot

This is a straightforward mixture problem.

Answers:

1. $\dfrac{25}{10,000} = \dfrac{1}{400}$ gallon

2. $\dfrac{1}{100} = \dfrac{\frac{1}{800} + x}{\frac{1}{2} + x} \quad \Leftrightarrow \quad x = \dfrac{1}{264}$ gallon

▼ Homework Problems

Core Exercises: 7, 22, 29, 36, 49, 54, 69

Sample Assignment: 7, 10, 16, 22, 26, 29, 31, 36, 43, 49, 54, 69, 74

GROUP WORK 1, SECTION 1.6

How Many People?

Jessica and Trogdor are getting married! They are planning the reception, and have come up with the following data:

- The reception hall is going to cost $1200 to rent.
- The reception hall will house a maximum of 500 people.
- The reception will take three hours.
- Each person's dinner is going to cost $8.
- On average, every person that drinks alcohol will cost an extra $9.
- About one-third of the attendees will drink alcohol.
- Each piece of wedding cake will cost $1.11.
- 90% of the guests will eat a piece of wedding cake.
- The DJ is going to charge $75 per hour.
- The decorations (flowers, streamers, bobble-head representations of the groom, etc.) are going to cost $200.

Answer the following questions:

1. How much would the reception cost if 50 people attended?

2. How many people could come if Jessica and Trogdor have a total of $3000 to spend?

3. Write an algebraic formula describing the cost of x people attending their reception.

Some Like it Hot

I like my chili spicier than my sister does. I like mine to be 1% habañero sauce, and she likes it to be 0.25% habañero sauce. Here is the plan: I'm going to make a gallon of chili the way my sister likes it. I'll measure out a half-gallon, and put it in a container for her. Then I will add some more habañero sauce so that the remaining chili will be the way I like it.

1. How much habañero sauce should I put in initially?

2. How much extra habañero sauce should I put in my portion after I've divided it up?

1.7 INEQUALITIES

▼ Suggested Time and Emphasis

1 class. Essential material.

▼ Points to Stress

1. Definition of inequalities.

2. Manipulation of linear and nonlinear inequalities.

3. Solving inequalities of the form $|A| < B$ and $|A| > B$.

▼ Sample Questions

- **Text Question:** Solve the inequality $(x - 1)(x - 3) < 0$.

  Answer: $1 < x < 3$
- **Drill Question:** Solve $|3x + 5| = 14$.

  Answer: $x = -\frac{19}{3}$ or $x = 3$

▼ In-Class Materials

- Just as a quadratic equation can have zero, one, or two solutions, quadratic inequalities can have zero, one, or infinitely many solutions. A good way to clarify this point is to solve the following with your students:

$$x^2 + 2x \leq 0$$
$$x^2 + 2x + 1 \leq 0$$
$$x^2 + 2x + 1 < 0$$
$$x^2 + 2x + 2 \leq 0$$

- A nice comparison is the difference between these two inequalities:

$$\frac{x}{x^2 + 4} < 0$$
$$\frac{x}{x^2 - 4} < 0$$

- Ask students if there is an inequality that is true for every value of x *except* a single number, say 22. See if they can come up with something like $(x - 22)^2 > 0$.

- One of the themes of this chapter is taking verbal descriptions and translating them into algebraic equations. Assume we know that a length of tubing (to three significant figures) is 11.6 cm. Because of significant figures, there is a range of possible exact lengths of tubing. For example, if the actual length is 11.6000323 cm, we would report the length as 11.6 cm. Have students try to express the range of values as an absolute value inequality: $|x - 11.6| \leq 0.05$.

- There is a particular type of inequality that shows up often in higher mathematics: $0 < |x - a| < \delta$. Ask students to graph $0 < |x - 3| < \frac{1}{10}$ and similar inequalities, emphasizing the idea that x is close to 3, but not equal to 3. For fun, you can now write the definition of "limit" on the blackboard, and see what you and the students can do with it at this stage. Note that $\dfrac{x^2 - 9}{x - 3}$ is not defined at $x = 3$, but is close to 6

43

when x is close to three. Then write the formal definition:

> We say $\lim\limits_{x \to 3} \dfrac{x^2 - 9}{x - 3} = 6$ **because for every** $\varepsilon > 0$, **there is a** δ **such that** $\left| \dfrac{x^2 - 9}{x - 3} - 6 \right| < \varepsilon$ **whenever** $0 < |x - 3| < \delta$.

Remember, putting this on the board at this point in the game is for fun only.

▼ Examples

- Solve $-5 < x^2 + 3x + 2 < 10$.
  Answer: $-\frac{3}{2} - \frac{1}{2}\sqrt{41} < x < -\frac{3}{2} + \frac{1}{2}\sqrt{41}$
- Quadratic inequalities involving absolute values that require thoughtful analysis:
  - $\left| x^2 - 8x + 6 \right| < 6 \quad \Rightarrow \quad x \in (0, 2) \cup (6, 8)$
  - $\left| x^2 - 8x + 6 \right| \geq 6 \quad \Rightarrow \quad x \in (-\infty, 0] \cup [2, 6] \cup [8, \infty)$

▼ Group Work 1: Looking for Patterns

This activity is designed to help students sketch solution sets, and get a feel for working with inequalities. Before handing this out, warn the students to be particularly careful on the second problem.

Answers:

1. (a) $(0, 1) \cup (3, \infty)$

(b) $[0, 1] \cup [3, \infty)$

(c) $(-\infty, 0] \cup [1, 3]$

(d) $\{0, 1, 3\}$

2. (a) $(-2, -1) \cup (1, 2)$

(b) $(-2, -1] \cup [1, 2)$

(c) $(-\infty, -2) \cup [-1, 1] \cup (2, \infty)$

(d) $\{\pm 1\}$

▼ Group Work 2: Teaching Tolerance

Before they start this activity, you may want to remind them that the volume of a sphere is given by $\frac{4}{3}\pi r^3$. After this activity is over, you might want to mention the following: According to engineers at NASA, the roundness tolerance of ball bearings used in the space shuttle is 0.000005 inches. For example, if a ball bearing is supposed to have diameter 0.7867 inches, no matter where you measure the diameter it must be greater than 0.786695 inches and less than 0.786705 inches.

Answers:

1. $\left|\frac{1}{3}x - 15\right| \le 0.1 \quad \Rightarrow \quad 44.7 \le x \le 45.3$

2. $\left|\frac{4}{3}\pi r^3 - 10\right| \le \frac{1}{5} \quad \Rightarrow \quad 1.3275345 \le r \le 1.3453559.$ Or, $\frac{1}{10}\sqrt[3]{7350}\pi^{-1/3} \le r \le \frac{1}{10}\sqrt[3]{7650}\pi^{-1/3}.$

▼ Homework Problems

Core Exercises: 11, 19, 32, 39, 44, 50, 61, 73, 80

Sample Assignment: 1, 6, 11, 19, 25, 32, 33, 39, 44, 50, 61, 72, 73, 80, 94, 122

Solve the following inequalities and equations, and graph their solution sets.

1. (a) $x^3 - 4x^2 + 3x > 0$

(b) $x^3 - 4x^2 + 3x \geq 0$

(c) $x^3 - 4x^2 + 3x \leq 0$

(d) $x^3 - 4x^2 + 3x = 0$

2. (a) $\dfrac{x^2 - 1}{x^2 - 4} < 0$

(b) $\dfrac{x^2 - 1}{x^2 - 4} \leq 0$

(c) $\dfrac{x^2 - 1}{x^2 - 4} \geq 0$

(d) $\dfrac{x^2 - 1}{x^2 - 4} = 0$

GROUP WORK 2, SECTION 1.7

Teaching Tolerance

When manufacturing items, we often have varying degrees of allowable tolerance. For example, assume a piece of metal needs to be 2 cm wide. If the metal is being used to make an attractive bracelet, any value between 1.9 cm and 2.1 cm would probably be okay. If it is being used to make a ruler, any value between 1.95 cm and 2.05 cm would probably be acceptable. If it is being used in an automobile engine, it would probably be best to have it measure between 1.999 cm and 2.001 cm.

We can express these possible ranges as $|x - 2| \leq 0.1$, $|x - 2| \leq 0.05$, and $|x - 2| \leq 0.001$.

1. Assume that we have a process where for every 3 cm^3 of batter we start with, we wind up with 1 cm^3 of Belderon. Assume that we want to wind up with 15 cm^3 of Belderon, with a tolerance of 0.1 cm^3. What is the allowable range of quantity of batter?

2. Now assume we are manufacturing steel ball bearings. We want to manufacture ball bearings with a volume between 9.8 mm^3 and 10.2 mm^3. What is the allowable range of the radius of each bearing?

1.8 COORDINATE GEOMETRY

▼ Suggested Time and Emphasis

1– 2 classes. Essential material.

▼ Points to Stress

1. The distance and midpoint formulas.

2. The relationship between a two-variable equation and its graph. (This is the most crucial concept.)

3. Sketching graphs by plotting points, using intercepts and symmetry.

4. Equations of circles and their graphs, including the technique of completing the square.

▼ Sample Questions

- **Text Question:** Circle the type of types of symmetry exhibited by each of the following figures.

  (a)   (b)

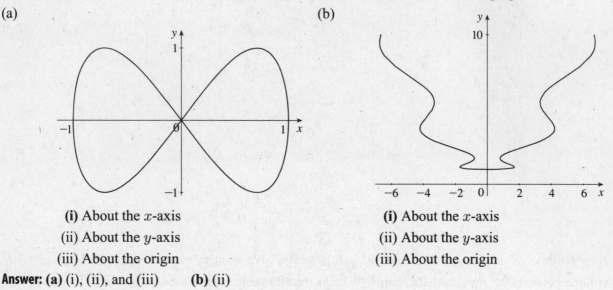

    (i) About the x-axis   **(i)** About the x-axis

    (ii) About the y-axis   **(ii)** About the y-axis

    (iii) About the origin   **(iii)** About the origin

  Answer: (a) (i), (ii), and (iii)   **(b)** (ii)

- **Drill Question:** Graph the circle with equation $x^2 + 2x + y^2 - 4y = 20$.

  Answer:

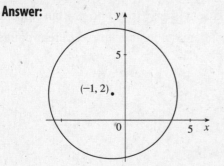

▼ In-Class Materials

- Obtain a transparency of a local map, and overlay it with an appropriate grid. Try to estimate the walking distance between the classroom and various points of interest. Then use the distance formula to find the distance "as the crow flies". This is discussed in Exercise 113 in the text.

- Assume that a meter stick is situated as in the diagram at right. Ask the students to find the 50 cm mark, and then the 25 cm mark.

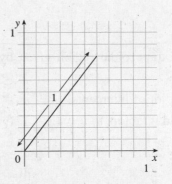

- I have always found this interesting, and your students may, too. Many modern cities are laid out in a grid similar to René Descartes' coordinate system. Paris, however, looks something like this:

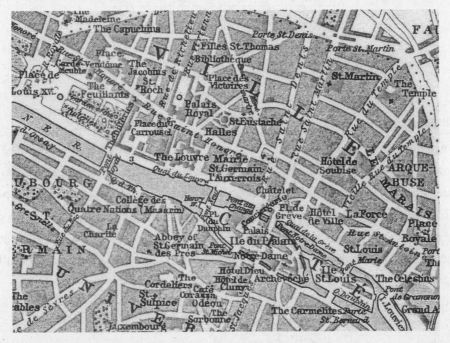

One can imagine René Descartes looking at such a map and saying, "There *must* to be a more organized way to arrange points in a plane!"

- Graph $y = ||x| - 1| - 2$ by plotting points. This is a nice curve because it is easy to get points, but students will not immediately see what the curve should look like. Have different students obtain different points, and plot them on a common graph on the board.

Answer:

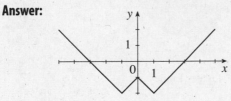

- Emphasize that the equation $(x - 2)^2 + (y + 3)^2 = 100$ and the equation $x^2 - 4x + y^2 + 6y = -3$ have the same graph — the same points satisfy both equations. Perhaps test $(2, 7)$ and $(1, 1)$ in both equations and notice that $(2, 7)$ satisfies both, and $(1, 1)$ fails to satisfy either. The only difference between the two equations is the form: it is easier to work with the first than the second.

49

▼ Examples

- Investigate the trapezoidal region given by the inequalities $x > 2$, $y > \frac{3}{2}x - 3$, $y > -x + 7$, and $y < -x + 12$.

- A curve with a lot of intercepts: $y = x^5 - 15x^4 + 85x^3 - 225x^2 + 274x - 120$ looks frightening until students are told it factors to $y = (x - 1)(x - 2)(x - 3)(x - 4)(x - 5)$.

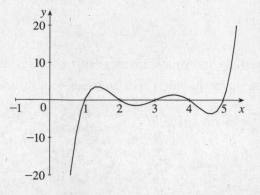

▼ Group Work 1: Taxicab Geometry

Taxicab geometry was first invented in the late 1800s, and is an accessible example of non-Euclidean geometry. In taxicab geometry, we assume a grid where we are allowed to travel only along the roads, and we define "distance" as driving distance. For example, in taxicab geometry, the distance between the point $(0, 0)$ and the point $(5, 6)$ is 11, because we would have to drive five blocks north and six blocks east to get from $(0, 0)$ to $(5, 6)$. There are analogues to circles, parabolas, and all the conic sections in taxicab geometry. This activity explores the distance formula in this context, and then checks to see whether the student really understands the definition of a circle.

If Chapter 11 is to be covered, note at that time that one can draw taxicab ellipses, hyperbolas, and parabolas.

Answers:

1. No, you are a four-mile drive away.

2.

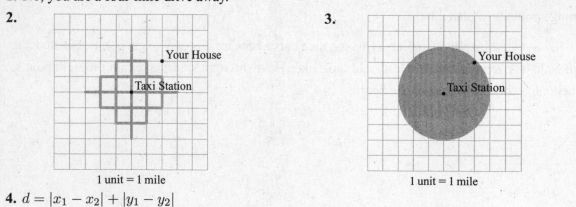

4. $d = |x_1 - x_2| + |y_1 - y_2|$

▼ Group Work 2: Discovering the Shift

This group work foreshadows Section 2.5: Transformations of Functions. The curves are obtainable by plotting points, although other techniques may be used. The first part deals with functions, although it doesn't use the term "function". The second part deals with $y^2 = x$, whose graph is also easily obtainable by plotting points.

Answers (Part One)

1. $y = x^2$: x- and y-intercepts $(0, 0)$

$y = (x - 1)^2$: x-intercept $(1, 0)$, y-intercept $(0, 1)$

$y = (x - 2)^2$: x-intercept $(2, 0)$, y-intercept $(0, 4)$

$y = (x - 3)^2$: x-intercept $(3, 0)$, y-intercept $(0, 9)$

$y = (x - 4)^2$: x-intercept $(4, 0)$, y-intercept $(0, 16)$

2.

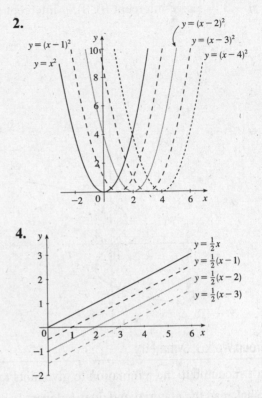

3. $y = \frac{1}{2}x$: x- and y-intercepts $(0, 0)$

$y = \frac{1}{2}(x - 1)$: x-intercept $(1, 0)$, y-intercept $\left(0, -\frac{1}{2}\right)$

$y = \frac{1}{2}(x - 2)$: x-intercept $(2, 0)$, y-intercept $(0, -1)$

$y = \frac{1}{2}(x - 3)$: x-intercept $(3, 0)$, y-intercept $\left(0, -\frac{3}{2}\right)$

4.

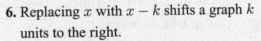

5.

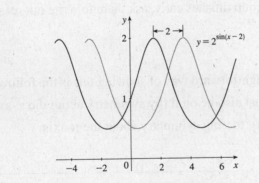

6. Replacing x with $x - k$ shifts a graph k units to the right.

Answers (Part Two)

1. $y^2 = x$: x- and y-intercepts $(0, 0)$.

$(y - 1)^2 = x$: x-intercept $(0, 1)$, y-intercept $(1, 0)$

$(y - 2)^2 = x$: x-intercept $(0, 2)$, y-intercept $(4, 0)$

$(y - 3)^2 = x$: x-intercept $(0, 3)$, y-intercept $(9, 0)$

$(y - 4)^2 = x$: x-intercept $(0, 4)$, y-intercept $(16, 0)$

2.

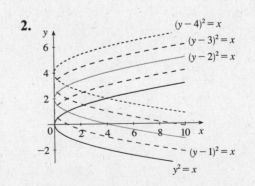

3. $y = \frac{1}{2}x$: x- and y-intercepts $(0,0)$

$y - 1 = \frac{1}{2}x$: x-intercept $(0,1)$, y-intercept $(-2,0)$

$y - 2 = \frac{1}{2}x$: x-intercept $(0,2)$, y-intercept $(-4,0)$

$y - 3 = \frac{1}{2}x$: x-intercept $(0,3)$, y-intercept $(-6,0)$

4.

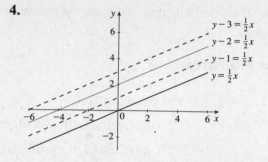

5.

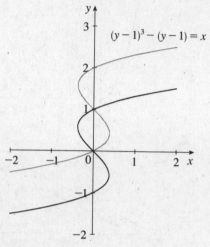

6. Replacing y with $y - k$ shifts a graph k units up.

7. The graph would be shifted 4 units down.

▼ Group Work 3: Symmetry

Don't succumb to the temptation to give hints too early here; this activity should be accessible to any student who has read the material and does not want to give up. If a group finishes early, ask them to write out reasons that certain graphs do not exist.

Answers:

Answers will vary. Problems 5, 6 and 7 are impossible. A straightforward way of showing this is the following pointwise argument: If (x, y) is on the curve, then $(-x, y)$ must also be on it (by symmetry about the x-axis), and then $(x, -y)$ must be on it (by symmetry about the origin), forcing symmetry about the y-axis.

▼ Homework Problems

Core Exercises: 5, 6, 8, 11, 28, 53, 54, 62, 64, 81, 92

Sample Assignment: 5, 6, 8, 11, 14, 27, 28, 53, 54, 62, 64, 75, 81, 92, 94, 105, 115

GROUP WORK 1, SECTION 1.8

Taxicab Geometry

Assume you live in a town where the streets form a grid.

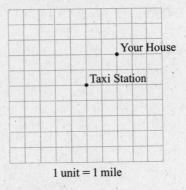

1 unit = 1 mile

1. The taxi dispatcher is willing to let the taxis travel only 3 miles to pick up a customer. Will she allow a taxi to leave her station to pick you up at your house?

2. Shade the region consisting of all points where the cab is allowed to make a pickup.

3. Now assume that, instead of a city, the taxi station and your house are located on a huge expanse of pavement, extending for miles in every direction, with no obstacles in sight. Shade the region where a cab would be allowed to make a pickup.

4. Create a "distance formula" the dispatcher could use to find how far the cab would travel.

GROUP WORK 2, SECTION 1.8

Discovering the Shift

Part One

1. Find the x- and y-intercepts of the curves $y = x^2$, $y = (x-1)^2$, $y = (x-2)^2$, $y = (x-3)^2$, and $y = (x-4)^2$.

2. Sketch the graph of each equation in Problem 1.

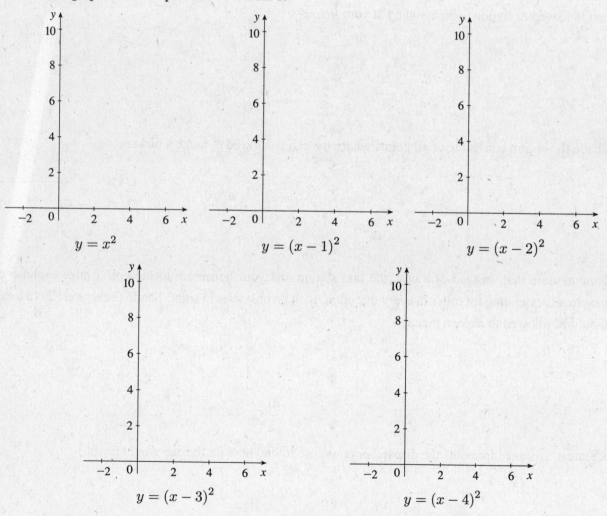

$y = x^2$ $y = (x-1)^2$ $y = (x-2)^2$

$y = (x-3)^2$ $y = (x-4)^2$

3. Find the x- and y-intercepts of the curves $y = \frac{1}{2}x$, $y = \frac{1}{2}(x-1)$, $y = \frac{1}{2}(x-2)$, and $y = \frac{1}{2}(x-3)$.

4. Sketch the graph of each equation in Problem 3.

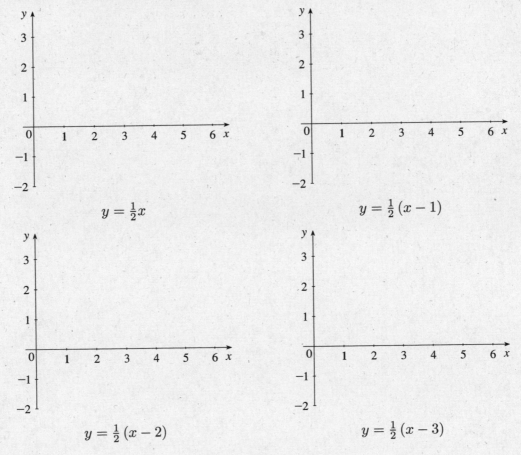

$y = \frac{1}{2}x$

$y = \frac{1}{2}(x-1)$

$y = \frac{1}{2}(x-2)$

$y = \frac{1}{2}(x-3)$

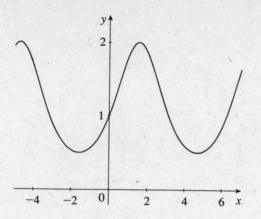

5. This is a graph of the complicated equation $y = 2^{\sin x}$.

On the same axes, sketch a graph of $y = 2^{\sin(x-2)}$. You don't need to know what "sin" means to do this problem.

6. This activity demonstrates an important principle about replacing x by $x - k$. What is that principle?

Part Two

1. Find the x- and y-intercepts of the curves $y^2 = x$, $(y-1)^2 = x$, $(y-2)^2 = x$, $(y-3)^2 = x$, and $(y-4)^2 = x$.

2. Sketch the graph of each equation in Problem 1.

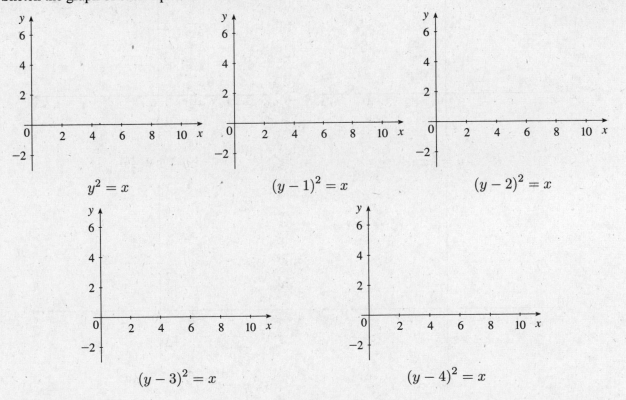

$y^2 = x$

$(y-1)^2 = x$

$(y-2)^2 = x$

$(y-3)^2 = x$

$(y-4)^2 = x$

3. Find the x- and y-intercepts of the curves $y = \frac{1}{2}x$, $y - 1 = \frac{1}{2}x$, $y - 2 = \frac{1}{2}x$, and $y - 3 = \frac{1}{2}x$.

4. Sketch the graph of each equation in Problem 3.

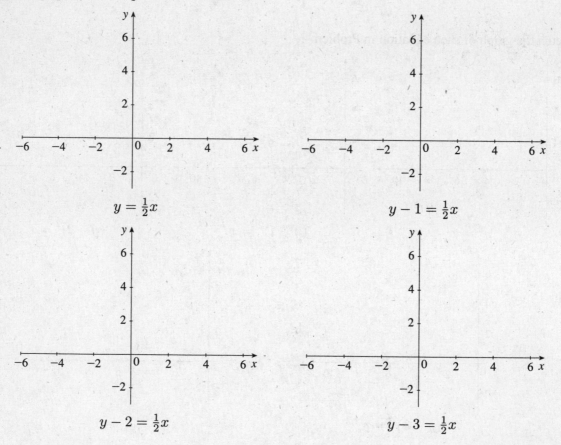

$$y = \frac{1}{2}x$$

$$y - 1 = \frac{1}{2}x$$

$$y - 2 = \frac{1}{2}x$$

$$y - 3 = \frac{1}{2}x$$

5. This is a graph of the complicated equation $y^3 - y = x$.

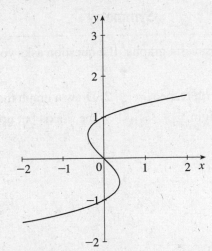

On the same axes, sketch a graph of $(y-1)^3 - (y-1) = x$.

6. This activity was designed to demonstrate an important principle about replacing y by $y - k$. What is that principle?

7. What do you think would happen if we replaced y by $y + 4$?

GROUP WORK 3, SECTION 1.8

Symmetry

For this activity you are asked to draw several graphs. If a question asks you to draw something that does not exist, write "Does not exist".

1. Draw a graph that is symmetrical with respect to the x-axis, the y-axis, and the origin.

2. Draw a graph that is symmetrical with respect to the x-axis but not the y-axis.

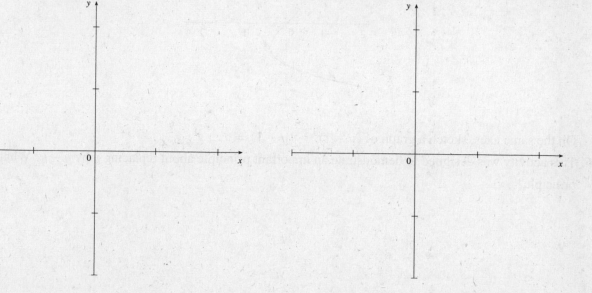

3. Draw a graph that is symmetrical with respect to the y-axis only.

4. Draw a graph that is symmetrical with respect to the origin.

5. Draw a graph that is symmetrical with respect to the x-axis and the y-axis, but not the origin.

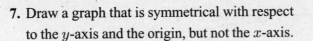

6. Draw a graph that is symmetrical with respect to the x-axis and the origin, but not the y-axis.

7. Draw a graph that is symmetrical with respect to the y-axis and the origin, but not the x-axis.

8. Draw a graph that is *not* symmetrical with respect to the x-axis, nor the y-axis, nor the origin.

1.9 GRAPHING CALCULATORS; SOLVING EQUATIONS AND INEQUALITIES GRAPHICALLY

▼ Suggested Time and Emphasis

1 class. Recommended material.

▼ Points to Stress

1. Approximating the solution to an equation by finding the roots of an expression graphically.

2. Approximating the solution to an inequality by graphing both sides of the inequality.

▼ Sample Questions

- **Text Question:** Give an advantage of solving an equation graphically, and an advantage of solving an equation algebraically.

- **Drill Question:** Solve the equation $x^3 - \sqrt{x} = 2x - 1$ to the nearest thousandth.
  Answer: $x \approx 0.2556$ or $x \approx 1.464$

▼ In-Class Materials

- Have the students find an viewing rectangles for $y = 3x + 1$, $y = -x^2 + 2$, and $y = x^6 - 100x^4 + 50$.

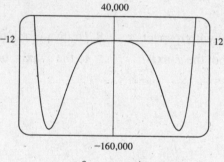

$$y = x^6 - 100x^4 + 50$$

- If graphing calculators are going to be an important part of the course, do not hurry the concept of finding appropriate windows. Let the students play with functions such as $\sin x$, $\ln x$, $\cos^{-1} x$, and so forth. At this stage, don't ask the students to worry too much about what they mean; let them play. Let them develop the idea of the variety of functions their calculators contain, and the idea that each function gives rise to its own special curve. In the unfortunate event that your students can't "play", perhaps ask them which functions are bounded or unbounded, which are symmetric about the y-axis, which are symmetric about the origin, and so on.

- Have the students determine the intersection points of $y = x^2 - 2$ and $y = -x^2 + 5x + 1$ both graphically and algebraically.
  Answers: $x = -\frac{1}{2}$, $x = 3$

- Have the students compare the values of $100x^2$ and $x^4 + 1$ for $x = 0$, $x = \frac{1}{2}$, $x = 1$, and $x = 2$. Then ask the question: For what values of x is $100x^2 > x^4 + 1$? See if they can use their calculators to approximate the answer.

62

Answers: $100x^2 > x^4 + 1$ for $x \in [-10, -0.1] \cup [0.1, 10]$, approximately.

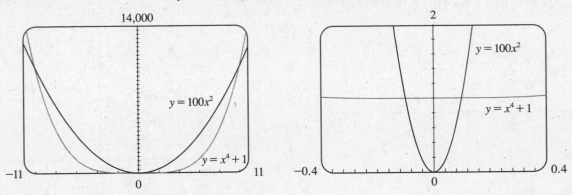

Notice that it is possible to find the right windows by trial and error, but sometimes plugging a number or two into the functions can give a clue as to the best y-range.

▼ Examples

Graphs that some calculators get wrong:

- $y = \sqrt{x-2}\sqrt{x-4}$: Some calculators do not give a graph with the correct domain.

- $y = \sin x + \frac{1}{100}\cos 100x$: The "standard" viewing rectangle misses the bumps that a rectangle of $[-0.1, 0.1] \times [-0.1, 0.1]$ will catch.

- $y = x^{1/3}$: Some calculators dislike taking negative numbers to rational powers, even when it is possible.

- $y = \dfrac{\sin\left(x - \sqrt{2}\right)}{x - \sqrt{2}}$: Calculators are not good at graphing functions with holes.

▼ Group Work 1: Some Interesting Curves

The idea here is to give the students some idea of the variety of functions that their calculator can create, and of some of the calculator's limitations as well. It is also an exercise in putting parentheses in the correct places. If a group finishes early, ask them to come up with their own interesting curve.

Answers:

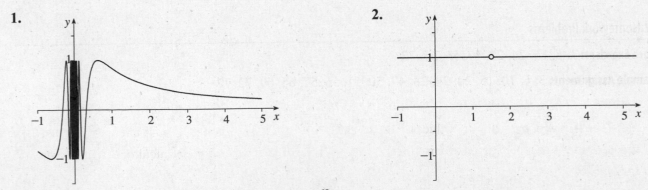

1.

2.

3.

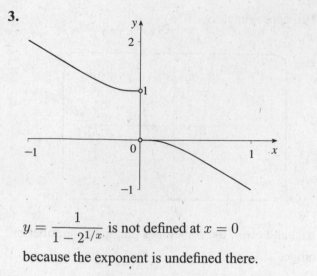

$y = \dfrac{1}{1 - 2^{1/x}}$ is not defined at $x = 0$

because the exponent is undefined there.

4.

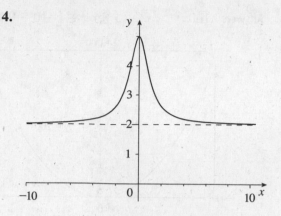

It appears that as x gets very large,

$y = \dfrac{3}{1 + x^2} + 2$ approaches 2.

5.

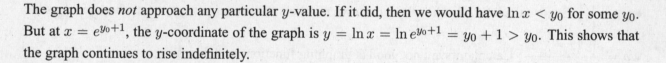

The graph does *not* approach any particular y-value. If it did, then we would have $\ln x < y_0$ for some y_0. But at $x = e^{y_0+1}$, the y-coordinate of the graph is $y = \ln x = \ln e^{y_0+1} = y_0 + 1 > y_0$. This shows that the graph continues to rise indefinitely.

▼ Group Work 2: The Small Shall Grow Large

If a group finishes early, ask them to similarly compare x^3 and x^4.

Answers:

1. $x^6 \geq x^8$ for $-1 \leq x \leq 1$
2. $x^3 \geq x^5$ for $-\infty < x \leq -1, 0 \leq x \leq 1$
3. $x^3 \geq x^{105}$ for $-\infty < x \leq -1, 0 \leq x \leq 1$. If the exponents are both even, the answer is the same as for Problem 1; if the exponents are both odd, the answer is the same as for Problem 2.

▼ Homework Problems

Core Exercises: 3, 6, 15, 24, 28, 47, 56, 65, 72

Sample Assignment: 3, 6, 10, 15, 20, 24, 28, 47, 50, 51, 56, 57, 65, 69, 72, 77

1. Sketch the graph of $y = \sin \dfrac{1}{x}$. Pay particular attention to what happens when x is close to zero.

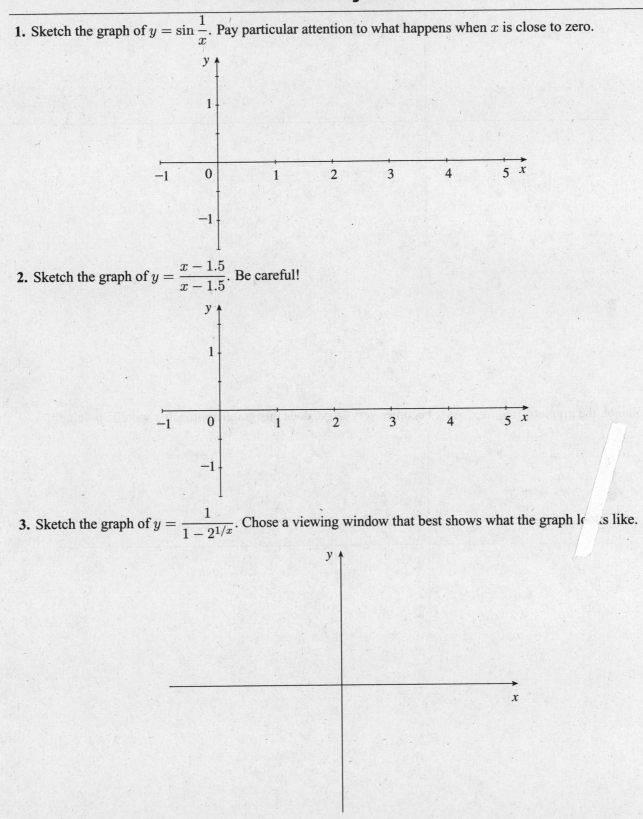

2. Sketch the graph of $y = \dfrac{x - 1.5}{x - 1.5}$. Be careful!

3. Sketch the graph of $y = \dfrac{1}{1 - 2^{1/x}}$. Chose a viewing window that best shows what the graph looks like.

4. Sketch the graph of $y = \dfrac{3}{1 + x^2} + 2$. As x becomes very large, does this graph approach a specific y-value?

5. Sketch the graph of $y = \ln x$. As x becomes very large, does this graph approach a specific y-value?

GROUP WORK 2, SECTION 1.9

The Small Shall Grow Large

---

1. For what values of x is $x^6 \geq x^8$? For what values is $x^6 \leq x^8$?

2. For what values of x is $x^3 \geq x^5$?

3. For what values of x is $x^3 \geq x^{105}$? Can you generalize your results?

1.10 LINES

▼ Suggested Time and Emphasis

1 class. Essential material.

▼ Points to Stress

1. Computing equations of lines in their various forms, given information such as a point and a slope, or two points.
2. The concepts of parallel, perpendicular, slope, vertical, horizontal, and rate of change as reflected in equations of lines.
3. Graphing lines from their equations.

▼ Sample Questions

- **Text Question:** Which of the three lines graphed below has the largest slope?

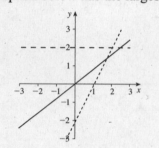

  Answer: The dotted line
- **Drill Question:** Find an equation of the line through the points $(2, 4)$ and $(3, -1)$.
  Answer: $y = -5x + 14$

▼ In-Class Materials

- One good way to get students used to slope is to have them do quick estimates. Stand in front of the class, raise your arm at various angles, and have them write down (or call out) estimates. Students should be able to tell a positive from a negative slope, and whether a slope is closer to $\frac{1}{3}$ than it is to 3. Also note that if the x- and y-scales on a graph are different, the appearance of the slope can be misleading.
- A classic example is to have the students come up with conversion formulas from Fahrenheit to centigrade and vice-versa, using the fact that in centigrade measurement, water freezes at $0°$ and boils at $100°$ ($-32°$ F and $212°$ F respectively.) Other conversion formulas can be found, using facts such as the following: 3 ft ≈ 0.914 m, 1 L ≈ 0.264 gal (US), a 250-calorie snack is equivalent to 0.991 BTU, etc.
- Go over an interpolation with the students. For example, compare your school's budget this year with that of ten years ago. Find the equation of the appropriate line. Then try to predict the budget five years ago, and see if a linear model was appropriate. (Linear models will be discussed more thoroughly in the next section.)
- Ask the students to figure out if three given points are vertices of a right triangle. They can go ahead and plot them, to get a guess going. Ask them to come up with a strategy, and reveal (or ideally elicit) the idea of writing equations of lines between each pair of points, and checking for perpendicular lines. $(3, 4)$, $(3, 12)$, and $(6, 5)$ do not form a right triangle; $(-2, -1)$, $(-2, 8)$, and $(8, -1)$ do.

- Don't neglect to give the students horizontal and vertical lines to explore—they often find equations of vertical lines challenging.

▼ Examples

Equations of some standard lines:

- Through $(3, 5)$ and $(-1, 13)$: $y = -2x + 11$
- Through $(6, -5)$ with a slope of $\frac{1}{3}$: $y = \frac{1}{3}x - 7$

▼ Group Work 1: I've Grown Accustomed to Your Growth

This activity uses the students' skills in finding equations of lines to foreshadow the idea that some growth is linear, and some is not linear.

Answers:

1. Yes $(m = 1)$, no, yes $(m \approx 2.08)$, yes $(m \approx 2.01)$
2. Equally spaced changes in x-values result in equally spaced changes in y-values.

▼ Group Work 2: Read Between the Lines

This is a drill-oriented activity, probably best worked on by the students individually, using their groups to check their work. It just goes over various bits of information that suffice to give the equation of a line.

Answers:

1. $y = -\frac{15}{2}x + 35$ 2. $x = 4$ 3. $y = -2x + 7$ 4. $y = 3$
5. $x = 2$ 6. $y = -2x + 7$ 7. $y = -\frac{1}{3}x + \frac{11}{3}$ 8. $x = 2$
9. Not enough information given   10. $y = \frac{1}{2}x$ 11. $y = 4x - 11$

▼ Group Work 3: Lines and Slopes

In this age of graphing calculators, students usually see graphs where the x- and y-scales are the same. This activity allows them to explore slopes when the scales are different, and allows them to connect linear relationships to the real world.

Answers:

1. (b), (a), (c)
2. (a), (c), (b)
3. Answers will vary. Make sure your students' answers are consistent with the slopes of the lines. Possible answers:
   (a) The accumulation of rain or snow during a storm.
   (b) The distance a jet plane has traveled from a given point in time.
   (c) The force exerted by a spring as it stretches.

▼ Homework Problems

Core Exercises: 1, 2, 7, 16, 21, 24, 26, 37, 46, 52

Sample Assignment: 1, 2, 4, 7, 13, 16, 18, 21, 24, 26, 30, 37, 38, 46, 52, 65, 75

GROUP WORK 1, SECTION 1.10

I've Grown Accustomed to Your Growth

1. Some of the following four tables of data have something in common: linear growth. By trying to find equations of lines, determine which of them represent linear growth. Which table has the slowest growth?

x	y
1	2
2	3
3	4
4	5

x	y
21.5	4.32
32.6	4.203
43.7	4.090
54.8	3.980

x	y
−3	1.1
−2.5	2.14
−2	3.18
−1.5	4.22

x	y
1	−5.00
3	−0.98
6	5.05
8	9.07

2. In a sentence, describe a property of linear growth that can be determined from a table of values.

Find the equations of the following lines. If there is not enough information given, write "Not enough information given".

1. The line through the points $(4, 5)$ and $(6, -10)$.

2. The line through the points $(4, 5)$ and $(4, -10)$.

3. The line through the point $(2, 3)$ with slope -2.

4. The horizontal line through the point $(2, 3)$.

5. The vertical line through the point $(2, 3)$.

6. The line through the point $(2, 3)$ that is parallel to the line $y = -2x + 11$.

7. The line through the point $(2, 3)$ that is perpendicular to the line $3x - y + 12 = 0$.

8. The line through the point $(2, 3)$ that is perpendicular to the line $y = 5$.

9. The line parallel to the line $y = -2x + 11$ and perpendicular to the line $y = \frac{1}{2}x + 12$.

10. The line with slope $\frac{1}{2}$ that passes through the origin.

11. The line parallel to the line $y = 4x - 2$ that passes through the point of intersection of the lines $y = x - 2$ and $y = 2x - 5$.

Lines and Slopes

1. Sort the following three lines from smallest slope to largest slope.

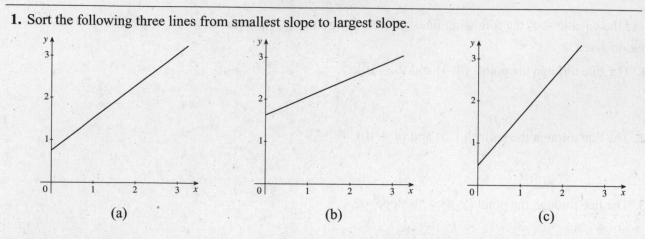

2. Sort the following three lines from smallest slope to largest slope.

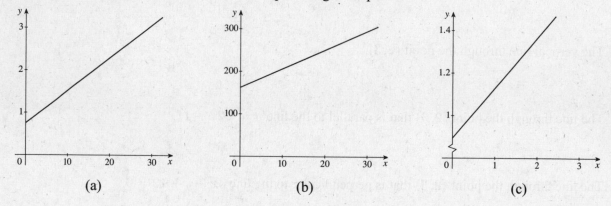

3. For each of the following graphs, describe a possible real-world situation that it might model. Make sure your answer is realistic.

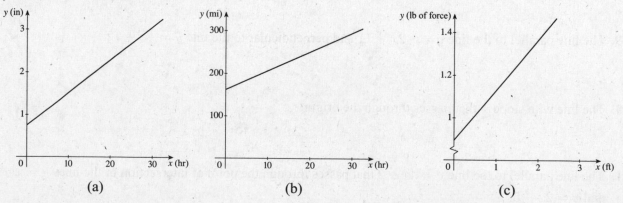

1.11 MAKING MODELS USING VARIATION

▼ Suggested Time and Emphasis

1 class. Recommended material.

▼ Point to Stress

Direct and inverse proportionality.

▼ Sample Questions

- **Text Question:**

  (a) If y is proportional to x, must there be a linear equation relating y and x?

  (b) If there is a linear equation relating y and x, must y be proportional to x?

  Answer: (a) Yes   **(b)** No

- **Drill Question:** The mass of a memo is proportional to the number of pages it contains. If a 100-page memo measures 89 g, how much mass would a 35 page memo have?

  Answer: $(0.89)\,35 = 31.15$ g

▼ In-Class Materials

- Have the students come up with as many examples of proportionality as they can. One effective way would be to give them a minute to write down as many as they could think of, then another couple of minutes to discuss their list with a neighbor, generating more. Finally, have them write down their answers on the board. With luck, some will accidentally give examples that are not proportional or that are inversely proportional. If these don't come up, you can ask, "What about the height of a person and that person's average rent?" or, "What about the cost of a computer and its weight, all other things being equal?"

- Point out that proportionality is a model, just like a linear model or any other kind of model. For example, show students an example of a scatter plot such as the one at right.
  Clearly there is no straight line that will go through the points, but we can model the relationship by a straight line to try to make predictions.

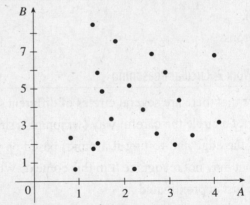

- Discuss the difference between a general linear relationship and direct variation: in a directly proportional relationship, the origin is a data point. For example, the number of cans of beans you buy and the price you pay are in direct proportion—zero cans cost zero dollars. If you have to pay a fee to get into the store (as in some discount stores) the two quantities are no longer in direct proportion.

- There are many proportional and inversely proportional relationships that the students already understand, but may not have thought about using that vocabulary. For example, the area of a circle is directly proportional to the square of its radius. The area of a rectangle is jointly proportional to its length and width. The time it takes to make a trip (of fixed distance) is inversely proportional to the average speed.

▼ Examples

- Newton's Law: The rate of change of temperature of an object is proportional to the difference between the current temperature of the object and the temperature of its surroundings.
- Torricelli's Law: The velocity at which liquid pours out of a cylindrical container (like orange juice out of a can with a hole at the bottom) is proportional to the square root of its height in the container.
- Einstein's Law: The energy of a photon is directly proportional to its frequency.
- Einstein's Theory of Relativity: The energy of a particle is proportional to its mass. (The constant of proportionality is the speed of light, squared.)

▼ Group Work 1: Powers of Magnification

All of these are real measurements taken by the author's brother, except for the second, which was altered slightly to make the inverse relationship work more closely. If a group finishes early, or if you want to go into more detail, point out that the measurement was actually "$100\times = 20$ microns" and discuss whether an inverse variation model is still appropriate.

Notice the premise of the problem: the mathematician doesn't quite understand the application, but understands the mathematics enough to answer the question. In industry, people who model often are not given the "big picture," but are still expected to answer questions based on the information they have, and on the underlying principles of mathematics.

Answers:

1. This is inversely proportional, since the larger the magnification, the smaller the pointer.
2. The constant is approximately 1600. The first three data points give 1600 exactly. The last point would give 1600 if it were actually 1.6. (If we are talking about a tenth of a micron, we can't rule out experimental error.)
3. 8 microns

▼ Group Work 2: Circular Reasoning

Make sure that there are several circles of different sizes around the room. Show the students how to measure perimeter of a circle the careful way (wrapping a string, and measuring the string) or the sloppy way (holding a ruler to the edge and rolling it around) based on your preference. The students already know the formula $C = \pi d$ but may not recognize it in this context. When they are finished, congratulate them and point out that they have just approximated π.

If this activity is too simple, have the students try to find the constant acceleration due to gravity (9.8 m/s^2), the constant of a spring, or the formula for the volume of a cylinder.

▼ Homework Problems

Core Exercises: 6, 7, 8, 12, 15, 18, 24, 25, 29

Sample Assignment: 6, 7, 8, 9, 12, 13, 15, 18, 20, 24, 25, 28, 29, 32, 39

I received this email from my brother, an amateur scientist, last month:

```
From:  "Melvin Shaw" <melvin@etaoinshrdlu.com>
To:  "Doug Shaw" <doug@shrdluetaoin.com>
Date:  Sat, 11 Jun 2011 14:11:54 -0600
Subject:  Math help needed!

Hey bro.  I took the following measurements of the pointer in my eyepiece at
the powers of magnification shown on the left:

40X = 40 microns
100X = 16 microns
400X = 4 microns
1000X = 1.5 microns

Are these random numbers, or are they related in some way?
```

Frankly, I didn't know what he was talking about; I didn't know what the × meant, nor what the pointer in the eyepiece was, exactly (Was it shrinking? Why?) But I knew some mathematics, and recognized this as a proportional relationship.

1. Was this a directly proportional relationship, or an inversely proportional relationship? How do you know?

2. Approximately what is the constant of proportionality?

3. If my brother had a $200\times$ lens, predict the "pointer measurement".

GROUP WORK 2, SECTION 1.11

Circular Reasoning

Find three differently sized circles in the room, or make them yourself using a compass.

1. What are the diameters of your three circles?

2. What are the circumferences of your three circles?

3. Many people believe that the circumference of a circle is directly proportional to its diameter. Do you think this is true? Using your data, approximate the constant of proportionality.

2 FUNCTIONS

2.1 WHAT IS A FUNCTION?

▼ Suggested Time and Emphasis

$\frac{1}{2}$–1 class. Essential material.

▼ Points to Stress

1. The idea of function, viewed as the dependence of one quantity on a different quantity.

2. The notation associated with numeric functions, including piecewise-defined functions.

3. Domains and ranges from an algebraic perspective.

4. Four different representations of functions (verbally, algebraically, visually, and numerically).

▼ Sample Questions

- **Text Question:** What is a function?

  Answer: Answers will vary. Anything that gets at the idea of assigning an element in one set to an element in another set should be given full credit.

- **Drill Question:** Let $f(x) = x + \sqrt{x}$. Find $f(0)$ and $f(4)$.

  Answer: $f(0) = 0$, $f(4) = 6$

▼ In-Class Materials

- If students are using calculators, discuss the ties between the idea of a function and a calculator key. Keys such as sin, cos, tan, and $\sqrt{}$ represent functions. It is easy to compute and graph functions on a calculator. Contrast this with equations such as $y^3 - x^3 = 2xy$, which have graphs but are not easy to work with, even with a calculator. (Even symbolic algebra calculators such as the TI-89 do not do well with all general relations.) Point out that the calculator often gives approximations to function values—applying the square root function key to the number 2 gives 1.4142136 which is close, but not equal, to $\sqrt{2}$.

- This course emphasizes functions where both the domain and range sets are numerical. One could give a more abstract definition of function, where D and R can be any set. For example, there is a function mapping each student in the class to his or her birthplace. A nice thing about this point of view is that it can be pointed out that the map from each student to his or her telephone number may *not* be a function, because a student may have more than one telephone number, or none at all.

- Function notation can trip students up. Start with a function such as $f(x) = x^2 - x$ and have your students find $f(0)$, $f(1)$, $f(\sqrt{3})$, and $f(-1)$. Then have them find $f(\pi)$, $f(y)$, and (of course) $f(x + h)$. Some students will invariably, some day, assume that $f(a + b) = f(a) + f(b)$ for all functions, but this can be minimized if plenty of examples such as $f(2 + 3)$ are done at the outset.

- Discuss the straightforward things to look for when trying to find the domain of a function: zero denominators and negative even roots. Discuss the domain and range of a function such as
$$f(x) = \begin{cases} x^2 & \text{if } x \text{ is an integer} \\ 0 & \text{if } x \text{ is not an integer} \end{cases}$$
If the class seems interested, perhaps let them think about
$$f(x) = \begin{cases} x^2 & \text{if } x \text{ is rational} \\ 0 & \text{if } x \text{ is irrational} \end{cases}$$

- Let $f(x) = \dfrac{x(x-2)}{x-2}$ and $g(x) = x$. Ask students if the functions are the same function. If they say "yes", ask them to compare the domains, or to compute $g(2)$ and $f(2)$. If they say "no", ask them to find a value such that $f(x) \neq g(x)$. [This activity assumes that students know the equation of a circle with radius r. If they do not, this may be a good opportunity to introduce the concept.]

▼ Examples

- Real-world piecewise functions:

    1. The cost of mailing a parcel that weighs w ounces (see Figure 1 in the text)

    2. The cost of making x photocopies (given that there is usually a bulk discount)

    3. The cost of printing x pages from a computer (at some point the toner cartridge must be replaced)

- A function with a nontrivial domain: $\sqrt{\dfrac{x^2 - 5x + 6}{x^2 - 2x + 1}}$ has domain $(-\infty, 1) \cup (1, 2] \cup [3, \infty)$.

▼ Group Work 1: Choosing a Calling Plan

This activity will require some advance work on the part of your students, but it will be worth it. It complements Example 3 in the text. The world is full of advertisements for long-distance services, phone plans, and the like. These often have figures such as "five cents per minute", but there are a lot of details behind the figures. There may or may not be a monthly fee. There may or may not be a minimum call length. (One commercial offered a 20-minute call for $1, but did not mention that a three-minute call also cost $1.) There may or may not be a fee change after a certain time. (One plan costs five cents per minute for the first twenty minutes and seven cents per minute thereafter.) There may also be a rate increase after a certain base number of minutes are used.

Have each student pick a plan (or you can assign plans to them) and research exactly how the plan works. In addition to the myriad phone and long distance plans, there are collect call plans, plans in which phone service is bundled with other services, etc. Students can also research the cost of an operator-assisted long distance call. After they have done so, this group work can be handed out.

Part 1 is for this section and is algebraic in nature. Part 2 is for the next section (although it can be done earlier) and involves drawing a graph of a piecewise function. Note that you may not want to discuss the greatest integer function at this point. In that case, you can let students assume that the call lengths are all an integral number of minutes.

You may have to "keep students honest" here—a careless student may take the phrase "five cents per minute" at face value and not worry about the fine print. Being able to listen carefully to a commercial or a salesperson and translate the pitch into mathematics is not a trivial skill.

It might be a good idea to collect students' findings and distribute them. Students can then be assigned to decide which plan is best for them, taking into account their average call length, and the amount of calling they do each month. (The monthly fees become important to a person who doesn't use the phone often.) An alternative form of this group work is provided that deals with text messages.

▼ Group Work 2: Finding a Formula

Make sure that students know the equation of a circle with radius r, and that they remember the notation for piecewise-defined functions. Divide the class into groups of four. In each group, have half of them work on each problem first, and then have them check each other's work. If students find these problems difficult, have them work together on each problem.

Answers: 1. $f(x) = \begin{cases} -x - 2 & \text{if } x \le -2 \\ x + 2 & \text{if } -2 < x \le 0 \\ 2 & \text{if } x > 0 \end{cases}$ **2.** $g(x) = \begin{cases} x + 4 & \text{if } x \le -2 \\ 2 & \text{if } -2 < x \le 0 \\ \sqrt{4 - x^2} & \text{if } 0 < x \le 2 \\ x - 2 & \text{if } x > 2 \end{cases}$

▼ Group Work 3: Rounding the Bases

On the board, review how to compute the percentage error when estimating π by $\frac{22}{7}$. (Answer: 0.04%) Have them work on the problem in groups. If a group finishes early, have them look at $h(7)$ and $h(10)$ to see how fast the error grows. Students have not seen exponential functions before, but Problem 3 is a good foreshadowing of Section 4.1.

Answers: 1. 17.811434627, 17, 4.56% **2.** 220.08649875, 201, 8.67% **3.** 45.4314240633, 32, 29.56%

▼ Homework Problems

Core Exercises: 2, 6, 11, 18, 21, 29, 32, 44, 47, 50, 55, 65

Sample Assignment: 2, 6, 7, 11, 18, 21, 22, 25, 29, 32, 36, 44, 47, 50, 55, 56, 63, 65, 72, 83

GROUP WORK 1, SECTION 2.1
Choosing a Calling Plan

1. You have been assigned to research a calling plan. What is the name of the plan you've investigated?

2. Is there a monthly fee?

For Questions 3--7, do not include monthly fees.

3. How much would it cost to make a twenty-minute call using your plan?

4. How much would it cost to make a five-minute call?

5. How much would it cost to make a one-minute call?

6. How much would it cost to make a three-hour call?

7. Write a function $c(t)$, where t is the duration of the call in minutes and $c(t)$ is the cost of the call.

8. How much would it cost to make 20 five-minute calls in a month? (Include the monthly fee.)

9. How much would it cost to make 2 fifty-minute calls in a month? (Include the monthly fee.)

10. Is this plan suitable for you? Why or why not?

GROUP WORK 1, SECTION 2.1

Choosing a Text Message Plan

---

1. You have been assigned to research a text message plan. What is the name of the plan you've investigated?

2. Is there a monthly fee?

For Questions 3--5, do not include monthly fees.

3. How much would it cost to send twenty messages in one month using your plan?

4. How much would it cost to send three hundred messages in one month?

5. How much would it cost to send just one message in one month?

6. Is there a maximum message length?

7. Now including the monthly fee, how much would it cost to send 20 messages in one month. 300 messages? A single message?

8. What is the average cost per message under this plan if you send 20 messages in one month. 300 message? A single message?

9. Write a function $c(n)$ modeling the total monthly cost c if n messages are sent that month.

10. Is this plan suitable for you? Why or why not?

GROUP WORK 2, SECTION 2.1

Finding a Formula

Find formulas for the following functions:

1.

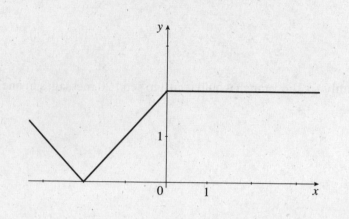

2.

GROUP WORK 3, SECTION 2.1

Rounding the Bases

1. For computational efficiency and speed, we often round off constants in equations. For example, consider the linear function
$$f(x) = 3.137619523x + 2.123337012$$
In theory, it is easy and quick to find $f(1)$, $f(2)$, $f(3)$, $f(4)$, and $f(5)$. In practice, most people doing this computation would probably substitute
$$f(x) = 3x + 2$$
unless a very accurate answer is called for. For example, compute $f(5)$ both ways to see the difference.

   The actual value of $f(5)$: _____

   The "rounding" estimate: _____

   The percentage error: _____

2. Now consider
$$g(x) = 1.12755319x^3 + 3.125694x^2 + 1$$
Again, one is tempted to substitute $g(x) = x^3 + 3x^2 + 1$.

   The actual value of $g(5)$: _____

   The "rounding" estimate: _____

   The percentage error: _____

3. It turns out to be dangerous to similarly round off exponential functions, due to the nature of their growth. For example, let's look at the function
$$h(x) = (2.145217198123)^x$$
One may be tempted to substitute $h(x) = 2^x$ for this one. Once again, look at the difference between these two functions.

   The actual value of $h(5)$: _____

   The "rounding" estimate: _____

   The percentage error: _____

2.2 GRAPHS OF FUNCTIONS

▼ Suggested Time and Emphasis

1 class. Essential material.

▼ Points to Stress

1. The Vertical Line Test.
2. Graphs of piecewise-defined functions.
3. The greatest integer function.

▼ Sample Questions

- **Text Question:** Your text discusses the greatest integer function $[\![x]\!]$. Compute $[\![2.6]\!]$, $[\![2]\!]$, $[\![-2.6]\!]$, and $[\![-2]\!]$.
  Answer: $[\![2.6]\!] = 2$, $[\![2]\!] = 2$, $[\![-2.6]\!] = -3$, $[\![-2]\!] = -2$

- **Drill Question:** Let $f(x) = x^2 + |x|$. Which of the following is the graph of f? How do you know?

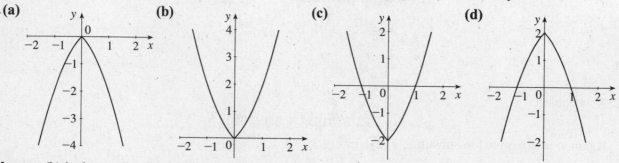

Answer: (b) is the graph of f, because $f(x) \geq 0$ for all x.

▼ In-Class Materials

- Draw a graph of fuel efficiency versus time on a trip, such as the one below. Lead a discussion of what could have happened on the trip.

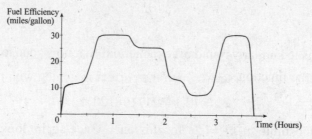

- In 1984, United States President Ronald Reagan proposed a plan to change the personal income tax system. According to his plan, the income tax would be 15% on the first $19,300 earned, 25% on the next $18,800, and 35% on all income above and beyond that. Describe this situation to the class, and have them graph (marginal) tax rate and tax owed versus income for incomes ranging from $0 to $80,000. Then have them try to come up with equations describing this situation.

- In the year 2000, Presidential candidate Steve Forbes proposed a "flat tax" model: 0% on the first $36,000 and 17% on the rest. Have your students do the same analysis, and compare the two models. As an extension, consider having them look at a current tax table and draw similar graphs.

86

- Discuss the shape, symmetries, and general "flatness" near 0 of the power functions x^n for various values of n. Similarly discuss $\sqrt[n]{x}$ for n even and n odd. A blackline master is provided at the end of this section, before the group work handouts.

▼ Examples

- A continuous piecewise-defined function

- A discontinuous piecewise-defined function

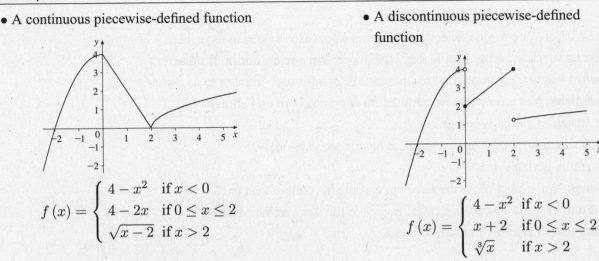

$$f(x) = \begin{cases} 4 - x^2 & \text{if } x < 0 \\ 4 - 2x & \text{if } 0 \le x \le 2 \\ \sqrt{x - 2} & \text{if } x > 2 \end{cases}$$

$$f(x) = \begin{cases} 4 - x^2 & \text{if } x < 0 \\ x + 2 & \text{if } 0 \le x \le 2 \\ \sqrt[3]{x} & \text{if } x > 2 \end{cases}$$

- Classic rational functions with interesting graphs

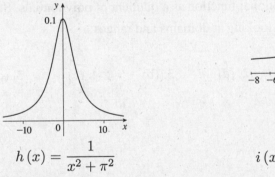

$$h(x) = \frac{1}{x^2 + \pi^2}$$

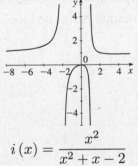

$$i(x) = \frac{x^2}{x^2 + x - 2}$$

▼ Group Work 1: Every Picture Tells a Story

Put students in groups of four, and have them work on the exercise. If there are questions, encourage them to ask each other before asking you. After going through the correct matching with them, have each group tell their story to the class and see if it fits the remaining graph.

Answers:

1. (b) **2.** (a) **3.** (c)

4. The roast was cooked in the morning and put in the refrigerator in the afternoon.

▼ Group Work 2: Functions in the Classroom

Before starting this one, review the definition of "function". Some of the problems can be answered only by polling the class after they are finished working. Don't forget to take leap years into account for the eighth problem. For an advanced class, anticipate Section 2.7 by quickly defining "one-to-one" and "bijection", then determining which of the functions have these properties.

Answers:

Chairs: Function, one-to-one, bijection (if all chairs are occupied)

Eye color: Function, not one-to-one

Mom & Dad's birthplace: Not a function; mom and dad could have been born in different places

Molecules: Function, one-to-one (with nearly 100% probability); inverse assigns a number of molecules to the appropriate student.

Spleens: Function, one-to-one, bijection. Inverse assigns each spleen to its owner.

Pencils: Not a function; some people may have more than one or (horrors!) none.

Social Security Number: Function, one-to-one; inverse assigns each number to its owner.

February birthday: Not a function; not defined for someone born on February 29.

Birthday: Function, perhaps one-to-one.

Cars: Not a function; some have none, some have more than one.

Cash: Function, perhaps one-to-one.

Middle names: Not a function; some have none, some have more than one.

Identity: Function, one-to-one, bijection. Inverse is the same as the function.

Algebra instructor: Function, not one-to-one.

▼ Group Work 3: Rational Functions

Remind students of the definition of a rational function as a quotient of polynomials. Students should be able to do this activity by plotting points and looking at domains and ranges.

Answers:

 1.

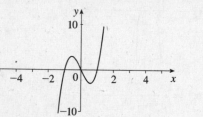

2. (d)   **3.** (b)   **4.** (e)   **5.** (c)   **6.** (a)

▼ Homework Problems

Core Exercises: 4, 7, 12, 16, 21, 38, 49, 52, 75

Sample Assignment: 4, 7, 12, 16, 21, 27, 30, 38, 44, 49, 52, 53, 63, 70, 75, 77, 84

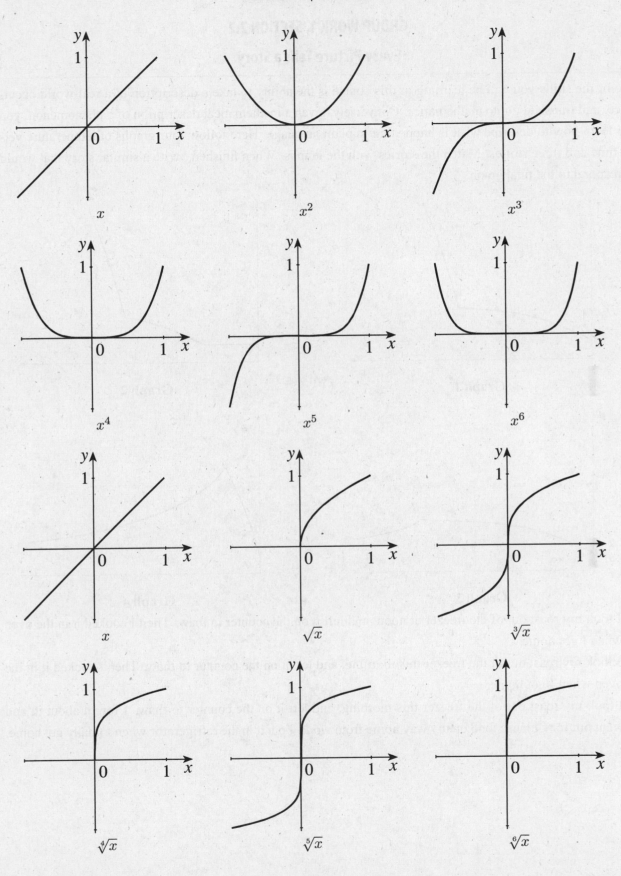

Every Picture Tells a Story

One of the skills you will be learning in this course is the ability to take a description of a real-world occurrence, and translate it into mathematics. Conversely, given a mathematical description of a phenomenon, you will learn how to describe what is happening in plain language. Here follow four graphs of temperature versus time and three stories. Match the stories with the graphs. When finished, write a similar story that would correspond to the final graph.

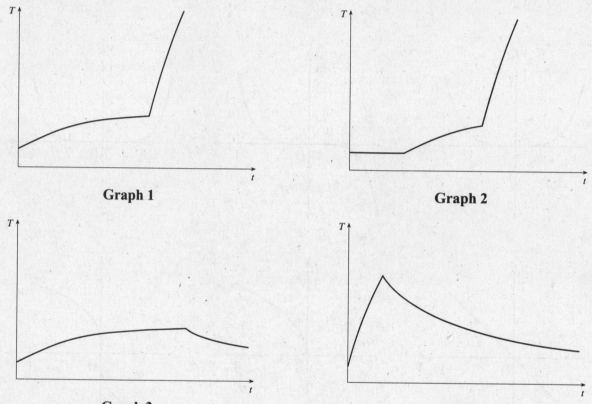

Graph 1   **Graph 2**

Graph 3   **Graph 4**

(a) I took my roast out of the freezer at noon, and left it on the counter to thaw. Then I cooked it in the oven when I got home.

(b) I took my roast out of the freezer this morning, and left it on the counter to thaw. Then I cooked it in the oven when I got home.

(c) I took my roast out of the freezer this morning, and left it on the counter to thaw. I forgot about it, and went out for Chinese food on my way home from work. I put it in the refrigerator when I finally got home.

Functions in the Classroom

Which of the following relations are functions?

Domain	Function Values	Function
All the people in your classroom	Chairs	f (person) = his or her chair
All the people in your classroom	The set {blue, brown, green, hazel}	f (person) = his or her eye color
All the people in your classroom	Cities	f (person) = birthplace of their mom and dad
All the people in your classroom	$\mathbb{R}$, the real numbers	f (person) = number of molecules in their body
All the people in your classroom	Spleens	f (person) = his or her own spleen
All the people in your classroom	Pencils	f (person) = his or her pencil
All the people in the United States	Integers from 0–999999999	f (person) = his or her Social Security number
All the living people born in February	Days in February, 2007	f (person) = his or her birthday in February 2007
All the people in your classroom	Days of the year	f (person) = his or her birthday
All the people in your classroom	Cars	f (person) = his or her car
All the people in your classroom	$\mathbb{R}$, the real numbers	f (person) = how much cash he or she has
All the people in your college	Names	f (person) = his or her middle name
All the people in your classroom	People	f (person) = himself or herself
All the people in your classroom	People	f (person) = his or her algebra instructor

Rational Functions

The functions below are sad and lonely because they have lost their graphs! Help them out by matching each function with its graph. One function's graph is not pictured here; when you are done matching, go ahead and sketch that function's graph.

1. $\dfrac{x^3 - x}{0.125}$

2. $\dfrac{x^2 - 1}{x^2 - 4}$

3. $\dfrac{x^2 - 4}{x^2 - 1}$

4. $\dfrac{x^2 - 1}{x + 0.5}$

5. $\dfrac{5x\left(x^2 - 1\right)}{x^2 + 1}$

6. $\dfrac{5x\left(x^2 - 1\right)}{-x^2 - 1}$

(a)

(b)

(c)

(d)

(e)

92

2.3   GETTING INFORMATION FROM THE GRAPH OF A FUNCTION

▼ Suggested Time and Emphasis

$\frac{1}{2}$–1 class. Essential material.

▼ Points to Stress

1. Gaining information about a function from its graph, including finding function values, domain and range.

2. Algebraic and geometric definitions of increasing and decreasing.

3. Finding local extrema of a function from its graph.

▼ Sample Questions

- **Text Question:** Draw a graph of a function with domain $[-10, 10]$ and range $[-2, 2]$. There should be at least one interval where the graph is increasing and at least one interval where the graph is decreasing.

  Answer: Answers will vary.

- **Drill Question:** If $f(x) = -x^2 + 9x + 2$, find the extreme value of f. Is it a maximum or a minimum?
  Answer: $f\left(\frac{9}{2}\right) = \frac{89}{4}$ is a maximum.

▼ In-Class Materials

- Explore domain and range with some graphs that have holes, such as the graphs of some of the functions in the previous section.

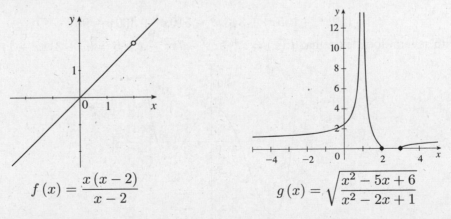

$$f(x) = \frac{x(x-2)}{x-2} \qquad g(x) = \sqrt{\frac{x^2 - 5x + 6}{x^2 - 2x + 1}}$$

- Draw a graph of electrical power consumption in the classroom versus time on a typical weekday, pointing out important features throughout, and using the vocabulary of this section as much as possible.

93

- Notice that it is fairly easy to tell where some functions are increasing and decreasing by looking at their graphs. For example, the graph of $f(x) = x^4 - 8x^2$ makes things clear. Note that in this case, the intervals are not immediately apparent from looking at the formula. However, for many functions such as $g(x) = x^3 - 3x^2 + x + 1$, it is very difficult to find the exact intervals where the function is increasing/decreasing. In this example, the endpoints of the intervals will occur at precisely $x = 1 \pm \frac{1}{3}\sqrt{6}$.

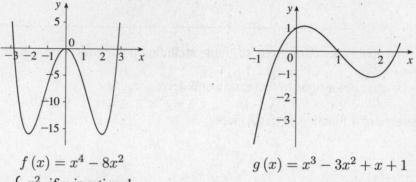

$$f(x) = x^4 - 8x^2 \qquad\qquad g(x) = x^3 - 3x^2 + x + 1$$

- Examine $f(x) = \begin{cases} x^2 & \text{if } x \text{ is rational} \\ 0 & \text{if } x \text{ is irrational} \end{cases}$ pointing out that it is neither increasing nor decreasing near $x = 0$. Stress that when dealing with new sorts of functions, it becomes important to know the precise mathematical definitions of such terms.

▼ Examples

- A function with two integer turning points and a flat spot:

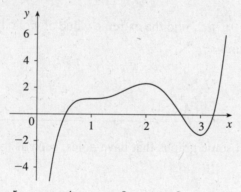

$$\tfrac{1}{6}\left(12x^5 - 105x^4 + 340x^3 - 510x^2 + 360x - 90\right)$$

- A function with several local extrema: $f(x) = x^4 + x^3 - 7x^2 - x + 6 = (x+3)(x+1)(x-1)(x-2)$

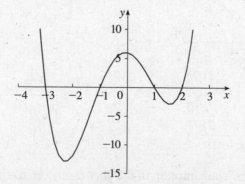

The extrema occur at $x \approx -2.254$, $x \approx -0.0705$, and $x \approx 1.5742$.

▼ Group Work 1: Calculator Exploration

This gives students a chance to graph things on their calculator and make conclusions. It will also serve as a warning that relying on calculator graphs without understanding the functions can lead one astray.

Notice that in calculus, when we say a function is increasing, we are saying it is increasing at every point on its domain. In this context, we are talking about increasing over an interval, which is slightly different. The curve $-1/x$, for example, is increasing at every point in its domain. Can we say it is decreasing over the interval $[-10, 1]$? No, because it is not defined in that interval. So the curve $-1/x$ is increasing over every interval for which it is defined.

Answers:

1. (c) **2.** (a) **3.** (a) (assuming positive intervals) **4.** (c) **5.** (c) **6.** (a) **7.** (b) **8.** (a) **9.** (c)

10. (c)

$$f(x) = 20x + x \sin x \qquad f(x) = 20x + x \sin x$$

▼ Group Work 2: The Little Dip

In this exercise students analyze a function with some subtle local extrema. After they have tried, reveal that there are two local maxima and two local minima.

After students have found the extrema, point out that if they take calculus, they will learn a relatively simple way to find the exact coordinates of the extrema.

Answers:

1.

2. There are local maxima at $x = -6$ and $x = \frac{5}{4}$, and local minima at $x = 1$ and $x = \frac{3}{2}$.

▼ Homework Problems

Core Exercises: 3, 7, 8, 20, 28, 31, 37, 43, 49

Sample Assignment: 3, 4, 7, 8, 16, 20, 21, 23, 28, 31, 37, 43, 46, 49, 55

Graph the following curves on your calculator. For each curve specify which of the following applies.

(a) The graph of f is increasing over every interval (assuming the curve is defined everywhere in that interval).

(b) The graph of f is decreasing over every interval (assuming the curve is defined everywhere in that interval).

(c) The graph of f is increasing over some intervals and decreasing over others.

1. $f(x) = x^2$

2. $f(x) = x^3$

3. $f(x) = \sqrt{x}$

4. $f(x) = \sin x$

5. $f(x) = \cos x$

6. $f(x) = \tan x$

7. $f(x) = e^{-x}$

8. $f(x) = \ln x$

9. $f(x) = 5x^4 - 1.01^x$

10. $f(x) = 20x + x \sin x$

Consider $f(x) = \frac{1}{5}x^5 + \frac{9}{16}x^4 - \frac{143}{24}x^3 + \frac{207}{16}x^2 - \frac{45}{4}x$.

1. Draw a graph of f.

2. Estimate the x-values of all local extrema. Make sure your estimates are accurate to three decimal places.

2.4 AVERAGE RATE OF CHANGE OF A FUNCTION

▼ Suggested Time and Emphasis

$\frac{1}{2}$–1 class. Essential material.

▼ Points to Stress

1. Average rate of change.

▼ Sample Questions

- **Text Question:**

  Let $f(t) = 3t + 2$.

  (a) What is the average rate of change of f from $t = 1$ to $t = 3$?

  (b) What is the average rate of change of f from $t = 1$ to $t = \pi$?

  Answer: (a) 3   **(b)** 3

- **Drill Question:** If $f(t) = |t^2 - |3t||$, what is the average rate of change between $t = -3$ and $t = -1$?

  Answer: 1

▼ In-Class Materials

- Students should see the geometry of the average rate of change — that the average rate of change from $x = a$ to $x = b$ is the slope of the line from $(a, f(a))$ to $(b, f(b))$. Armed with this knowledge, students now have a way of estimating average rate of change: graph the function (making sure that the x- and y-scales are the same), plot the relevant points, and then estimate the slope of the line between them.

- It is possible, at this point, to foreshadow calculus nicely. Take a simple function such as $l(t) = t^2$ and look at the average rate of change from $t = 1$ to $t = 2$. Then look at the average rate of change from $t = 1$ to $t = \frac{3}{2}$. If students work in parallel, they should be able to fill in the following table:

From	To	Average Rate of Change
$t = 1$	2	3
$t = 1$	1.5	2.5
$t = 1$	1.25	2.25
$t = 1$	1.1	2.1
$t = 1$	1.01	2.01
$t = 1$	1.001	2.001

Note that these numbers seem to be approaching 2. This idea is pursued further in the group work.

- Assume that a car drove for two hours and traversed 120 miles. The average rate of change is clearly 60 miles per hour. Ask the students if it was possible for the car to have gone over 60 mph at some point in the interval, and explain how. Ask the students if it was possible for the car to have stayed under 60 mph the whole time. Ask the students if it was possible for the car never to have gone exactly 60 mph. Their intuition will probably say that the car had to have had traveled exactly 60 mph at one point, but it will be hard for them to justify. The truth of this statement is an example of the Mean Value Theorem from calculus.

▼ Examples

If $f(x) = x^3 - x$, the average rate of change from $x = 1$ to $x = 4$ is

$$\frac{f(4) - f(1)}{4 - 1} = \frac{(4^3 - 4) - (1^3 - 1)}{3} = \frac{(64 - 4) - (1 - 1)}{3} = \frac{60}{3} = 20$$

▼ Group Work: Small Intervals

If you have the time, and really wish to foreshadow calculus, have the students find the limit starting with $x = 1$ and then again with $x = 3$. Then see if they can find the pattern, and discover that the average value is going to approach $3a^2$ if we start at a.

Students won't remember every detail of this problem in a year, obviously. So when you close, try to convey the main idea that as we narrow the interval, the average values approach a single number, and that everything blows up if we make the interval consist of a single point. You may want to mention that exploring this phenomenon is a major part of the first semester of calculus.

Answers:

1. 19   **2.** 15.25   **3.** 12.61   **4.** 12.0601   **5.** 12.006001   **6.** 11.9401   **7.** 12   **8.** You get $\dfrac{0}{0}$, which is undefined.

▼ Homework Problems

Core Exercises: 4, 5, 8, 9, 12, 17, 22, 24, 27

Sample Assignment: 3, 4, 5, 8, 9, 12, 13, 17, 20, 22, 24, 27, 28, 31

GROUP WORK, SECTION 2.4

Small Intervals

Let us consider the curve $y = x^3$. Assume I am interested only in what is happening near $x = 2$. It is clear that the function is getting larger there, but my question is, how quickly is it increasing? One way to find out is to compute average rates of change.

1. Find the average rate of change between $x = 2$ and $x = 3$.

2. The number 2.5 is even closer to the number 2. Remember, I only really care about what is happening very close to $x = 2$. So compute the average rate of change between $x = 2$ and $x = 2.5$.

3. We can get closer still. Compute the average rate of change between $x = 2$ and $x = 2.1$.

4. Can we get closer? Sure! Compute the average rate of change between $x = 2$ and $x = 2.01$.

5. Compute the average rate of change between $x = 2$ and $x = 2.001$.

6. We can also approach 2 from the other side. Compute the average rate of change between $x = 2$ and $x = 1.99$.

7. Your answers should be approaching some particular number as we get closer and closer to 2. What is that number?

8. Hey, the closest number to 2 is 2 itself, right? So go ahead and compute the average rate of change between $x = 2$ and $x = 2$. What happens?

2.5 TRANSFORMATIONS OF FUNCTIONS

▼ **Suggested Time and Emphasis**

1 class. Essential material.

▼ **Points to Stress**

1. Transforming a given function to a different one by shifting, stretching, and reflection.

2. Using the technique of reflection to better understand the concepts of even and odd functions.

▼ **Sample Questions**

- **Text Question:** What is the difference between a vertical stretch and a vertical shift?

  Answer: A vertical stretch extends the graph in the vertical direction, changing its shape. A vertical shift simply moves the graph in the vertical direction, preserving its shape.

- **Drill Question:** Given the graph of $f(x)$ below, sketch the graph of $\frac{1}{2}f(x) + 1$.

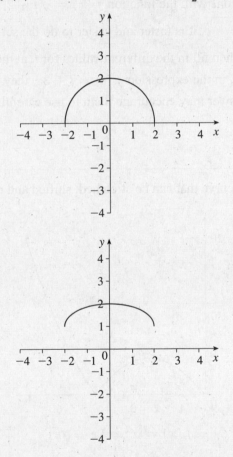

Answer:

▼ **In-Class Materials**

- Students will often view this section as a process of memorizing eight similar formulas. Although it doesn't hurt to memorize how to shift, reflect, or stretch a graph, emphasize to students the importance of understanding what they are doing when they transform a graph. The group work "Discovering the Shift" (in Section 1.8) should help students understand and internalize. Tell students that if worse comes to worst, they can always plot a few points if they forget in which direction the graphs should move.

- Show the class a function they have not learned about yet, such as $f(x) = \sin x$. (If students know about sin, then show them $\arctan$ or e^{-x^2}—any function with which they are unfamiliar.) Point out that even though they don't know a lot about $\sin x$, once they've seen the graph, they can graph $\sin x + 3$, $\sin(x - 1)$, $2 \sin x$, $-\sin x$, etc.

- Graph $f(x) = x^2$ with the class. Then anticipate Section 3.1 by having students graph $(x - 2)^2 - 3$ and $(x + 1)^2 + 2$, finally working up to $g(x) = (x - h)^2 + k$. If you point out that any equation of the form $g(x) = ax^2 + bx + c$ can be written in this so-called *standard form*, students will have a good start on the next section in addition to learning this one.

- This is a good time to start discussing parameters. Ask your students to imagine a scientist who knows that a given function will be shaped like a stretched parabola, but has to do some more measurements to find out exactly what the stretching factor is. In other words, she can write $f(x) = -ax^2$, noting that she will have to figure out the a experimentally. The a is not a variable, it is a parameter. Similarly, if we are going to do a bunch of calculations with the function $f(x) = \sqrt[3]{x + 2}$, and then do the same calculations with $\sqrt[3]{x + 3}$, $\sqrt[3]{x - \pi}$, and $\sqrt[3]{x - \frac{2}{3}}$, it is faster and easier to do the set of calculations just once, with the function $g(x) = \sqrt[3]{x + h}$, and then fill in the different values for h at the end. Again, this letter h is called a parameter. Ask the class how, in the expression $f(t) = t + 3s$, they can tell which is the variable, and which is the parameter—the answer may encourage them to use careful notation.

▼ Examples

A distinctive-looking, asymmetric curve that can be stretched, shifted and reflected:

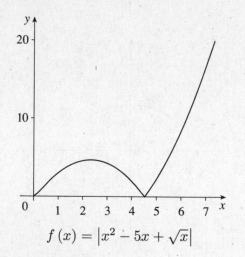

$$f(x) = \left| x^2 - 5x + \sqrt{x} \right|$$

▼ Group Work 1: Label Label Label, I Made It Out of Clay

Some of these transformations are not covered directly in the book. If the students are urged not to give up, and to use the process of elimination and testing individual points, they should be able to complete this activity.

Answers: 1. (d) **2.** (a) **3.** (f) **4.** (e) **5.** (i) **6.** (j) **7.** (b) **8.** (c) **9.** (g) **10.** (h)

▼ Group Work 2: Which is the Original?

The second problem has a subtle difficulty: the function is defined for all x, so some graphs show much more of the behavior of $f(x)$ than others do.

Answers: 1. $2f(x+2), 2f(x), f(2x), f(x+2), f(x)$ **2.** $2f(x), f(x), f(x+2), f(2x), 2f(x+2)$

▼ Homework Problems

Core Exercises: 4, 7, 11, 15, 20, 38, 44, 45, 48, 62, 77

Sample Assignment: 4, 6, 7, 11, 14, 15, 20, 38, 44, 45, 48, 51, 53, 58, 62, 77, 80, 83, 89

Label Label Label, I Made it Out of Clay

This is a graph of the function $f(x)$:

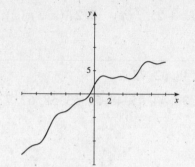

Give each graph below the correct label from the following:

(a) $f(x+3)$ (b) $f(x-3)$ (c) $f(2x)$ (d) $2f(x)$ (e) $|f(x)|$

(f) $f(|x|)$ (g) $2f(x)-1$ (h) $f(2x)+2$ (i) $f(x)-x$ (j) $1/f(x)$

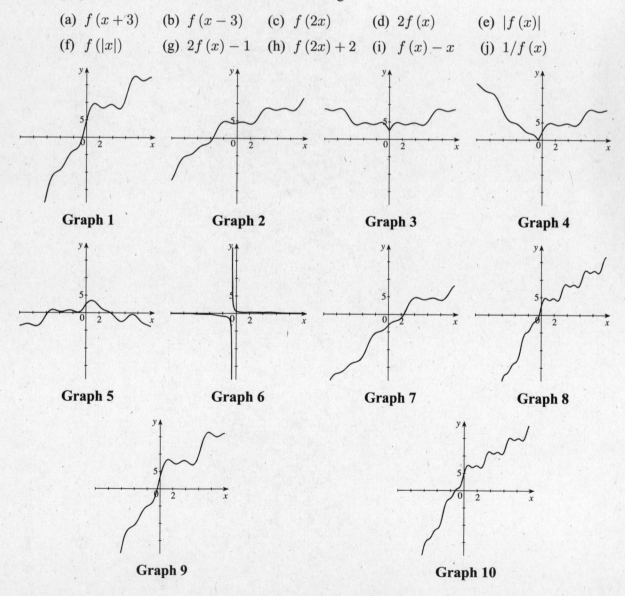

Graph 1   Graph 2   Graph 3   Graph 4

Graph 5   Graph 6   Graph 7   Graph 8

Graph 9   Graph 10

Below are five graphs. One is the graph of a function $f(x)$ and the others include the graphs of $2f(x)$, $f(2x)$, $f(x+2)$, and $2f(x+2)$. Determine which is the graph of $f(x)$ and match the other functions with their graphs.

1.

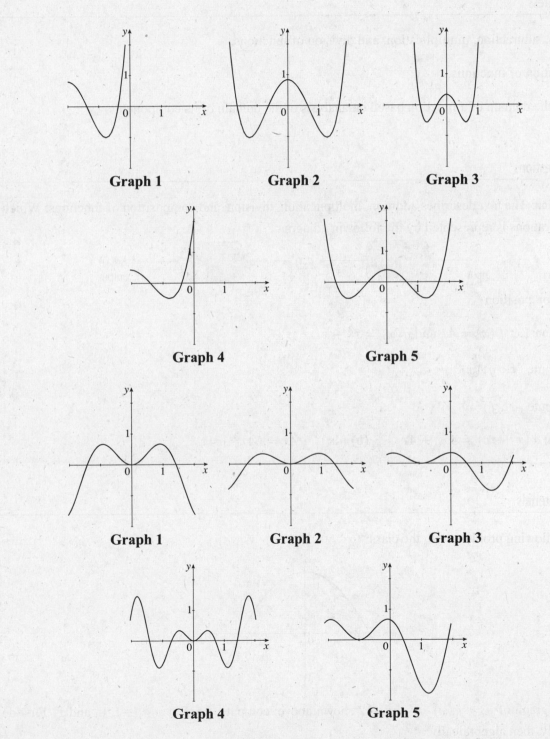

Graph 1   Graph 2   Graph 3

Graph 4   Graph 5

2.

Graph 1   Graph 2   Graph 3

Graph 4   Graph 5

2.6 COMBINING FUNCTIONS

▼ Suggested Time and Emphasis

$\frac{1}{2}$–1 class. Essential material.

▼ Points to Stress

1. Addition, subtraction, multiplication, and division of functions.

2. Composition of functions.

3. Finding the domain of a function based on analysis of the domain of its components.

▼ Sample Questions

- **Text Question:** The text describes addition, multiplication, division, and composition of functions. Which of these operations is represented by the following diagram?

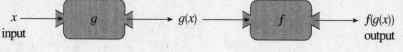

  Answer: Composition

- **Drill Question:** Let $f(x) = 4x$ and $g(x) = x^3 + x$.

  (a) Compute $(f \circ g)(x)$.

  (b) Compute $(g \circ f)(x)$.

  Answer: (a) $4(x^3 + x) = 4x^3 + 4x$ **(b)** $(4x)^3 + 4x = 64x^3 + 4x$

▼ In-Class Materials

- Do the following problem with the class:

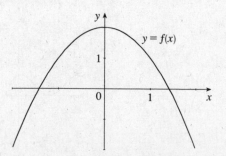

  From the graph of $y = f(x) = -x^2 + 2$ shown above, compute $f \circ f$ at $x = -1$, 0, and 1. First do it graphically, then algebraically.

- Show the tie between algebraic addition of functions and graphical addition. For example, let $f(x) = 1 - x^2$ and $g(x) = x^2 + \frac{1}{2}x - 1$. First add the functions graphically, as shown below, and then show how this result can be obtained algebraically: $(1 - x^2) + (x^2 + \frac{1}{2}x - 1) = \frac{1}{2}x$.

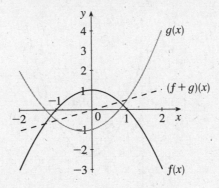

- Point out that it is important to keep track of domains, especially when doing algebraic simplification. For example, if $f(x) = x + \sqrt{x}$ and $g(x) = 3x^2 + \sqrt{x}$, even though $(f - g)(x) = x - 3x^2$, its domain is not $\mathbb{R}$ but $\{x \mid x \geq 0\}$.

- Function maps are a nice way to explain composition of functions. To demonstrate $g \circ f(x)$, draw three number lines labeled x, $f(x)$, and $g(x)$, and then indicate how each number x goes to $f(x)$ which then goes to $g(f(x))$. For example, if $f(x) = \sqrt{x}$ and $g(x) = 2x - 1$, the diagram looks like this:

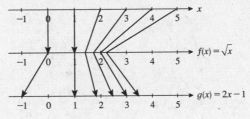

- After doing a few basic examples of composition, it is possible to foreshadow the idea of inverses, which will be covered in the next section. Let $f(x) = 2x^3 + 3$ and $g(x) = x^2 - x$. Compute $f \circ g$ and $g \circ f$ for your students. Then ask them to come up with a function $h(x)$ with the property that $(f \circ h)(x) = x$. They may not be used to the idea of coming up with examples for themselves, so the main hints they will need might be "don't give up," "when in doubt, just try something and see what happens," and "I'm not expecting you to get it in fifteen seconds." If the class is really stuck, have them try $f(x) = 2x^3$ to get a feel for how the game is played. Once they have determined that $h(x) = \sqrt[3]{\dfrac{x - 3}{2}}$, have them compute $(h \circ f)(x)$ and have them conjecture whether, in general, if $(f \circ g)(x) = x$ then $(g \circ f)(x)$ must also equal x.

▼ Examples

Combined functions with graphs: Let $f(x) = x^2 - 3x + 2$ and $g(x) = -\sqrt{x}$.

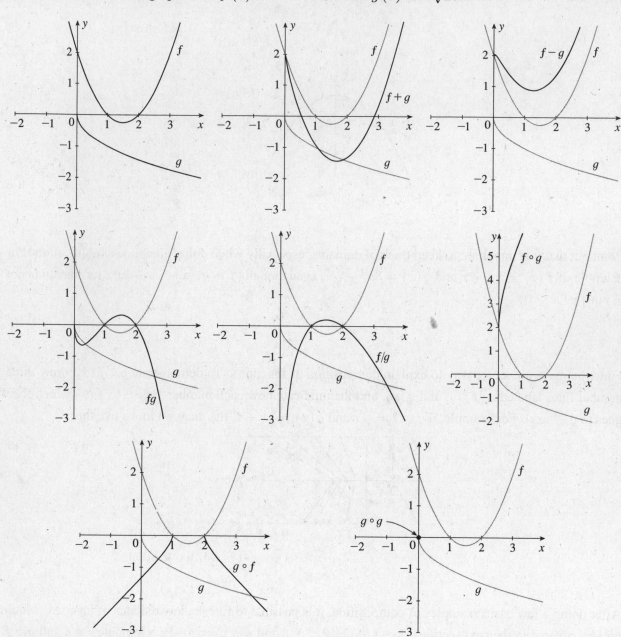

▼ Group Work 1: Transformation of Plane Figures

This tries to remove the composition idea from the numerical context, and introduces the notion of symmetry groups. It is a longer activity than it seems, and can lead to an interesting class discussion of this topic.

Answers:

1. (a) $f\left(\ulcorner\right) = \urcorner$ **(b)** $g\left(\urcorner\right) = \ulcorner$ **(c)** $f\left(f\left(\llcorner\right)\right) = \urcorner$ **(d)** $g\left(g\left(\urcorner\right)\right) = \urcorner$

2. This is false. For example, $(f \circ g)\left(\text{⌐}\right) = \text{L}$, but $(g \circ f)\left(\text{⌐}\right) = \text{⌐}$.

3. It is true: reversing something thrice in a mirror gives the same result as reversing it once.

4. It rotates the shape $270°$ clockwise or, equivalently, $90°$ counterclockwise.

▼ Group Work 2: Odds and Evens

This is an extension of Exercise 70 in the text. Students may find the third problem difficult to start. You may want to give selected table entries on the board first, before handing the activity out, to make sure students understand what they are trying to do.

Answers:

1.

a	b	$a+b$
even	even	even
odd	even	odd
even	odd	odd
odd	odd	even

2.

a	b	$a \cdot b$
even	even	even
odd	even	even
even	odd	even
odd	odd	odd

3.

f	g	$f+g$	fg	$f \circ g$	$g \circ f$
even	even	even	even	even	even
even	odd	neither	odd	even	even
odd	even	neither	odd	even	even
odd	odd	odd	even	odd	odd
neither	neither	unknown	unknown	unknown	unknown

▼ Group Work 3: It's More Fun to Compute

Each group gets one copy of the graph. During each round, one representative from each group stands, and one of the questions below is asked. The representatives write their answer down, and all display their answers at the same time. Each representative has the choice of consulting with their group or not. A correct solo answer is worth two points, and a correct answer after a consult is worth one point.

1. $(f \circ g)(5)$ **5.** $(g \circ g)(5)$ **9.** $(g \circ f)(1)$

2. $(g \circ f)(5)$ **6.** $(g \circ g)(-3)$ **10.** $(f \circ f \circ g)(4)$

3. $(f \circ g)(0)$ **7.** $(g \circ g)(-1)$ **11.** $(g \circ f \circ f)(4)$

4. $(f \circ f)(5)$ **8.** $(f \circ g)(1)$ **12.** $(f \circ g \circ f)(4)$

Answers: 1. 0   **2.** 0   **3.** 1   **4.** 5   **5.** 1   **6.** 1   **7.** 1   **8.** 0   **9.** 2   **10.** 1   **11.** 1   **12.** 1

▼ Homework Problems

Core Exercises: 1, 6, 7, 16, 21, 25, 29, 38, 46, 54

Sample Assignment: 1, 6, 7, 10, 11, 16, 21, 25, 26, 29, 38, 44, 46, 54, 58, 66, 68

GROUP WORK 1, SECTION 2.6

Transformation of Plane Figures

So far, when we have been talking about functions, we have been assuming that their domains and ranges have been sets of numbers. This is not necessarily the case. For example, look at this figure:

Let's let our domain be all the different ways we can move this figure around, including flipping it over:

$$D = \left\{ \text{L}, \text{Γ}, \text{⌐}, \text{⌐}, \text{⌐}, \text{L}, \text{Γ}, \text{⌐} \right\}$$

Now let f be the function that rotates the shape 90° clockwise: $f\left(\text{L}\right) = \text{Γ}$. Let g be the function that flips the shape over a vertical line drawn through the center: $g\left(\text{L}\right) = \text{⌐}$

1. Find the following:

(a) $f\left(\text{Γ}\right)$ **(b)** $g\left(\text{⌐}\right)$ **(c)** $f\left(f\left(\text{L}\right)\right)$ **(d)** $g\left(g\left(\text{⌐}\right)\right)$

2. Is it true that $f \circ g = g \circ f$? Why or why not?

3. Is it true that $g \circ g \circ g = g$? Why or why not?

4. Write, in words, what the function $f \circ f \circ f$ does to a shape.

GROUP WORK 2, SECTION 2.6

Odds and Evens

1. Let a be an odd number, and b be an even number. Fill in the following table (the first row is done for you).

a	b	$a + b$
even	even	even
odd	even	
even	odd	
odd	odd	

2. We can also multiply numbers together. Fill in the corresponding multiplication table:

a	b	$a \cdot b$
even	even	
odd	even	
even	odd	
odd	odd	

3. Now we let f and g be (nonzero) functions, not numbers. We are going to think about what happens when we combine these functions. When you fill in the table, you can write "unknown" if the result can be odd *or* even, depending on the functions. You can solve this problem by drawing some pictures, or by using the definition of odd and even functions.

f	g	$f + g$	fg	$f \circ g$	$g \circ f$
even	even				
even	odd				
odd	even				
odd	odd				
neither	neither				

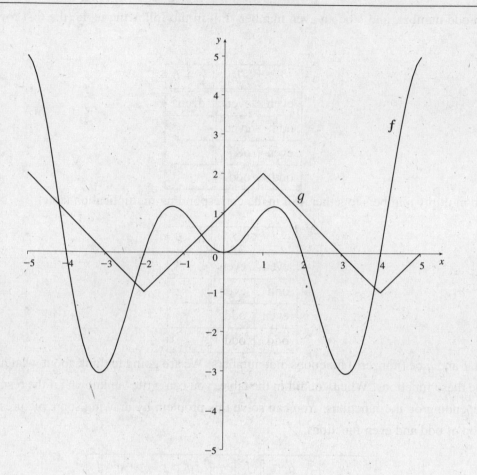

2.7   ONE-TO-ONE FUNCTIONS AND THEIR INVERSES

▼ **Suggested Time and Emphasis**

1–2 classes. Essential material.

▼ **Points to Stress**

1. One-to-one functions: their definition and the Horizontal Line Test.

2. Algebraic and geometric properties of inverse functions.

3. Finding inverse functions.

▼ **Sample Questions**

- **Text Question:** The function f is graphed below. Sketch f^{-1}, the inverse function of f.

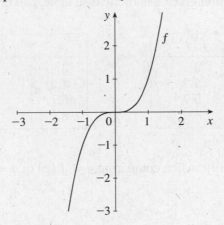

Answer:

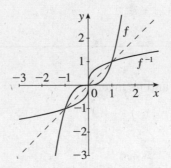

- **Drill Question:** If $f(-2) = 4$, $f(-1) = 3$, $f(0) = 2$, $f(1) = 1$ and $f(2) = 3$, what is $f^{-1}(2)$?

  Answer: 0

▼ **In-Class Materials**

- Make sure students understand the notation: f^{-1} is not the same thing as $\dfrac{1}{f}$.

- Starting with $f(x) = \sqrt[3]{x - 4}$, compute $f^{-1}(-2)$ and $f^{-1}(0)$. Then use algebra to find a formula for $f^{-1}(x)$. Have the class try to repeat the process with $g(x) = x^3 + x - 2$. Note that facts such as $g^{-1}(-2) = 0$, $g^{-1}(0) = 1$, and and $g^{-1}(8) = 2$ can be found by looking at a table of values for $g(x)$ but that algebra fails to give us a general formula for $g^{-1}(x)$. Finally, draw graphs of f, f^{-1}, g, and g^{-1}.

113

- Pose the question: If f is always increasing, is f^{-1} always increasing? Give students time to try prove their answer.

  Answer: This is true. Proofs may involve diagrams and reflections about $y = x$, or you may try to get them to be more rigorous. This is an excellent opportunity to discuss concavity, noting that if f is concave up and increasing, then f^{-1} is concave down and increasing.

- Point out that the idea of "reversing input and output" permeates the idea of inverse functions, in all four representations of "function". When finding inverse functions algebraically, we explicitly reverse x and y. When drawing the inverse function of a graph, by reflecting across the line $y = x$ we are reversing the y- and x-axes. If $c(x)$ is the cost (in dollars) to make x fruit roll-ups, then $c^{-1}(x)$ is the number of fruit roll-ups that could be made for x dollars—again reversing the input and the output. Finally, show the class how to find the inverse of a function given a numeric data table, and note that again the inputs and outputs are reversed.

x	$f(x)$
1	3
2	4.2
3	5.7
4	8

x	$f^{-1}(x)$
3	1
4.2	2
5.7	3
8	4

- Make sure to discuss units carefully: when comparing $y = f(x)$ to $y = f^{-1}(x)$, the units of y and x trade places.

▼ Examples

- The graph of a complicated function and its inverse:

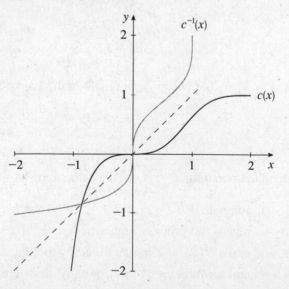

▼ Group Work 1: Inverse Functions: Domains and Ranges

While discussing the domains and ranges of inverse functions, this exercise foreshadows later excursions into the maximum and minimum values of functions.

If a group finishes early, ask them this question:

"Now consider the graph of $f(x) = \sqrt{2x - 3} + 2$. What are the domain and range of $f(x)$? Try to figure out the domain and range of $f^{-1}(x)$ by looking at the graph of f. In general, what information do you need to be able to compute the domain and range of $f^{-1}(x)$ from the graph of a function f?"

Answers:

1. It is one-to-one, because the problem says it climbs steadily.

2. a^{-1} is the time in minutes at which the plane achieves a given altitude.

3. Reverse the data columns in the given table to get the table for the inverse function. The domain and range of a are $0 \le t \le 30$ and $0 \le a \le 29{,}000$, so the domain and range of a^{-1} are $0 \le x \le 29{,}000$ and $0 \le a^{-1} \le 30$.

4. You can expect to turn on your computer after about 8.5 minutes.

5. a is no longer 1-1, because heights are now achieved more than once.

Bonus The domain of f^{-1} is the set of all y-values on the graph of f, and the range of f^{-1} is the set of all x-values on the graph of f.

▼ Group Work 2: The Column of Liquid

If students need a hint, you can mention that the liquid used in the drugstore is mercury.

Answers:

1. The liquid is 1 cm high when the temperature is $32°$ F.

2. The liquid is 10 cm high when the temperature is $212°$ F

3. The inverse function takes a height in cm, and gives the temperature. So it is a device for measuring temperature.

4. A thermometer

▼ Group Work 3: Functions in the Classroom Revisited

This activity starts the same as "Functions in the Classroom" from Section 2.2 At this point, students have learned about one-to-one functions, and they are able to explore this activity in more depth.

Answers:

Chairs: Function, one-to-one, bijection (if all chairs are occupied). If one-to-one, the inverse assigns a chair to a person.

Eye color: Function, not one-to-one

Mom & Dad's birthplace: Not a function; mom and dad could have been born in different places

Molecules: Function, one-to-one (with nearly 100% probability); inverse assigns a number of molecules to the appropriate student.

Spleens: Function, one-to-one, bijection. Inverse assigns each spleen to its owner.

Pencils: Not a function; some people may have more than one or (horrors!) none.

Social Security Number: Function, one-to-one; inverse assigns each number to its owner.

February birthday: Not a function; not defined for someone born on February 29.

Birthday: Function, perhaps one-to-one. If one-to-one, the inverse assigns a day to a person.

Cars: Not a function; some have none, some have more than one.

Cash: Function, perhaps one-to-one. If one-to-one, the inverse assigns an amount of money to a person.

Middle names: Not a function; some have none, some have more than one.

Identity: Function, one-to-one, bijection. Inverse is the same as the function.

Algebra instructor: Function, not one-to-one.

▼ Homework Problems

Core Exercises: 4, 5, 13, 17, 22, 28, 31, 37, 44, 54, 76

Sample Assignment: 4, 5, 10, 13, 17, 22, 28, 31, 34, 36, 37, 44, 45, 54, 60, 63, 75, 76, 85

Inverse Functions: Domains and Ranges

Let $a(t)$ be the altitude in feet of a plane that climbs steadily from takeoff until it reaches its cruising altitude after 30 minutes. We don't have a formula for a, but extensive research has given us the following table of values:

t	$a(t)$
0.1	50
0.5	150
1	500
3	2000
7	8000
10	12,000
20	21,000
25	27,000
30	29,000

1. Is $a(t)$ a one-to-one function? How do you know?

2. What does the function a^{-1} measure in real terms? Your answer should be descriptive, similar to the way $a(t)$ was described above.

3. We are interested in computing values of a^{-1}. Fill in the following table for as many values of x as you can. What quantity does x represent?

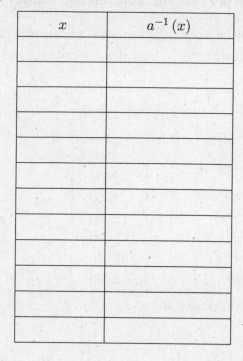

x	$a^{-1}(x)$

What are the domain and range of a? What are the domain and range of a^{-1}?

4. You are allowed to turn on electronic equipment after the plane has reached 10,000 feet. Approximately when can you expect to turn on your laptop computer after taking off?

5. Suppose we consider $a(t)$ from the time of takeoff to the time of touchdown. Is $a(t)$ still one-to-one?

The Column of Liquid

It is a fact that if you take a tube and fill it partway with liquid, the liquid will rise and fall based on the temperature. Assume that we have a tube of liquid, and we have a function $h(T)$, where h is the height of the liquid in cm at temperature T in °F.

1. It is true that $h(32) = 1$. What does that mean in physical terms?

2. It is true that $h(212) = 10$. What does that mean in physical terms?

3. Describe the inverse function h^{-1}. What are its inputs? What are its outputs? What does it measure?

4. There is a device, currently available at your local drugstore, that measures the function h^{-1}. What is the name of this device?

Functions in the Classroom Revisited

Which of the following are functions? Of the ones that are functions, which are one-to-one functions? Describe what the inverses tell you.

Domain	Function Values	Function
All the people in your classroom	Chairs	f (person) = his or her chair
All the people in your classroom	The set {blue, brown, green, hazel}	f (person) = his or her eye color
All the people in your classroom	Cities	f (person) = birthplace of their mom and dad
All the people in your classroom	ℝ, the real numbers	f (person) = number of molecules in their body
All the people in your classroom	Spleens	f (person) = his or her own spleen
All the people in your classroom	Pencils	f (person) = his or her pencil
All the people in the United States	Integers from 0–999999999	f (person) = his or her Social Security number
All the living people born in February	Days in February, 2007	f (person) = his or her birthday in February 2007
All the people in your classroom	Days of the year	f (person) = his or her birthday
All the people in your classroom	Cars	f (person) = his or her car
All the people in your classroom	ℝ, the real numbers	f (person) = how much cash he or she has
All the people in your college	Names	f (person) = his or her middle name
All the people in your classroom	People	f (person) = himself or herself
All the people in your classroom	People	f (person) = his or her algebra instructor

3 POLYNOMIAL AND RATIONAL FUNCTIONS

3.1 QUADRATIC FUNCTIONS AND MODELS

▼ Suggested Time and Emphasis

1 class. Essential material.

▼ Points to Stress

1. Graphing quadratic functions, including obtaining the exact coordinates of the vertex by completing the square.

▼ Sample Questions

- **Text Question:** If $f(x) = 4x^2 + 16x + 5$, why would it be useful to complete the square?
  Answer: Completing the square would reveal the zeros of the function.

- **Drill Question:** Find the vertex of the quadratic function $f(x) = -x^2 + 9x + 2$.
  Answer: $\left(\frac{9}{2}, \frac{89}{4}\right)$

▼ In-Class Materials

- A straightforward way to demonstrate the utility of quadratic functions is to demonstrate how thrown objects follow parabolic paths. Physically throw an actual ball (perhaps trying to get it into the wastebasket) and have the class observe the shape of the path. Note that not only can thrown objects' paths be modeled by parabolas, their height as a function of time can (on Earth) be modeled by quadratic functions of the form $f(x) = -16t^2 + v_0 t + s_0$, where t is in seconds, f is in feet, v_0 is initial velocity, and s_0 is initial height.

- Show students how quadratic functions can come up in an applied context. If a demand function is linear then the revenue will be quadratic. For example, if the number of shoes you can sell is given by $10000 - 3c$, where c is the cost per shoe, then the revenue is $R = c(10000 - 3c)$. If we are thinking of costs in a narrow possible range, we can usually approximate revenue in such a way.

- Having covered quadratic functions, it is not a big leap to talk about quadratic inequalities. After graphing $f(x) = x^2 + 4x - 5$, find the intervals described by $x^2 + 4x + 5 > 0$, $x^2 + 4x + 5 \geq 0$, $x^2 + 4x + 5 < 0$, and $x^2 + 4x + 5 \leq 0$.

▼ Examples

A quadratic function that can be graphed by hand: $f(x) = -2x^2 + 12x - 13 = -2(x-3)^2 + 5$

121

▼ Group Work: The Penny Drop

This is a classic type of physics problem with the differentiation omitted.

Answers:

1. $t = \frac{5}{16} = 0.3125$ s
2. $t = \frac{5}{16} = 0.3125$ s
3. $\frac{4825}{16} \approx 301.56$ ft
4. $\frac{5}{16}\left(1 + \sqrt{193}\right) \approx 4.654$ s
5. It is moving at 138.9 ft/s downward.

▼ Homework Problems

Core Exercises: 2, 7, 16, 29, 42, 46, 55, 64, 67

Sample Assignment: 2, 7, 16, 21, 29, 31, 42, 44, 46, 50, 54, 55, 64, 67, 75

GROUP WORK, SECTION 3.1

The Penny Drop

Suppose we are standing on top of a 300-ft tower and we are holding a shiny new penny. We do not hurl it down, for that would be dangerous and wrong. We toss it *up* at a velocity of 10 feet per second, and then when it comes down, it just happens to plummet to the ground below.

At a time t seconds after the toss, the velocity is given by $v(t) = -32t + 10$. (Note that positive velocity corresponds to the penny moving up, as it does initially, and negative velocity corresponds to it moving down, as it does eventually.) The distance from the sidewalk, in feet, is given by $p(t) = -16t^2 + 10t + 300$.

1. At what time is the penny's velocity zero?

2. When is the penny at its highest point?

3. What is the maximum height achieved by the penny?

4. How long is the penny in the air?

5. How fast is it going when it hits the ground?

3.2   POLYNOMIAL FUNCTIONS AND THEIR GRAPHS

▼ Suggested Time and Emphasis

1 class. Essential material.

▼ Points to Stress

1. The terminology and notation associated with polynomial functions.

2. Characteristics of polynomial graphs: smoothness, continuity, end behavior, and boundaries on the number of local maxima and minima.

3. Graphing polynomials using the zeros (taking into account multiplicity) and end behavior.

▼ Sample Questions

- **Text Question:** Which of the following are polynomial functions?

   (a) $f(x) = -x^3 + 2x + 4$

   (b) $f(x) = (\sqrt{x})^3 - 2(\sqrt{x})^2 + 5(\sqrt{x}) - 1$

   (c) $f(x) = (x - 2)(x - 1)(x + 4)^2$

   (d) $f(x) = \dfrac{x^2 + 2}{x^2 - 2}$

   Answer: (a) and (c)

- **Drill Question:** Sketch the graph of the polynomial $f(x) = x^3 + 5x^2 + 6x$.
   Answer:

   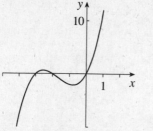

▼ In-Class Materials

- This section teaches students how to quickly sketch the graph of a polynomial function like $f(x) = (x - 1)(x - 2)^2(x - 3)$. Point out that these methods cannot be used to find the precise coordinates of the two local minima, nor can they describe how fast the function is increasing as x increases. That precision will come with calculus.

- This is one application of the Intermediate Value Theorem for Polynomials:

Consider $f(x) = 90x^3 + 100x^2 + 10x + 1$ and $g(x) = 91x^3 - 60x^2$. Have students graph each on their calculator, if they can find a good window. It will be tough. After giving them some time, put some graphs on the board.

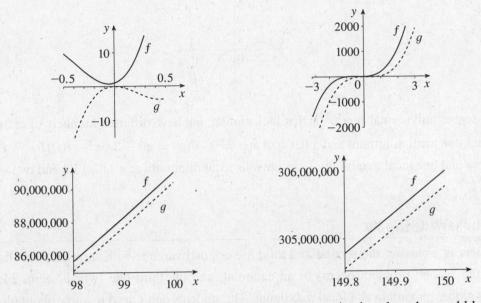

It certainly looks like these two curves never cross. One way to prove that they do would be to actually find the crossing point—to solve $f(x) - g(x) = 0$. But a quicker way is to use the Intermediate Value Theorem for Polynomials. Let $h(x) = f(x) - g(x)$. We know $g(x)$ will cross $f(x)$ when $h(x) = 0$. Now $h(0)$ is positive, and $h(1000)$ is negative. We don't *need* to go hunting for the value of x that makes $h(x) = 0$; we can simply invoke the intermediate value property to prove that such an x does exist.

- Explore, using technology, the concept of families of functions. Take, for example, the easy-to-graph curve $y = x^3 - x$. Add in a constant: $y = x^3 - x + 1$, $y = x^3 - x + 2$, $y = x^3 - x - 1$. Using material from Chapter 2, students should be able to predict what these graphs look like. Now add in a quadratic term: $y = x^3 + \frac{1}{2}x^2 - x$, $y = x^3 + x^2 - x$, $y = x^3 + 8x^2 - x$, $y = x^3 + -x^2 - x$. By graphing these curves on the same axes, have students attempt to put into words the effect that an x^2 term has on this cubic function.

- When discussing local extrema, make sure students understand that just because a fifth-degree polynomial (for example) *can* have four local extrema, doesn't mean it *must* have four local extrema. Have students graph $f(x) = x^5$ as a quick example, and then $f(x) = x^5 - x^3$ as an example of a fifth-degree polynomial with two local extrema. Have students try to come up with a proof that there can't be a fifth-degree polynomial with exactly one or three local extrema.

▼ Examples

- A polynomial function with zeros of various multiplicities:

$$f(x) = x^6 + x^5 - x^4 - x^3 = (x-1)x^3(x+1)^2$$

- Two sixth-degree polynomial functions that look similar, but have different numbers of extrema: $f(x) = x^6 - 3x^3$ has one local minimum and a flat spot at $x = 0$. $f(x) = x^6 - 3.0x^3 - 0.015x^4 + 0.09x$ has two local minima and one local maximum — an obvious local minimum at $x \approx 1.145$, and two subtle extrema at $x \approx \pm 0.1$.

▼ Group Work 1: The Waste-Free Box

The first problem is a classic; the second and third are original variants with surprising results. The global maximum in the second problem occurs at an endpoint, and the third one, which seems identical to the second, has its global maximum at a local maximum. The students don't need to know about global and local extrema to solve this problem—they just have to understand what they are doing when they are modeling the phenomenon, and looking for an extreme value.

Set up the activity by actually building a box for students out of an $8.5'' \times 11''$ sheet of paper, so they can see exactly what is going on before they try to construct a mathematical model.

Answers:

1. $V(x) = x(8.5 - 2x)(11 - 2x)$
2. The domain is $0 \le x \le 4.25$.
3. 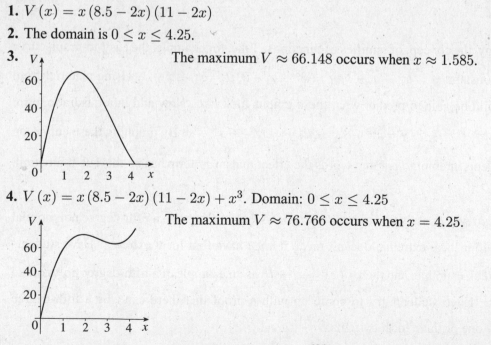 The maximum $V \approx 66.148$ occurs when $x \approx 1.585$.

4. $V(x) = x(8.5 - 2x)(11 - 2x) + x^3$. Domain: $0 \le x \le 4.25$

   The maximum $V \approx 76.766$ occurs when $x = 4.25$.

5. There is no open-topped box. We cut the biggest squares we can and then throw away the scrap. Because the box needs a bottom, it is a less efficient user of materials than the handsome pen-and-pencil holder.

6. In the $6'' \times 10''$ case, $V(x) = x(6 - 2x)(10 - 2x) + x^3$. Domain: $0 \leq x \leq 3$

The maximum $V \approx 35$ occurs when $x \approx 1.39096$.

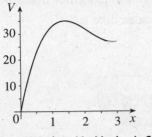

▼ Group Work 2: My Mother's Gifts

This exercise is primarily about taking a verbal description of a problem and translating it into a (polynomial) function. It also explores some large growth rates.

Answers:

1. 396 cm^3

2. 4940 cm^3

3. $V(x) = x(x + 9)(x + 16) = x^3 + 25x^2 + 144x$

4. 512 cm^2

5. 1888 cm^2

6. $A(x) = 2x(x + 9) + 2x(x + 16) + 2(x + 9)(x + 16) = 6x^2 + 100x + 288$

7. Solving $6x^2 + 100x + 288 = 11{,}000$, we find that $x \approx 34.7338$, so according to his claim, I will be 34 when he makes his last one. But he will never stop!

8. $73{,}100 \text{ cm}^3$ or about $2\frac{1}{2}$ cubic feet

▼ Homework Problems

Core Exercises: 4, 6, 13, 16, 20, 29, 31, 52, 83

Sample Assignment: 4, 6, 7, 10, 13, 16, 20, 21, 29, 31, 34, 42, 50, 52, 73, 77, 83

Assume we take a sheet of standard $8.5'' \times 11''$ typing or "notebook" paper. We can transform it into a box by cutting identical squares of side length x from each corner, and folding up the sides, like so:

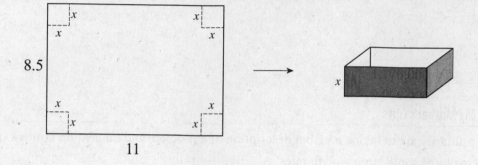

1. Express the volume V of the box as a function of x.

2. What is the domain of V?

3. Draw a graph of the function V and use it to estimate the maximum volume for such a box.

The previous problem is a classic problem often given to calculus students. People have been doing this problem for centuries, never caring about those four squares, those cast-off pieces of paper. What is to be their fate? They are often thrown out—sometimes (cruel irony!) in the very box that they helped to create! Should we stand for this waste of paper? The answer is "No!", particularly since we can use the four squares to make a handsome pen-and-pencil holder, by taping them together to form their own box. This new box will have neither top nor bottom, but it still can be used to hold pens and pencils.

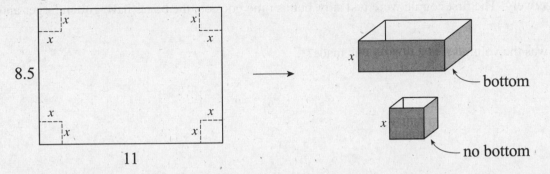

4. What is the maximum possible combined volume of an open-topped box plus a handsome pen-and-pencil holder that can be made by cutting four squares from an $8.5'' \times 11''$ sheet of paper?

5. Describe the open-topped box that results from this maximal case. Intuitively, why do we get the result that we do?

6. Repeat this problem for a $6'' \times 10''$ piece of paper.

GROUP WORK 2, SECTION 3.2
My Mother's Gifts

I have a brother who is sixteen years older than I am, and a sister who is nine years older. Every Mother's Day, since I was two, my father (who is a competent woodworker) has made the same gift for my mother. He gives her a box whose length, width and height (in centimeters) are my brother's, my sister's, and my age, respectively. The first couple were just silly, but as time goes on, the boxes have gotten larger and more useful.

1. What was the volume of the first box he made?

2. What was the volume of the box he made when I was ten?

3. Write a formula that gives the volume of the box he will make when I am x years old.

Dad doesn't just give her the box unadorned. He always puts a gift in the box, and wraps it up in wrapping paper. He then draws a mortar-and-pestle on it (Mom was a pharmacist) and tapes on a stick of gum (don't ask).

4. How much wrapping paper did he have to use for that first box? Give your answer in cm^2.

5. How much wrapping paper did he have to use when I was ten?

6. Write a formula that gives the amount of wrapping paper he will have to use when I am x years old.

7. A standard roll of wrapping paper has an area of about 11,000 cm^2. Dad has said he is going to stop building these boxes when they take more than a roll to wrap up. How old will I be when he makes his last box? Do you think he will really stop?

8. What will be the volume of that "final" box?

3.3   DIVIDING POLYNOMIALS

▼ Suggested Time and Emphasis

$\frac{1}{2}$–1 class. Essential material.

▼ Points to Stress

1. The division algorithm for polynomials.

2. Synthetic division.

3. The Remainder and Factor Theorems.

▼ Sample Questions

- **Text Question:** It is a fact that $x^3 + 2x^2 - 3x + 1 = (x + 2)\left(x^2 + 1\right) + (-4x - 1)$. Fill in the blanks:

$$\boxed{} \qquad \text{Remainder: } \boxed{}$$

$$x^2 + 1 \; \overline{\smash{\big)}\; x^3 + 2x^2 - 3x + 1}$$

Answers: $x + 2$, $-4x - 1$

- **Drill Question:** Divide $x^3 + 2x^2 - 3x + 1$ by $x + 2$.

Answer: $\dfrac{x^3 + 2x^2 - 3x + 1}{x + 2} = x^2 - 3 + \dfrac{7}{x + 2}$ or "$x^2 - 3$, remainder 7"

▼ In-Class Materials

- At this time, the teaching of long division in elementary schools is inconsistent. It will save time, in the long run, to do an integer long division problem for students, cautioning them to pay attention to every step in the process, because you are going to be extending it to polynomials. For example, divide 31,673 by 5 using the long division algorithm. Then show how the answer can be written as $\dfrac{31{,}673}{5} = 6334 + \dfrac{3}{5}$ or 6334 R 3. They will not be used to writing the result this way: $31673 = 5\,(6334) + 3$. It is important that they understand the form

$$\text{dividend} = \text{divisor} \cdot \text{quotient} + \text{remainder}$$

because that is the form in which the division algorithm is presented, both in this course, and any future math course involving generalized division. If students don't seem to understand (or start moving their lips as if beginning the process of rote memorization) it may even be worth the time to write out a simple example, such as $35 = 3\,(11) + 2$, so students realize that this is a trivial restatement of the fact that $\frac{35}{3} = 11$ R 2.

132

- After doing a routine example, such as $\dfrac{x^4 + 3x^3 - x^2 - x + 3}{x^2 + 2x - 1} = x^2 + x - 2 + \dfrac{1 + 4x}{x^2 + 2x - 1}$, verify the answer by having students go through the multiplication. In other words, write $\left(x^2 + 2x - 1\right)\left(x^2 + x - 2\right) + (4x + 1)$ and multiply it out to verify that the result is $x^4 + 3x^3 - x^2 - x + 3$.

- Students often miss the crucial idea that synthetic division is a technique that works only for divisors of the form $x - c$. They also tend to believe that synthetic division is a magic process that has nothing to do with the long division they have just learned. To disabuse them of these notions, divide the polynomial $x^3 - x^2 + x - 1$ by $x - 2$ using both methods, showing all work, and then have students point out the similarities between the two computations. They should see that the two processes are essentially the same, the only difference being that synthetic division minimizes the amount of writing and thinking.

- One important application of polynomial division is finding asymptotes for rational functions. This is a good time to introduce the concept of a horizontal asymptote. This idea is explored in Group Work 1: Asymptology. A good example to discuss with students are $f(x) = \dfrac{2x^2 + 3x + 5}{x^2 - 4x + 2}$. Use long division to write this as $f(x) = 2 + \dfrac{11x + 1}{x^2 - 4x + 2}$. Now note what happens to the second term for large values of x. If students have calculators, they can go ahead and try $x = 100$, $x = 100{,}000$, and $x = 1{,}000{,}000{,}000$. Show how, graphically, this corresponds to a horizontal asymptote. Now point out that the 2 came from only the highest-degree term in the numerator and the highest-degree term in the denominator. Now discuss the possibilities for horizontal asymptotes in the rational functions $\dfrac{x^2 + 2x + 2}{3x^2 + 2x + 2}$, $\dfrac{x^2 + 2x + 2}{x - 7}$, and $\dfrac{x^2 + 2x + 2}{x^5 - x + 4}$. In all cases, go ahead and do the long division, so the students see the possibilities. (The second one has no horizontal asymptote. The idea of an oblique asymptote is covered in the group work.)

▼ Examples

- Fourth-degree polynomial functions with zeros at $x = -3$, 1, and 2:

$$f(x) = (x + 3)^2 (x - 1)(x - 2) = x^4 + 3x^3 - 7x^2 - 15x + 18$$
$$f(x) = (x + 3)(x - 1)^2 (x - 2) = x^4 - x^3 - 7x^2 + 13x - 6$$
$$f(x) = (x + 3)(x - 1)(x - 2)^2 = x^4 - 2x^3 - 7x^2 + 20x - 12$$

- An example to use in demonstrating the remainder and factor theorems: $f(x) = x^3 - x^2 - 14x + 24$ has zeros $x = -4$, 2, and 3; $f(0) = 24$, $f(1) = 10$, and $f(-1) = 36$.

▼ Group Work: Asymptology

In addition to encouraging practice with polynomial functions, this activity uses concepts that every economics student will have to learn.

It is not necessary to do all three parts of this activity. Depending on time pressure, you may want to stop after Part 1 or after Part 2. It will take at least one full class period to do all three parts.

Stress to students that this activity involves what happens to a function in the long run, as opposed to what they have been thinking about so far, which is what happens for relatively small values of x. Perhaps put a figure like this on the board:

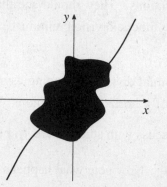

The first part will lead students to discover the idea of a horizontal asymptote. When all (or most) of students are done with this page, regain the attention of the class, and discuss this concept with them, perhaps doing another example. Make sure to be picky on their use of "=" and "≈" here, because the distinction is a major idea in this context. Take the time to give them a good understanding of what they have discovered. The second part leads students to the idea of an oblique asymptote, and the third page talks of quadratic asymptotes. (If you wish, you can generalize this idea with your students.)

The last problem on each part is intended to be used with graphing technology; the other problems do not need it.

Answers:

1. **(a)** 0.0568   **(b)** 0.000510   **(c)** 5×10^{-10}

   (d) $n(x)$ is getting closer and closer to zero. It is incorrect to say that $n(x) = 0$.

   (e) $n(x)$ is getting closer and closer to zero. It is incorrect to say that $n(x) = 0$.

2. **(a)** $3x^2 - 6x + 29 = (x^2 - 2x + 8)\, 3 + 5$ **(b)** $f(x) = 3 + \dfrac{5}{x^2 - 2x + 8}$

   (c) $f(x)$ gets close to 3.   **(d)**

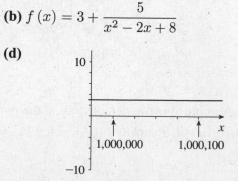

3.

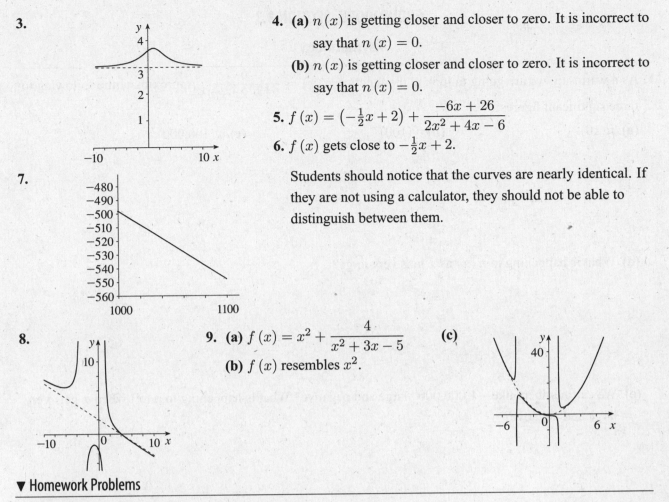

4. (a) $n(x)$ is getting closer and closer to zero. It is incorrect to say that $n(x) = 0$.

(b) $n(x)$ is getting closer and closer to zero. It is incorrect to say that $n(x) = 0$.

5. $f(x) = \left(-\frac{1}{2}x + 2\right) + \dfrac{-6x + 26}{2x^2 + 4x - 6}$

6. $f(x)$ gets close to $-\frac{1}{2}x + 2$.

Students should notice that the curves are nearly identical. If they are not using a calculator, they should not be able to distinguish between them.

7.

8.

9. (a) $f(x) = x^2 + \dfrac{4}{x^2 + 3x - 5}$

(b) $f(x)$ resembles x^2.

(c)

▼ Homework Problems

Core Exercises: 3, 10, 17, 20, 28, 41, 46, 55, 60

Sample Assignment: 3, 6, 10, 11, 17, 20, 28, 35, 41, 46, 48, 55, 58, 60, 63, 66, 69

1. As a warm-up, we are going to look at the function $n(x) = \dfrac{5}{x^2 - 2x + 8}$. Approximate the following to three significant figures:

   (a) $n(10)$ **(b)** $n(100)$ **(c)** $n(100{,}000)$

   (d) What is happening to $n(x)$ as x gets very large?

   (e) We call numbers like $-1{,}000{,}000$ "large and negative" What is happening to $n(x)$ when x gets very large and negative?

2. Now we are going to consider $f(x) = \dfrac{3x^2 - 6x + 29}{x^2 - 2x + 8}$.

   (a) Use polynomial division to write $3x^2 - 6x + 29$ in the form $\left(x^2 - 2x + 8\right) Q(x) + R(x)$, where $Q(x)$ and $R(x)$ are polynomials.

   (b) Use your answer to part (a) to write $f(x)$ in the form $f(x) = Q(x) + \dfrac{R(x)}{x^2 - 2x + 8}$.

(c) Now use what you learned in Question 1 to figure out what is happening to $f(x)$ when x is very large.

(d) Without using a calculator, sketch an approximate graph of $f(x)$ for $1,000,000 \le x \le 1,000,100$.

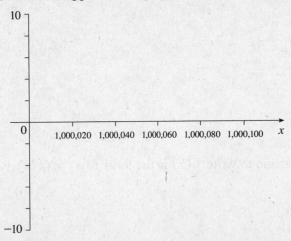

3. If you have a graphing calculator, graph both $f(x)$ and the curve $y = 3$ on the same axes, on the interval $-10 \le x \le 10$. What do you notice?

4. We now consider $f(x) = \dfrac{-x^3 + 2x^2 + 5x + 14}{2x^2 + 4x - 6}$. Again we are going to warm up by looking at a simpler

rational function, $n(x) = \dfrac{-6x + 26}{2x^2 + 4x - 6}$.

(a) What is happening to $n(x)$ as x gets very large and positive?

(b) What is happening to $n(x)$ as x gets very large and negative?

5. Now use polynomial division to write $f(x)$ in the form $f(x) = Q(x) + \dfrac{R(x)}{2x^2 + 4x + 6}$.

6. Use your answers to Questions 4 and 5 to figure out what is happening to $f(x)$ as x gets large. This will require more thought than it did on the previous page, but go ahead and put it into words.

7. We are now going to sketch some graphs without using a calculator.

   (a) Graph the line $y = -\frac{1}{2}x + 2$ (in the range $1000 \le x \le 1100$) on the axes below.

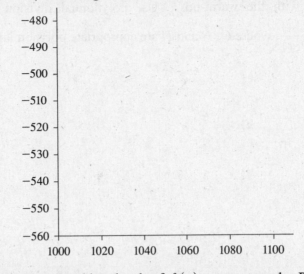

   (b) Using your answer to Question 6, add a sketch of $f(x)$ to your graph. Plot a few points of $f(x)$ afterwards, to confirm that your sketch is reasonable.

8. If you have a graphing calculator, graph both $f(x)$ and the curve $y = -\frac{1}{2}x + 2$ on the same axes, on the interval $-10 \le x \le 10$. What do you notice?

9. We now consider the function $f(x) = \dfrac{x^4 + 3x^3 - 5x^2 + 4}{x^2 + 3x - 5}$.

(a) We will dispense with the warm-ups. Use polynomial division to write $f(x)$ in the form $f(x) = Q(x) + \dfrac{R(x)}{D(x)}$, where Q, R and D are appropriate polynomial functions.

(b) When x gets large, what polynomial function will $f(x)$ most closely resemble? Why?

(c) If you have a graphing calculator, graph $f(x)$ and your answer to part (b) on the axes below.

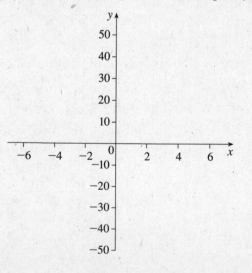

3.4 REAL ZEROS OF POLYNOMIALS

▼ Suggested Time and Emphasis

$\frac{1}{2}$–1 class. Essential material.

▼ Points to Stress

1. The Rational Zeros Theorem: The rational zeros of a polynomial function are always quotients of factors of the constant and the leading terms.
2. Factoring large polynomials using the Rational Zeros Theorem and the quadratic formula.
3. Bounding the number and size of zeros of a polynomial function.

▼ Sample Questions

- **Text Question:** Consider $f(x) = x^6 - 2x^5 - x^4 + 4x^3 - x^2 - 2x + 1$.

    (a) According to the Rational Zeros Theorem, how many possible rational zeros can this polynomial have?

    (b) List all the rational zeros of $f(x)$. Ignore multiplicities and show your work.

    Answer:

    (a) 2

    (b) Both 1 and -1 are zeros of f. This can be shown by manually calculating $f(1)$ and $f(-1)$.

- **Drill Question:** Factor $f(x) = x^3 - 6x + 4$.

    Answer: $f(x) = (x - 2)\left(x + 1 + \sqrt{3}\right)\left(x + 1 - \sqrt{3}\right)$

▼ In-Class Materials

- Students often misinterpret the Rational Zeros Theorem in two ways. Some believe that it classifies *all* the real zeros of a polynomial function, not just the rational ones. Others believe that it apples to *all* polynomial functions, not just the ones with integer coefficients. Start with the simple quadratic $p(x) = x^2 - 2$, pointing out that the candidates for rational zeros are ± 1 and ± 2. None of these candidates are zeros of $p(x)$, but it is simple to find that there are two real zeros: $x = \pm\sqrt{2}$. Then move to a polynomial with one real zero and two irrational ones, such as the one in the Drill Question: $p(x) = x^3 - 6x + 4$. Ask students if they can come up with a polynomial with three real, irrational zeros. One example is $p(x) = x^3 - 3x - \sqrt{2}$ (the zeros are $-\sqrt{2}$ and $\frac{1}{2}\sqrt{2} \pm \frac{1}{2}\sqrt{6}$). This might be perceived as a bit of a cheat, so follow up by asking them if they can come up with a polynomial with integer coefficients and three real, irrational zeros ($x^3 - 5x + 1$ works, for example). The fact that there are three real roots can be determined from a graph; the fact that none are rational can be determined using the Rational Zeros Theorem.

- Ask students why we do not advocate using synthetic division to find the roots of a polynomial such as $p(x) = x^2 + 9x + 20$, $p(x) = x^2 + 9x - 7$, or even $p(x) = x^2 + \pi x - \sqrt[5]{2}$. Hopefully, they will arrive at the conclusion that the quadratic formula is easier to use and will find all the zeros, not just the rational ones. Point out that there is a formula, analogous to the quadratic formula, for third-degree polynomials, but that it is much harder to use. (For those interested, this formula is included below as a bonus.) There is one for fourth-degree polynomials as well. It has been proved that there is no such formula for arbitrary fifth-degree polynomials. In other words, we can find the exact roots for any polynomial up through a fourth-degree polynomial, but there are some polynomials, fifth-degree and higher, whose roots we can only approximate. See Exercises 107 and 108 in the text.

- Point out that being able to find the zeros of a polynomial allows us to solve many types of problems. The text gives several examples of applied problems (and there are many more, of course). For example, we can now find the intersection points between two polynomial curves [if $f(x) = g(x)$, then $f(x) - g(x) = 0$]. If $p(x)$ is a polynomial with an inverse, we can find $p^{-1}(k)$ for a specific k by solving $p(x) - k = 0$. In addition, being able to factor polynomials is very important. For example, the graph of $f(x) = \dfrac{x^3 - 4x}{x^3 + 6x^2 + 11x + 6}$ has a hole at $x = -2$, vertical asymptotes at $x = -1$ and $x = -3$, and x-intercepts at $(2, 0)$ and $(0, 0)$. This information is easily obtained if we write $f(x)$ as $\dfrac{(x + 2)(x - 2)x}{(x + 1)(x + 2)(x + 3)}$.

▼ Examples

- A polynomial with many rational zeros:

$$f(x) = 6x^5 + 17x^4 - 40x^3 - 45x^2 + 14x + 8$$

Factored form: $(2x - 1)(3x + 1)(x + 4)(x + 1)(x - 2)$

Zeros: $x = \frac{1}{2}, -\frac{1}{3}, -4, -1$, and 2

- A polynomial with one rational zero, and four irrational zeros that can be found by elementary methods:

$$f(x) = 2x^5 - 10x^3 + 12x - x^4 + 5x^2 - 6 = (2x - 1)(x^2 - 2)(x^2 - 3)$$

Zeros: $x = \frac{1}{2}, \pm\sqrt{2}$, and $\pm\sqrt{3}$

▼ Bonus: Solving a Cubic Equation

As you know, given an equation of the form $ax^2 + bx + c = 0$ we have a formula that will give us all possible solutions:

$$x = \frac{-b \pm \sqrt{b^2 - 4ac}}{2a}$$

Notice that this gives us the exact solutions, not approximations.

We now solve $ax^3 + bx^2 + cx + d = 0$. First, we "depress the cubic". This does not involve telling the cubic that its favorite band has broken up, its favorite television show has been cancelled, and that nobody has ever really loved it. It means finding a way to remove the coefficient of the x^2 term. (This is done in Exercise 107 in the text, and was first done by Nicolo Fontana Tartaglia in the 1500s.) We make the substitution $x = s - \dfrac{b}{3a}$. In other words we are going to solve

$$a\left(s - \frac{b}{3a}\right)^3 + b\left(s - \frac{b}{3a}\right)^2 + c\left(s - \frac{b}{3a}\right) + d = 0$$

for the variable s, and after we have done so we will use $x = s - \dfrac{b}{3a}$ to find x. Why does this help us?

Because after all the arithmetic, the above equation will simplify to

$$s^3 + ps + q = 0$$

for some p and q.

Exercise 108 points out that one solution to this cubic is

$$s = \sqrt[3]{\frac{-q}{2} + \sqrt{\frac{q^2}{4} + \frac{p^3}{27}}} + \sqrt[3]{\frac{-q}{2} - \sqrt{\frac{q^2}{4} + \frac{p^3}{27}}}$$

So after you depress your cubic, you can find one solution s using this formula. You can then subtract $\dfrac{b}{3a}$ to get a solution x to the original equation. Then synthetic division gives you a quadratic to solve to get the other two solutions.

Note that if the original equation has three real roots, then this equation will be difficult to use, because you will have to deal with some nasty complex numbers and take care to take correct square roots.

▼ Group Work 1: Supply and Demand

Answers:

1. 10,000 people would take a treat (or one person would take 10,000 of them). We could not afford to make any.

2. We could afford to make 1,509,200 treats if we charged such an exorbitant price, but nobody would buy one.

3. $S(x) - D(x) = 0$. This happens when $x = 2$. We should charge $2 per treat.

▼ Group Work 2: Sketch the Graph

This is a straightforward activity, where students use the zeros of a polynomial function to sketch its graph.

Answers:

$f(x) = (4x - 3)^2 (x - 2) (x + 1)^2$, which has roots $x = \frac{3}{4}$, 2, and -1.

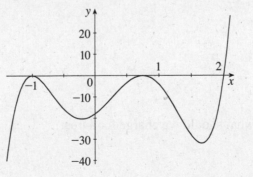

▼ Homework Problems

Core Exercises: 1, 7, 17, 28, 43, 50, 54, 60, 75, 80

Sample Assignment: 1, 7, 12, 17, 19, 28, 33, 43, 46, 50, 54, 57, 60, 66, 73, 75, 80, 85, 101

Supply and Demand

Assume that we are in the business of making and selling tacky, deluxe 10 ounce cat treats in the likenesses of fading celebrities. Economists tell us that there is a function $D(x)$ that tells us how many treats consumers will buy at a price x. They also tell us that there is a function $S(x)$ that tells us how many we can afford to make if we are selling them at a price x. Therefore, they say, we should set our price at the point where $S(x) = D(x)$. They also tell us that we can assume a completely rational consumer, that cat treats never go bad, that there is no international treat cartel that we have to deal with, and that price-fixing and tariffs do not exist. The economists live in a very nice world; speak quietly so as not to frighten them.

Anyway, assume that for $0 \leq x \leq 100$, $S(x) = x^3 + 3x^2 + 4792x$. (This is due to economies of scale. If we are charging \$100 for a cat treat, we can afford to make a heck of a lot of them.)   And also assume that for $0 \leq x \leq 100$, $D(x) = x^2 - 200x + 10{,}000$. (In the given interval, this model says that the more we charge, the fewer people are willing to buy a cat treat.)

1. If we give away the treats for free, how many people would be willing to take a treat? How many could we afford to make if we were giving them away for free?

2. If we were charging \$100 per treat, how many people would buy them? How many could we afford to make if we were selling them at \$100 per treat?

3. According to the economists, what should we charge for a treat?

Sketch the graph of $f(x) = 16x^5 - 24x^4 - 39x^3 + 40x^2 + 21x - 18$. First plot the intercepts, then plot some points between the intercepts, and finally sketch the whole graph.

3.5 COMPLEX NUMBERS

▼ Suggested Time and Emphasis

1 class. Essential material.

▼ Points to Stress

1. Arithmetic operations with complex numbers.
2. Complex numbers as roots of equations.

▼ Sample Questions

- **Text Question:** Write out all solutions (real and complex) to the equation $z^2 = -9$.

  Answer: $z = \pm 3i$
- **Drill Question:** Simplify $\dfrac{3i + 2}{3 + 4i}$.

  Answer: $\frac{18}{25} + \frac{1}{25}i$

▼ In-Class Materials

- Students often believe that the relationship between real and complex numbers is similar to the relationship between rational and irrational numbers—they don't see that the number 5 can be thought of as complex $(5 + 0i)$ as well as real. Perhaps show them this extension of Figure 1 in Section 1.1:

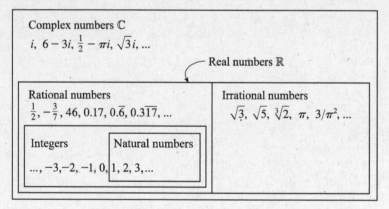

- One doesn't have to think of complex numbers as a philosophical abstraction. Many applied fields use complex numbers, because the result of complex arithmetic leads to real-world understanding. One can think of complex numbers as points in the plane with the real and imaginary axes replacing the x- and y-axes. (In that sense, the complex numbers become a geometric extension of a number line.) Now we can model walking two feet North and one foot East as $1 + 2i$, and one foot North and three feet East as $3 + i$. The sum of the two numbers now has a physical significance: the final location. Multiplication has a meaning, too: When we multiply two complex numbers (thinking of them as points on the plane) we are multiplying their distances from the origin and adding their vector angles. So when we say $i^2 = -1$ we are really just saying that a 90° angle plus a 90° angle is a 180° angle. The statement $i = \sqrt{-1}$ is then a notational aid. Engineers represent waves of a fixed frequency as a magnitude and a phase angle. This interpretation of a complex number is well suited to that model.

- The text states an important truth: that every quadratic equation has two solutions (allowing for multiplicities) if complex numbers are considered. Equivalently, we can say that every quadratic expression $ax^2 + bx + c$ can be factored into two linear factors $(x - z_1)(x - z_2)$, where z_1 and z_2 are complex numbers (and possibly real). An important, easy-to-understand generalization is the Fundamental Theorem of Algebra: Every nth degree polynomial can be factored into n linear factors, if we allow complex numbers. (If we do not, it can be shown that every nth degree polynomial can be factored into linear factors and irreducible quadratic factors) The Fundamental Theorem will be covered explicitly in Section 3.6.

- There is a certain similarity to dividing complex numbers and rationalizing denominators. Make this similarity explicit by having the students do these two problems:

  - Rationalize the denominator of $\dfrac{8}{3 + \sqrt{2}}$. (Answer: $\frac{24}{7} - \frac{8}{7}\sqrt{2}$)

  - Simplify $\dfrac{8}{3 + 2i}$. (Answer: $\frac{24}{13} - \frac{16}{13}i$)

▼ Examples

Sample operations with complex numbers: Let $a = 3 + 2i$ and $b = 7 - 2i$. Then

$$a + b = 10$$
$$a - b = -4 + 4i$$
$$ab = 25 + 8i$$
$$\frac{a}{b} = \tfrac{17}{53} + \tfrac{20}{53}i$$

▼ Group Work 1: Complex Roots

Students should be encouraged, in solving the first problem, to try things out and to explore. Make sure they know in advance that there isn't some method out there that they should have learned and can look up in the textbook. A sufficiently clever student may solve the first problem without the use of the hint sheet. If this happens, have the student attempt to find the square root of $-3 - 4i$ without the hint sheet. After the students have given Problem 1 the "old college try", hand out the hint sheet.

Problem 2 on the hint sheet may require the students to solve $b^4 - 3b^2 + 2 = 0$. Allow them to figure out how to solve it—it is a good foreshadowing of the next section. You may want to give them the hint that it can be factored as $(b^2 - x)(b^2 - y)$.

Answer:

$\pm\frac{\sqrt{2}}{2}(1 + i)$. Note that students are not expected to get this problem without going through the hint sheet.

Hint Sheet Answers:

1. $(a^2 - b^2) + (2ab)i = 0 + 1i \iff a^2 - b^2 = 0$ and $2ab = 1 \iff a = \pm\frac{1}{\sqrt{2}}, b = \pm\frac{1}{\sqrt{2}}$. The square roots of i are $\frac{\sqrt{2}}{2} + \frac{\sqrt{2}}{2}i$ and $-\frac{\sqrt{2}}{2} - \frac{\sqrt{2}}{2}i$.

2. $\sqrt{-3 - 4i} = 1 - 2i$ and $-1 + 2i$, using the same method.

▼ Group Work 2: Find the Error

This is another "old standard" that will show the students that it is important to be careful when manipulating complex numbers. The students should write their answer out completely, so you can make sure that they really understand the error—it will be easy for them to write vague statements that dance around the mistake without actually explaining it. If students finish early, ask them if it is true that $\frac{1}{i} = -i$.

Answer:

The rule $\sqrt{\frac{a}{b}} = \frac{\sqrt{a}}{\sqrt{b}}$ works only if a and b are real and positive. It is true that $\frac{1}{i} = -i$. Also, when writing $\sqrt{z}$ for complex values of z, it is unclear which of the two possible values is the principal square root.

▼ Homework Problems

Core Exercises: 6, 7, 17, 26, 31, 38, 44, 48, 53, 60, 67

Sample Assignment: 6, 7, 14, 17, 26, 31, 33, 38, 44, 45, 48, 53, 56, 60, 67, 72, 75, 76, 79

GROUP WORK 1, SECTION 3.5

Complex Roots

So far we have learned how to find square roots of real numbers. For example, $\sqrt{9} = 3$ or -3. Also, $\sqrt{-9} = 3i$ or $-3i$, if we allow $i = \sqrt{-1}$. We can check our work: $3^2 = 9$ and $(-3)^2 = 9$ so we know that we were right when we said that $\sqrt{9} = \pm 3$. Similarly $(3i)^2 = -9$ and $(-3i)^2 = -9$ so we know that we were right when we said $\sqrt{-9} = \pm 3i$.

It turns out that, once we are in the world of complex numbers, real numbers aren't the only ones that have square roots.

Find $\sqrt{i}$. Notice that "$\sqrt{i}$" is not a sufficient answer—it is simply restating what we are trying to find! "$i^{1/2}$" has the same problem. We are looking for a complex number $z = a + bi$ with the property that $z^2 = i$.

GROUP WORK 1, SECTION 3.5

Complex Roots (Hint Sheet)

Finding $\sqrt{i}$ isn't easy, huh? But you can do it with the knowledge you have of complex numbers. We want to find $a + bi$ with the property that it is the square root of i. In other words:

$$(a + bi)^2 = i$$

We can write this as

$$(a + bi)^2 = 0 + 1i$$

You know how to simplify the left-hand side. You will get an expression with two parts: a real part and an imaginary part. Set the real part equal to zero, the imaginary part equal to one, and find a and b which satisfy the equation.

1. The square roots of 9 are $3 + 0i$ and $-3 + 0i$.

   The square roots of -9 are $0 + 3i$ and $0 - 3i$.

   The square roots of i are _____ + _____ i and _____ + _____ i.

2. You can now find the square root of *any* complex number!

   The square roots of $-3 - 4i$ are _____ + _____ i and _____ + _____ i.

3. Check your answers to Problem 2 by squaring them.

GROUP WORK 2, SECTION 3.5

Find the Error

It is a beautiful autumn day. You and your friends are playing horseshoes, and to make it even more fun, you are playing the rule that after every toss you have to mention something that you learned in school. "Shakespeare wrote in iambic pentameter," says one friend as her horseshoe lands three feet from the post. "Theodore Roosevelt backed antitrust legislation, our national park system, and was the first US citizen to win the Nobel Peace Prize," says another friend, quickly, as his horseshoe lands nine inches from the post. "Mathematicians use the symbol i to denote the square root of negative one, and everything works out," you say, as your horseshoe lands a foot from the post. Another horseshoe sails over your head and rings the post as a small voice yells, "LIES!"

The three of you turn around to see a wild-eyed boy, with several horseshoes in one hand, and his lollipop in the other. "What do you mean, lies?" you ask. "Complex numbers aren't the most intuitive things in the world, hence the use of the adjective 'complex,' but they are certainly consistent with the rest of mathematics, if we allow the concept of i."

"LIES I say, and LIES I mean!" yells the boy. He takes a horseshoe and writes the following in the dirt:

$$\frac{-1}{1} = \frac{1}{-1}$$

"True or false?" demands the boy. You say "True," and your friends nod in assent. They love you. You are their leader.

The boy then says, "And we can take the square root of both sides?"

$$\sqrt{\frac{-1}{1}} = \sqrt{\frac{1}{-1}}$$

"Of course," you say. Your friends do not have to agree with you out loud, because they are looking on you with admiration and respect.

The boy continues to write in the dirt:

$$\frac{\sqrt{-1}}{\sqrt{1}} = \frac{\sqrt{1}}{\sqrt{-1}}$$
$$\frac{i}{1} = \frac{1}{i}$$

"Fine by me!" you say, wondering why the boy continues to write such obvious banalities. "Fine by us!" chorus your friends.

The boy asks you for help with his cross-multiplying. You oblige:

$$i \cdot i = 1 \cdot 1$$
$$-1 = 1$$

There is an uncomfortable pause. You look to your friends, but they are not making eye contact. A single tear is about to run down one of their cheeks. Is all of mathematics a big lie? Are negative numbers really the same as positive numbers? If that is true, could you please write a letter to my credit card company, telling them that they actually owe *me* a few thousand dollars?

Or is it possible that somewhere, somehow, someone made a mistake? Find the error.

3.6 COMPLEX ZEROS AND THE FUNDAMENTAL THEOREM OF ALGEBRA

▼ Suggested Time and Emphasis

1 class. Essential material.

▼ Points to Stress

1. The Complete Factorization Theorem.

2. The Conjugate Zeros Theorem.

3. The Linear and Quadratic Factors Theorem.

▼ Sample Questions

- **Text Question:** Let $f(x) = x^3 + ax^2 + bx + c$.

  (a) What is the maximum number of zeros this polynomial function can have?

  (b) What is the minimum number of real zeros this polynomial function can have?

  Answer: (a) 3   **(b)** 1

- **Drill Question:** Consider the polynomial $f(x) = x^5 - 2x^4 + 16x^3 + 8x^2 + 20x + 200$. It is a fact that -2 is a zero of this polynomial, and that $(x - 1 - 3i)^2$ is a factor of this polynomial. Using this information, factor the polynomial completely.

  Answer: $f(x) = (x - 1 - 3i)^2 (x - 1 + 3i)^2 (x + 2)$

▼ In-Class Materials

- Stress the power of the Complete Factorization Theorem and how it dovetails with the Linear and Quadratic Factors Theorem. Once we allow complex numbers, we can view *all* polynomial functions as functions of the form $f(x) = a(x - c_1)(x - c_2) \ldots (x - c_n)$; simple products of linear factors. If we don't want to allow complex numbers (the preference of many students), we still can write all polynomials almost as simply, as the product of linear and (irreducible) quadratic factors.

- Point out that when graphing $y = f(x)$, the real zeros appear as x-intercepts, as expected. Remind students how the multiplicities of the real zeros can be seen. A multiplicity of 1 crosses the x-axis, an even multiplicity touches the x-axis, and an odd multiplicity greater than one crosses the x-axis and is flat there. (See Section 3.2.) Note that the complex zeros don't appear on real plane.

- Exercise 74 discusses roots of unity—the zeros of polynomials of the form $f(x) = x^n - 1$ or, equivalently, the solutions of $x^n = 1$. It is easy to find the real solutions, 1 if n is odd and ± 1 if n is even. Exercise 74 prompts students to solve $x^n = 1$ for $n = 2$, 3, and 4. If your students have been exposed to trigonometric functions, then you can show them the general formula: $x^n = 1 \iff x = \cos\left(\dfrac{2\pi k}{n}\right) + i\sin\left(\dfrac{2\pi k}{n}\right)$ for $k = 0, \ldots, n$.

Interestingly enough, if you plot the solutions in the complex plane, there is a wonderful amount of symmetry. Even if you don't want to discuss the general formula, you can show your students where the roots of unity live.

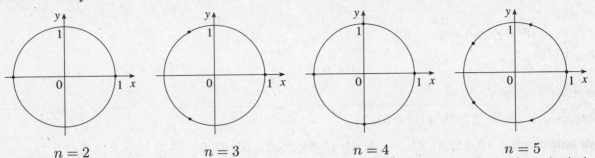

$$n = 2 \qquad n = 3 \qquad n = 4 \qquad n = 5$$

The complex roots of unity can be thought of as points that are evenly distributed around the unit circle.

- It is possible to use the techniques of the previous sections to solve polynomials with nonreal coefficients. If you want to demonstrate this fact, consider the polynomial $f(z) = z^3 + (2 - 3i) z^2 + (-3 - 6i) + 9i$, and use synthetic division to obtain $f(z) = (z - 1)(z + 3)(z - 3i)$

▼ Examples

- A polynomial that is the product of two irreducible quadratic terms:

$$f(x) = x^4 + 2x^3 + 9x^2 + 2x + 8 = \left(x^2 + 1\right)\left(x^2 + 2x + 8\right)$$

This can be factored by noting that $x = i$ is a zero, and therefore $x = -i$ is a zero, and then dividing by $\left(x^2 + 1\right)$.

- A polynomial that is the product of two linear terms and an irreducible quadratic term:

$$f(x) = x^4 + 5x^3 + 10x^2 + 16x - 32 = \left(x^2 + 2x + 8\right)(x - 1)(x + 4)$$

▼ Group Work: Complex Roots

Students should, at this point, be able to factor a polynomial by dividing out linear factors (found by the Rational Roots Theorem) and then using the quadratic formula, if necessary, on what is left. This technique only works if there are at most two nonrational roots. This activity allows them to explore a quartic function with four complex roots.

Allow students to puzzle over Problem 3, but give them the Hint Sheet if it doesn't look like their puzzling is getting anywhere.

Answers:

1. $\pm 1, \pm 2, \pm 4, \pm 5, \pm 10, \pm 20$

2. This polynomial has no real zero. This can be determined by evaluating f at each of the 12 possible zeros, by synthetic division and use of bounding theorems, or by graphing f.

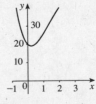

3. $(x - i)(x + i)\left[x - (4 + 2i)\right]\left[x - (4 - 2i)\right]$

153

Answers (Hint Sheet)

1. Synthetic division works here.
2. $x = -i$ is a zero.
3. $x^2 + 1$
4. $f(x) = (x^2 + 1)(x^2 - 8x + 20)$
5. $\pm i, 4 \pm 2i$

▼ Homework Problems

Core Exercises: 7, 10, 20, 27, 38, 47, 54, 63, 71

Sample Assignment: 7, 10, 15, 20, 27, 30, 38, 44, 47, 54, 56, 59, 63, 67, 71, 74

Complex Roots

Consider the polynomial function $f(x) = x^4 - 8x^3 + 21x^2 - 8x + 20$.

1. According to the Rational Zeros Theorem, what are the possible rational zeros of this polynomial?

2. Which of the possible rational zeros are, in fact, zeros of f?

3. Factor this polynomial.

1. Factoring $f(x) = x^4 - 8x^3 + 21x^2 - 8x + 20$ looks like it is going to be difficult, eh? Well, here is a hint. The imaginary number i is a zero of the polynomial. Verify that this is correct.

2. According to the Conjugate Zeros Theorem, the fact that $x = i$ is one zero of this polynomial informs you of another zero of this polynomial. What is that zero?

3. Use your answer to the previous parts to come up with an irreducible quadratic that is a factor of f.

4. Factor f into irreducible quadratic factors.

5. What are all the zeros of f?

3.7   RATIONAL FUNCTIONS

▼ Suggested Time and Emphasis

2 classes. Essential material.

▼ Points to Stress

1. Various kinds of asymptotes and end behavior of functions, particularly rational functions.

2. Graphing rational functions.

▼ Sample Questions

- **Text Question:** What is a slant asymptote?

  Answer: Answers will vary

- **Drill Question:** Find all the asymptotes of the rational function $f(x) = \dfrac{x^2 + 1}{2x^2 - 5x - 3}$.

  Answer: Horizontal asymptote at $y = \frac{1}{2}$, vertical asymptotes at $x = -\frac{1}{2}$ and $x = 3$

▼ In-Class Materials

- This is a good time to remind students of parameters. For example, give each section of the class a different value of c and have them sketch $f(x) = \dfrac{x}{x^2 - c}$.

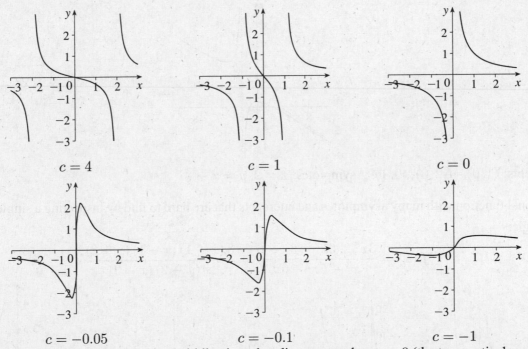

$$c = 4 \qquad\qquad c = 1 \qquad\qquad c = 0$$

$$c = -0.05 \qquad\qquad c = -0.1 \qquad\qquad c = -1$$

  Note that when c is positive, there is a middle piece that disappears when $c = 0$ (the two vertical asymptotes become one). Note how the curve still gets large at $x = 0$ when c is small and negative.

- If the group work "Asymptology" in Section 3.3 was assigned, it should be reviewed at this point, because it lays the groundwork for this section's discussion of asymptotes. Students should see how the concepts they have previously discovered are described in the text.

- A bit of care should be exercised when checking vertical asymptotes. For example, have students examine $f(x) = \dfrac{x^2 + 3x + 2}{x^2 - 1}$. If they are alert, they will notice an apparent x-intercept at $x = -1$, making it impossible to follow the text's dictum: "When choosing test values, we must make sure that there is no x-intercept between the test point and the vertical asymptote." The reason is that there is not a vertical asymptote at $x = -1$ is that there is a hole there, as seen when f is factored: $f(x) = \dfrac{(x+1)(x+2)}{(x+1)(x-1)}$. See Exercise 91 in the text.

- A good example to do with students is $f(x) = \dfrac{1}{x^2 + 1}$. A curve of this type is called a *Witch of Agnesi*. Its history may amuse your students. Italian mathematician Maria Agnesi (1718–1799) was a scholar whose first paper was published when she was nine years old. She called a particular curve *versiera* or "turning curve". John Colson from Cambridge confused the word with *avversiera* or "wife of the devil", and translated it "witch".

▼ Examples

- A rational function with a slant asymptote:

$$f(x) = \frac{x^2 + x - 2}{x - 2} = \frac{(x-1)(x+2)}{x-2}$$

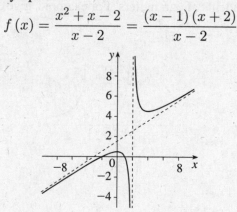

Intercepts: $(1, 0)$, $(-2, 0)$, $(0, 1)$. Asymptotes: $x = 2$, $y = x + \frac{3}{2}$

- A rational function with many asymptotes and intercepts that are hard to find by inspecting a single viewing rectangle:

$$f(x) = \frac{3x^3 + 6x^2 - 3x - 6}{x^3 - 5x^2 + 6x} = \frac{3(x+1)(x-1)(x+2)}{x(x-2)(x-3)}$$

Intercepts: $(1, 0)$, $(-1, 0)$, $(-2, 0)$. Asymptotes: $x = 0$, $x = 2$, $x = 3$, $y = 3$

- A rational function with no asymptote:

$$f(x) = \frac{x^4 + 3x^2 + 2}{x^2 - 4x + 5} = \frac{(x^2 + 1)(x^2 + 2)}{x^2 - 4x + 5}$$

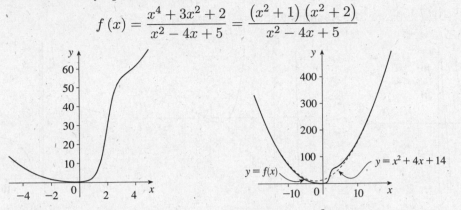

Note that the end behavior of this function is similar to that of $y = x^2 + 4x + 14$.

▼ Group Work 1: Fun with Asymptotes

This activity extends the concepts of this section and reviews the idea of odd and even functions.

Answers:

1. Answers will vary. There should be vertical asymptotes at $x = \pm\frac{1}{2}$ and $x = \pm 1$.

2. Answers will vary. There should be asymptotes at $x = \pm 1$, $x = \pm 2$, and $y = 2$.

3. There are vertical asymptotes at $x = \pm 1.5$. This is not a rational function.

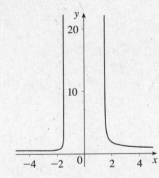

▼ Group Work 2: Putting It All Together

At first, students may just try to put this in their calculators. You may want to give them the hint that it will be difficult to find a viewing window that shows all the features of this graph by trial and error. When they've done some of the mathematical analysis of this graph, they should be encouraged to draw graphs using several windows, given that no one range is completely illustrative.

Answer:

Intercepts: $\left(-\frac{1}{2}, 0\right)$, $\left(\frac{3}{2}, 0\right)$, $(1, 0)$. Asymptotes: $x = 0$, $x = -1$, $y = 4$

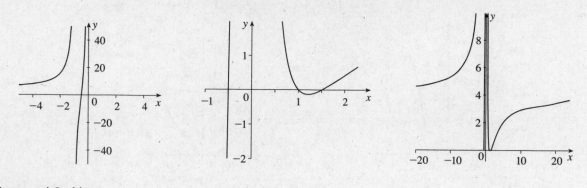

▼ Homework Problems

Core Exercises: 5, 8, 13, 22, 42, 49, 67, 84, 91

Sample Assignment: 5, 6, 8, 13, 19, 22, 28, 39, 42, 49, 55, 63, 67, 70, 84, 86, 91

Fun with Asymptotes

1. Draw an odd function that has the lines $x = \frac{1}{2}$ and $x = -1$ among its vertical asymptotes.

2. Draw an even function that has $x = 1$, $x = -2$, and $y = 2$ among its asymptotes.

3. Analyze the vertical asymptotes of $f(x) = \dfrac{3x^2 + 4x + 5}{\sqrt{16x^4 - 81}}$. Is this a rational function?

Sketch the graph of $f(x) = \dfrac{4x^3 - 8x^2 + x + 3}{x^3 + x^2}$.

4 EXPONENTIAL AND LOGARITHMIC FUNCTIONS

4.1 EXPONENTIAL FUNCTIONS

▼ Suggested Time and Emphasis

1 class. Essential material.

▼ Points to Stress

1. The definition of an exponential function, including what it means to raise a to an irrational number.
2. The geometry of exponential functions and their transformations.
3. Periodically compounded interest.

▼ Sample Questions

- **Text Question:** Sketch a graph of $y = \left(\frac{1}{2}\right)^x$.

  Answer:

  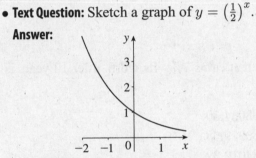

- **Drill Question:** Find the total amount of money in an account after 2 years if $100 is invested at an interest rate of 5.5% per year, compounded quarterly.

  Answer: $111.54

▼ In-Class Materials

- Start to draw a graph of $y = 2^x$, using a carefully measured scale of one inch per unit on both axes. Point out that after one foot, the height would be over 100 yards (the length of a football field). After two feet, the height would be 264 miles, after three feet it would be 1,000,000 miles (four times the distance to the moon), after three and a half feet it would be in the heart of the sun. If the graph extended five feet to the right, $x = 60$, then y would be over one light year up.

- Point out this contrast between exponential and linear functions: For equally spaced x-values, linear functions have constant *differences* in y-values, whereas pure exponential functions have constant *ratios* in y-values. Use this fact to show that the following table describes an exponential function, not a linear one.

x	y
-6.2	0.62000
-2.4	0.65100
1.4	0.68355
5.2	0.71773
9.0	0.75361
12.8	0.79129

- Estimate where $3^x > x^3$ and where $2^x > x^8$ using technology. Notice that exponential functions start by growing much more *slowly* than polynomial functions, and then wind up growing much more *quickly*. For example, if one were to graph x^2 versus x using one inch per unit, then when $x = 60$, y would be only 100 yards, as opposed to a light year for $y = 2^x$. (The sun is only 8 light minutes from the earth.)

▼ Examples

- A shifted exponential curve:

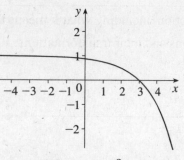

$$f(x) = -2^{x-3} + 1$$

- A comparison of compounding rates: \$2000 is put in an IRA that earns 7%. Its worth after 10 years is given in the following table.

Compounded annually	\$3934.30
Compounded semi-annually	\$3979.58
Compounded monthly	\$4019.32
Compounded weekly	\$4025.61
Compounded daily	\$4027.24
Compounded hourly	\$4027.50

Note: Most calculators will not be able to determine the amount earned if the interest is compounded, say, every tenth of a second. Underflow errors in the microprocessor will make the computation difficult.

▼ Group Work 1: I've Grown Accustomed to Your Growth

Before handing out this activity, it may be prudent to review the rules of exponentiation. This exercise enables students to discover for themselves the equal ratio property of exponential functions.

Answers:

1. Yes ($m = 1$), no, yes ($m \approx 2.08$), yes ($m \approx 2.01$)
2. Equally spaced changes in x-values result in equally spaced changes in y-values
3. Equally spaced changes in x values result in equally proportioned changes in y-values with the same ratio.
   $b = 2$, $b = 0.9975$, $b = 2.25$, $b = 3$
4. The "$ + C$" gets in the way when taking the ratio. However, the property is close to being true when A and b are large compared to C.

▼ Group Work 2: Comparisons

The purpose of this group work is to give students a bit of "picture sense". It is acceptable if they do this by looking at the graphs on their calculators, setting the windows appropriately.

Answers:

1. $0 < x < 1.374$ and $x > 9.940$
2. $0 < x < 1.051$ and $x > 95.7169$
3. $0 < x < 1.17$ and $x > 22.5$
4. $0 < x < 1.34$ and $x > 10.9$
5. $0 < x < 1.077$ and $x > 58.7702$

▼ Homework Problems

Core Exercises: 6, 9, 12, 21, 28, 42, 47, 52, 55

Sample Assignment: 6, 8, 9, 12, 18, 21, 23, 28, 35, 38, 42, 47, 52, 55, 59

I've Grown Accustomed to Your Growth

1. Two or three of the following four tables of data have something in common: linear growth. Without trying to find complete equations of lines, determine which of them are linear growth, and determine their rate of change:

x	y
1	2
2	3
3	4
4	5

x	y
21.5	4.32
32.6	4.203
43.7	4.090
54.8	3.980

x	y
-3	1.1
-2.5	2.14
-2	3.18
-1.5	4.25

x	y
1	-5.00
3	-0.98
6	5.05
8	9.07

2. In a sentence, describe a property of linear growth that can be determined from a table of values.

3. The following four tables of data have something in common: exponential growth. Functions of the form $y = Ab^x$ (or Ae^{kx}) have a property in common analogous to the one you stated in Question 2. Find the property, and then find the value of b.

x	y
1	5
2	10
3	20
4	40

x	y
21.5	4.32
32.6	4.203
43.7	4.090
54.8	3.980

x	y
-3	1.1
-2.5	1.65
-2	2.475
-1.5	3.7125

x	y
1	0.8
3	7.2
6	194.4
8	1749.6

4. Unfortunately, the above property does not hold for functions of the form $y = Ab^x + C$. What goes wrong? For what kinds of values of A, b, and C does the property come close to being true?

GROUP WORK 2, SECTION 4.1

Comparisons

You have learned that an exponential function grows faster than a polynomial function. Find the values of $x > 0$ for which

1. $2^x \geq x^3$.

2. $(1.1)^x \geq x^2$.

3. $2^x \geq x^5$.

4. $3^x \geq x^5$.

5. $2^x > x^{10}$.

4.2   THE NATURAL EXPONENTIAL FUNCTION

▼ **Suggested Time and Emphasis**

$\frac{1}{2}$–1 class. Essential material.

▼ **Points to Stress**

1. The base e.
2. Continuously compounded interest.

▼ **Sample Questions**

- **Text Question:** Sketch a graph of $y = e^x$.

  Answer:

  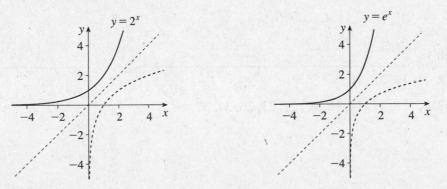

- **Drill Question:** Find the total amount of money in an account after 2 years if $100 is invested at an interest rate of 5.5% per year, compounded continuously.

  Answer: $111.63

▼ **In-Class Materials**

- Have your students fill out the following table, using their calculators, to give them a feel for $y = e^x$.

x	2^x	3^x	e^x
-2	$\frac{1}{4} = 0.25$	$\frac{1}{9} \approx 0.111$	≈ 0.135
-1	$\frac{1}{2} = 0.5$	$\frac{1}{3} \approx 0.333$	≈ 0.368
0	1	1	1
1	2	3	≈ 2.718
2	4	9	≈ 7.389
3	8	27	≈ 20.086

- Anticipate the next section by having students sketch the graphs of the inverse functions of 2^x and e^x by reflecting them across the line $y = x$.

169

▼ Examples

- A shifted exponential curve:

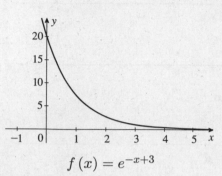

$$f(x) = e^{-x+3}$$

- A continuation of the previous section's analysis: $2000 is put in an IRA that earns 7%. Its worth after 10 years is given in the following table.

Compounded annually	$3934.30
Compounded monthly	$4019.32
Compounded daily	$4027.24
Compounded hourly	$4027.50
Compounded continuously	$4027.51

Note: Most calculators will not be able to determine the amount earned if the interest is compounded, say, every tenth of a second. Underflow errors in the microprocessor will make the computation difficult.

▼ Group Work 1: Finding a

The way we approximate e in this exercise foreshadows the computation that comes up when the derivative of e^x is used in calculus. Hand out the first page. Ideally, the students will realize that the value of a they are looking for in part 3 is between 2 and 3. If they don't, they may require the hint that part 1 implies that 2 is too small, and part 2 implies that 3 is too big. (These facts are not proved in the activity.)

After the students get close to 2.7, hand out the second page.

Answers:

1. **(a)** No, because $h = 0$ results in a zero denominator.   **(b)** 1, 0.7177, 0.6956, 0.6934   **(c)** 0.6931

2. **(a)** No, because $h = 0$ results in a zero denominator.   **(b)** 2, 1.1612, 1.1047, 1.0992   **(c)** 1.0986

3. 2.7   4. 0.9999   5. 1

▼ Homework Problems

Core Exercises: 2, 4, 8, 11, 17, 22, 31

Sample Assignment: 2, 4, 5, 8, 11, 14, 16, 17, 22, 23, 26, 31, 37

Finding a

There is a problem that looks kind of silly on the face of it, but turns out to be very important in the development of calculus. In this activity we introduce the problem, and attempt to find a solution. Please present all answers to at least four decimal places unless directed otherwise.

1. Consider the function $f(h) = \dfrac{2^h - 1}{h}$.

   (a) Is $f(0)$ defined? Why or why not?

   (b) Compute $f(1)$, $f(0.1)$, $f(0.01)$, and $f(0.001)$.

   (c) As h gets closer and closer to zero, does f approach a value? If so, what is that value?

2. Repeat part 1 using $f(h) = \dfrac{3^h - 1}{h}$.

3. It turns out to be important to find a number a such that as h gets closer and closer to zero, $f(h) = \dfrac{a^h - 1}{h}$ gets closer and closer to 1. Try to find such a value of a, accurate to one decimal place.

4. Now let $a = 2.718$. As h gets closer and closer to zero, what does $f(h) = \dfrac{2.718^h - 1}{h}$ approach?

5. Using the e^x key on your calculator, repeat part 4 for $f(h) = \dfrac{e^h - 1}{h}$.

4.3 LOGARITHMIC FUNCTIONS

▼ Suggested Time and Emphasis

1 class. Essential material.

▼ Points to Stress

1. Definition of the logarithm function as the inverse of the exponential function, from both a numeric and geometric perspective.

2. Properties of the logarithm function, emphasizing the natural and common logarithms.

▼ Sample Questions

- **Text Question:** It is a fact that $10^{\pi} \approx 1385.46$. Is it possible to approximate $\log 1385.46$ without the use of a calculator? If so, then approximate this number. If not, why not?

  Answer: $\log_{10} 1385.46 \approx \pi$

- **Drill Question:** Compute $\log_4 \frac{1}{64}$

  Answer: -3

▼ In-Class Materials

- When the logarithm function is graphed on a calculator, it appears to have a horizontal asymptote. Point out that the graph is misleading in that way. Start a graph of $y = \log_{10} x$ on the blackboard, noting the domain and the vertical asymptote. Using the scale of 1 inch $= 1$ unit (on the x-axis) and 1 foot $= 1$ unit (on the y-axis), plot some points:

x	0.1	1	2	3	4	5	6	7	8	9	10
$\log_{10} x$	-1	0	0.30	0.47	0.60	0.70	0.78	0.85	0.90	0.95	1

Now ask how many inches we would have to go out to get up to $y = 2$ feet. (Answer: 100 inches, or $8\frac{1}{3}$ feet.) If the blackboard is large enough, plot the point $(100, 2)$. Then ask how far we would have to go to get up to $y = 5$ feet. (Answer: 1.57 miles.) Note that it takes close to a mile and a half to go from $y = 4$ to $y = 5$, and that (if you graphed it out) it would look a lot like there is a horizontal asymptote. Find the distance from your classroom to a city or landmark in another state, and ask the class to estimate the log of that distance, using the same scale.

- Sketch a graph of $f(x) = 2 \log_2(x + 3)$. Sketch the inverse function, then find an algebraic formula for the inverse. Foreshadow the next section by showing that the graph of $f(x)$ is the same as that of $g(x) = \log_2\left((x + 3)^2\right)$.

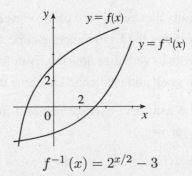

$f^{-1}(x) = 2^{x/2} - 3$

173

- Ask your students if they have ever had to deal with recharging the battery for a music device or a laptop. Assume that the battery is dead, and it takes an hour to charge it up half way. Ask them how much it will be charged in two hours. (The answer is 75% charged.) They may have noticed that, when charging a laptop battery, it takes a surprisingly long time for the monitor to change from "99% charged" to "100% charged." It turns out that the time it takes to charge the battery to $n\%$ is given by $t = -k \ln \left(1 - \frac{n}{100}\right)$; in our example $k = 1.4427$. Have students compute how long it would take the battery to get a 97% charge, a 98% charge, and a 99% charge. (Remind them that it took only an hour to go from 0% to 50%.) Graph t versus n to demonstrate that the battery will never be fully charged according to this model.

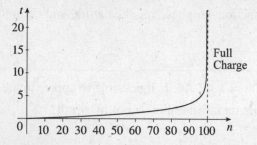

- Show students semilog graph paper (available at university bookstores, from your friendly neighborhood physics teacher, or from websites such as `http://www.csun.edu/science/ref/measurement/data/graph_paper.html`.) Point out how the distance between the y-axis lines is based on the logarithm of the y-coordinate, not on the y-coordinate itself. Have them graph $y = 2^x$ on semilog graph paper.

▼ Examples

A shifted logarithmic curve:

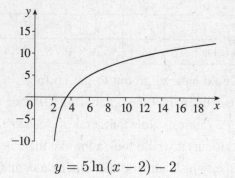

$$y = 5 \ln (x - 2) - 2$$

▼ Group Work 1: The Evan Operation

This activity can be enjoyed on two levels. One level of thought would stop after students used trial and error to discover that the Evan Function concatenates any two numbers. A more challenging level of thought would get students to verbalize how the Evan function works: why it does what it does. An advanced class might be given the goal, and challenged to come up with an expression for the Evan function themselves.

Problem 4 can serve as a springboard for discussions of commutativity, associativity, and identity, or it can stand on its own.

In this exercise, $[\![x]\!]$ denotes the greatest integer function.

Answers:

1. (a) 15   **(b)** 42,134   **(c)** 5,231,553   **(d)** 8,501,245   **(e)** 4,226,483,173

2. Evaning is the same as concatenating (writing one next to the other).

3. It is not possible, because negative numbers are outside the domain of the log function

4. (b) and (d) are true, (a) is false, and (c) is not even well defined.

5. $[\![\log_{10} b]\!] + 1$ tells us how many digits are in b. We then take a, add that many zeros to its end, and then add b.

▼ Group Work 2: Learning Curves

Phrases like "the learning curve is steep" and "the learning curve is shallow" come up occasionally in academia, and many don't know what they mean. This activity will use the idea of a learning curve to play with some of the functions that have been learned thus far. Either start the activity by handing out the worksheet, or by doing the first problem as a class, and then handing out the sheet.

Answers:

1.

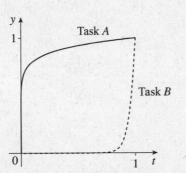

2. Task A. After saying it a couple of times, you pretty much know it.

3. Task B. There is a long period where improvment is slow, and then the learning takes place quickly.

4., 5. Answers will vary. Notice that for most activities of this nature, even though there is no horizontal asymptote, the slope of the learning curve will tend to approach zero (as happens for $y = \ln x$).

6. (a) Make sure students address the horizontal asymptote at $y = 1$ and the concavity change.

    (c) Make sure students address the fact that the y-intercept is not zero.

    (d) Make sure that students address the fact that there is no horizontal asymptote, and that improvement gets slower and slower (perhaps as discussed in Problem 5).

    (f) Make sure students address the periodic "plateaus" in improvement.

    (g) Make sure students address the "dips" where they get worse before they get better. (Games such as darts work like this, where as someone gets better, that person gets less and less lucky "fallout".)

7. It means that improvement is very rapid, implying that the task is easy to learn.

▼ Homework Problems

Core Exercises: 3, 6, 10, 13, 21, 32, 46, 65, 87

Sample Assignment: 3, 4, 6, 10, 11, 13, 17, 21, 27, 32, 36, 38, 46, 56, 65, 68, 87

GROUP WORK 1, SECTION 4.3

The Evan Operation

Consider two positive integers a and b. We know how to compute $a + b$, $a - b$, a/b, and ab. There is another thing we can compute: $a \circledast b$, pronounced "a Evan b". To Evan two numbers together, we perform the following calculation:

$$a \circledast b = a \left(10^{[\![\log_{10} b]\!]+1} \right) + b$$

1. Compute the following without the use of a calculator.

   (a) $1 \circledast 5$

   (b) $42 \circledast 134$

   (c) $5231 \circledast 553$

   (d) $8 \circledast 501{,}245$

   (e) $42{,}264 \circledast 83{,}173$

2. Describe, in words, what it means to Evan two integers together.

3. What happens when we try to Evan negative integers?

4. Which of the following statements are true for arbitrary positive integers a, b, and c?

(a) $a \circledast b = b \circledast a$

(b) $a \circledast (b \circledast c) = (a \circledast b) \circledast c$

(c) $a \circledast 0 = a$

(d) $0 \circledast b = b$

5. Revisit your answer to Part 2. Explain, in words, why $a\left(10^{\llbracket \log_{10} b \rrbracket + 1}\right) + b$ does what you say it does.

GROUP WORK 2, SECTION 4.3

Learning Curves

In psychology, we often graph the amount of material learned as a function of time spent studying or practicing. For example, assume I wanted to learn the capitals of all fifty states in the United States. I know the capitals of five states off the top of my head, and after ten minutes I can probably learn ten more. Ten more minutes will give me ten more, and then I'm going to slow down—I'll start forgetting. But if I put a solid three hours into it, I will know all fifty. If we plot these data on a graph, then I have a "learning curve".

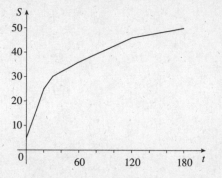

Different types of tasks have different learning curves, and, of course, the learning curves for each person are different. But for some tasks, the overall shape is similar for many people.

Let's look at two activities we are trying to learn how to do. Task A's curve is given by $y = \sqrt[10]{t}$ and Task B's is given by $y = t^{20}$.

1. Sketch both learning curves.

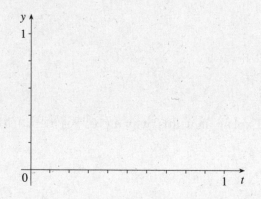

2. One of the tasks is memorizing a five digit number. Is this most likely Task A or Task B? Why?

3. It was interesting watching my five-year-old daughter learn to ride a bicycle. She experienced a period of frustration, where her improvement was slow. She couldn't balance. Suddenly, her mind and body seemed to "click" and she was able to ride perfectly, and started asking me how to pop wheelies, if she could ride to kindergarten by herself, and if unicycles were expensive. Did her learning curve look more like that of Task A or that of Task B? Why?

4. Both of the above tasks stopped at $y = 1$. We can think of $y = 1$ as "knowing the number" and "being able to ride down the street without falling off" Give an example of a task where there is no y-boundary; where one can start learning, and get better and better at the task without limit.

5. Draw the learning curve of the task you described in Part 4.

6. Come up with tasks that fit the following learning curves. Sketching their graphs, starting at $t = 0$, will be helpful.

(a) $L(t) = \dfrac{1}{1 + e^{-t+4}}$

(b) $L(t) = \dfrac{t}{10}$

(c) $L(t) = \dfrac{t}{10} + \dfrac{1}{2}$

(d) $L(t) = \ln(t + 1)$

(e) $L(t) = t^2$ for $0 \leq t \leq 1$

(f) $L(t) = x + \sin x$ for $0 \leq x \leq 9.5$

(g) $L(t) = x + 1.25 \sin x$ for $0 \leq x \leq 9$

7. If someone describes a task to you and says, "The learning curve is steep," what does that mean?

4.4   LAWS OF LOGARITHMS

▼ Suggested Time and Emphasis

$1-1\frac{1}{2}$ classes. Essential material.

▼ Point to Stress

The laws of logarithms, including the change of base formula.

▼ Sample Questions

- **Text Question:** Given that $\log_2 3 \approx 1.58496$, approximately what is $\log_2 9$?
  Answer: $\log_2 9 \approx 3.16992$

- **Drill Question:** Express $5 \log (x+2) - \frac{1}{3} \log x$ as a single logarithm.

  Answer: $\log \left(\dfrac{(x+2)^5}{\sqrt[3]{x}} \right)$

▼ In-Class Materials

- Make sure your students do not neglect the warning after Example 4. Perhaps have them write out all the rules of logarithms they have learned so far, organized this way:

The Equivalence Definition	$y = \log_m x$ is equivalent to $x = m^y$
The Conversion Rule	$\log_m (\text{thing}) = \dfrac{\log_n (\text{thing})}{\log_n (m)}$
The Combining Rules	$\log_m \left(m^{\text{thing}} \right) = \text{thing}$ $m^{\log_m (\text{thing})} = \text{thing}$
The Arithmetic Rules	$\log_m 1 = 0$ $\log_m (ab) = \log_m a + \log_m b$ $\log_m \left(\dfrac{a}{b} \right) = \log_m a - \log_m b$ $\log_m \left(a^b \right) = b \log_m a$
The Non-Rules	$\log_m (a+b) = \log_m (a+b)$ $\dfrac{\log_m a}{\log_m b} = \dfrac{\log_m a}{\log_m b}$ $(\log_m a)^b = (\log_m a)^b$

  Perhaps if your students memorize the non-rules, they will be less likely to indulge in algebraic mischief under exam pressure.

- Note, without necessarily emphasizing, the importance of domains when applying the log rules. For example, $\ln \left(\frac{-5}{-6} \right)$ is not equal to $\ln (-5) - \ln (-6)$.

180

- Mention how logarithms were used to do calculations before the advent of the calculator. For example, every scientist had tables like these:

x	$\ln x$
4.4	1.48160
4.5	1.50408
4.6	1.52606
4.7	1.54756
4.8	1.56862

x	$\ln x$
9.8	2.28238
9.9	2.29253
10.0	2.30259
10.1	2.31254
10.2	2.32239

To find $\sqrt[3]{100}$, for example, the scientist would write

$$\sqrt[3]{100} = 10^{2/3}$$

$$\ln\left(\sqrt[3]{100}\right) = \ln\left(10^{2/3}\right)$$

$$= \tfrac{2}{3}\ln(10)$$

Then he or she would look up $\ln(10)$ from the table to get

$$\ln\left(\sqrt[3]{100}\right) \approx \tfrac{2}{3}(2.30259)$$

$$\approx 1.53506$$

And to find $\sqrt[3]{100}$, he or she would try to find 1.53506 in the right-hand column of the table. The result is that $\sqrt[3]{100}$ is between 4.6 and 4.7. In practice, the distance between table entries was much closer than 0.1. For a quicker, less accurate estimate, a slide rule was used.

▼ Examples

- A set of logarithms that can be combined:

$$a\ln(b+c) + \frac{3}{4}(\ln a - \ln b) = \ln\left((b+c)^a \sqrt[4]{\left(\frac{a}{b}\right)^3}\right)$$

- A set of logarithms that can be expanded:

  Given $\ln 2 \approx 0.693$ and $\ln 3 \approx 1.099$, compute $\ln\frac{8}{9}\sqrt[5]{6}$.

$$\frac{8}{9}\sqrt[5]{6} = \frac{2^3}{3^2}(2 \cdot 3)^{1/5}$$

$$\ln\left(\frac{8}{9}\sqrt[5]{6}\right) = 3\ln 2 - 2\ln 3 + \tfrac{1}{5}(\ln 2 + \ln 3)$$

$$\approx 0.240569$$

▼ Group Work 1: Irrational, Impossible Relations

One of the joys of precalculus is that there are some deep, graduate-level mathematical results that can be explored using nothing more than the techniques of algebra and one's coconut. Start by asking students this true-or-false question:

$$\log_2 3 = \frac{4953}{3125}$$

The answer is, of course, "false". Next, review the definitions of rational and irrational numbers, and hand out the first sheet. The hint sheet should be given out only after students have tried to show that $\log_2 3$ is irrational, or at least discussed it enough to understand what they are trying to show. If a group finishes early, have them show that $\log_2 a$ is always irrational if a is an odd integer.

Answers:

1. $-\gamma$ **2.** $-\gamma$ **3.** $\dfrac{\gamma}{2}$ **4.** $\log_2 3 = \dfrac{\ln 3}{\ln 2}$

5. The proof is outlined in the hint sheet.

Answers (Hint Sheet):

1. $2^{a/b} = 3 \;\Rightarrow\; \sqrt[b]{2^a} = 3 \;\Rightarrow\; 2^a = 3^b$

2. If $a = b = 0$, then $\log_2 3 = 0/0$, which is undefined.

3. $2^a = 2 \cdot 2 \cdot \cdots \cdot 2$, and $3^b = 3 \cdot 3 \cdot \cdots \cdot 3$, so these numbers can never be equal, because the left is always divisible by two, and the right never is (unless $b = 0$).

4. It is irrational because it cannot be written as a ratio of two integers.

▼ Group Work 2: The Slide Rule

If possible, give each group a slide rule. If you don't happen to have a lot of real slide rules around, a slide rule cutout is provided. Teach the students how to use the slide rule to multiply:

To multiply a times b, move the 1 on the top over the a on the bottom. Then locate the b on the top, and right below it will be ab. Below is an example, where we multiply 6 by 8 to get 48.

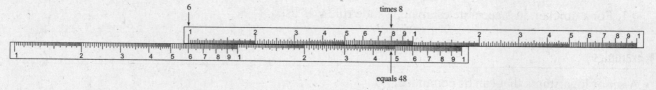

Accuracy isn't the main issue here (real slide rules have a very thin guide that slides perpendicular to the rules, with an embedded hair to ensure accuracy.) The idea is to see how it works.

After students have learned to multiply, hand out the activity sheet.

Answers:

Problems 1–5 are trivial. Note that Problem 5 can be done by multiplying 8×1.2 and remembering to multiply the answer by 10.

6. The numbers are not equally spaced. In fact, they are spaced based on the log of the number. In other words, the 2 is $\log 2$ units from the 1, the 3 is $\log 3$ units from the 1, the 4 is $\log 4$ units from the 1, etc. That is why the numbers get closer and closer together. When you slide the top, you are in effect *adding* the two logarithms. So when we move the slide over the six, and look at the eight, we are adding $\log 6 + \log 8$ The total distance is then $\log (6 \times 8) = \log 48$. And when we look below the 8, we see the number that is $\log 48$ units from the 1, which is 48. In short: We are adding logs, which in effect multiplies the numbers.

▼ Homework Problems

Core Exercises: 1, 2, 9, 14, 28, 33, 46, 48, 55

Sample Assignment: 1, 2, 3, 9, 14, 18, 28, 33, 35, 44, 46, 48, 53, 55, 72

1. If $\log_2 x = \gamma$, then what is $\log_{1/2} x$?

2. If $\log_b x = \gamma$, then what is $\log_{1/b} x$ (assuming $b > 1$)?

3. If $\log_b x = \gamma$, then what is $\log_{b^2} x$?

4. We are going to estimate $\log_2 3$. Of course, in fifth grade, you memorized that $\log_2 3 \approx 1.584962501$. Suppose you didn't have this fact memorized. There is no $\log_2 3$ button on your calculator! How would you compute it?

5. Unfortunately, the calculator gives us only a finite number of digits. If $\log_2 3$ were a rational number, we would be able to express it as a fraction, giving us perfect accuracy. Do you think it is rational or irrational? Try to prove your result.

Irrational, Impossible Relations (Hint Sheet)

So, you realize that it's not easy to determine whether $\log_2 3$ is rational!

One way to attempt to show that $\log_2 3$ is rational is to assume that it is, and try to find integers a and b such that $\log_2 3 = \dfrac{a}{b}$. If we can show that there are no such a and b, then $\log_2 3$ *cannot* be rational.

1. Assume that $\log_2 3 = \dfrac{a}{b}$. Show that a and b must then satisfy $2^a = 3^b$

2. Notice that $a = 0$, $b = 0$ satisfies $2^a = 3^b$. Show that this fact doesn't help us.

3. Find $a \neq 0$ and $b \neq 0$ that satisfy $2^a = 3^b$, or show that no such $\{a, b\}$ exists.

4. Is $\log_2 3$ rational or irrational? Why?

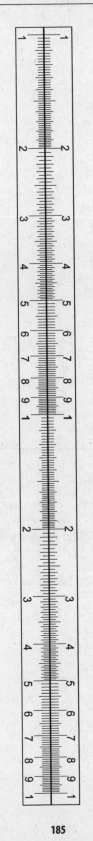

Before we ask the million-dollar question, it is important that you are familiar with the operation of a slide rule. Use your slide rule to do the following computations. (We are aware that you don't *need* a slide rule to do them, the idea here is to learn how a slide rule works.)

1. $2 \times 4 =$

2. $5 \times 5 =$

3. $1.3 \times 8 =$

4. $6 \times 8 =$

5. $8 \times 12 =$

And now, the big question:

6. Why does the slide rule work? What is this magical property it possesses that allows us to multiply in this way?

   Hint: It has something to do with the section you have just covered in class.

4.5   EXPONENTIAL AND LOGARITHMIC EQUATIONS

▼ Suggested Time and Emphasis

1 class. Essential material. Can be combined with Section 4.6.

▼ Point to Stress

Solving equations involving exponential and logarithmic functions, algebraically and graphically.

▼ Sample Questions

- **Text Question:** Solve the equation $4 + 3\log(2x) = 16$.

  Answer: $x = 5000$

- **Drill Question:** If I invest $2000 at an annual interest rate of 3%, compounded continuously, how long will it take the investment to double?

  Answer: $\dfrac{\ln 2}{0.03} \approx 23$ years

▼ In-Class Materials

- At this point students know the algebraic rules for working with exponential and logarithmic functions. Stress that if these rules do not suffice to solve an equation, there is a good chance they cannot find an exact solution. Give students an equation such as $x^2 = 2\ln(x+2)$ (Example 9) and have them try to solve it algebraically. The correct answer is that students cannot do so, but you will find that many make up rules and somehow wind up with a solution.

- Review the concept of inverse functions. Have students find the inverse of functions such as $f(x) = 2^{x^3+1}$ and $f(x) = \ln(x-5) + e^3$.

- Build up some tough problems from simple ones. For example, first have students solve $x^2 + 2x - 15 = 0$. Then have them solve $(e^x - 1)^2 + 2(e^x - 1) - 15 = 0$. One can go even further with $\ln\left((e^x - 1)^2 + 2(e^x - 1) - 14\right) = 0$.

▼ Examples

- Solve $\log(x^2 - 1) - \log(x + 1) = 3$.
  Answer: $x = 1001$

- Solve $(\ln x - 2)^3 - 4(\ln x - 2) = 0$.
  Answer: $x = 1, e^2, e^4$

▼ Group Work 1: The Rule of 72

If a group finishes early or has trouble with Problem 7, have them redo Problems 1–5 for annual compounding. Another good continuation is the following: is it true that the length of time it will take an investment to quadruple is always twice the amount that it will take the money to double? Prove your answer or provide a counterexample. The proofs that the students write may surprise you with their quality and use of the properties of exponents and logarithms.

Answers:

1. 13.86 years

2. The doubling time is not affected by changes in principal. Algebraically, the P_0 drops out of the exponential growth equation. Intuitively, the doubling time is a property of the ratio of two numbers, not a property of the numbers themselves.

3. Estimate: 14.4 years, a 3.90% error.

4.

Interest Rate	Actual Doubling Time	Estimated Doubling Time	Error
3%	23.1 years	24 years	3.90%
8%	8.66 years	9 years	3.92%
12%	5.78 years	6 years	3.81%
18%	3.85 years	4 years	3.90%

The Rule of 72 is accurate to within 4% for the given range of interest rates.

5. If r is the interest rate (as a number, not a percentage), then the doubling time is $D = \dfrac{\ln 2}{r}$.

6. $100 \ln 2 \approx 69$. This estimate gives a doubling time of 13.8, for an error of 0.4%.

7. If the compounding is assumed to be annual, 72 works best for values of r between 3% and 15%. For example, 10% compounded annually doubles every 7.2735 years. The rule of 72 gives 7.2, a good approximation, and the rule of 69 gives 6.9, a bad one.

▼ Group Work 2: Every Nest Egg Needs a Bird

This activity involves some repetitive calculation. Stress that part of working in a group effectively is to figure out how best to divide up the work.

Answers:

1. $2000e^{(0.07)47} + 2000e^{(0.07)46} + 2000e^{(0.07)45} + 2000e^{(0.07)44} + 2000e^{(0.07)43} + 2000e^{(0.07)42}$
$$+ 2000e^{(0.07)41} + 2000e^{(0.07)40} + 2000e^{(0.07)39} + 2000e^{(0.07)38} = \$399{,}759.00$$

2. $\displaystyle\sum_{n=0}^{37} 2000e^{(0.07)n} = \$366{,}753.00$

3. Most people are surprised by this fact.

▼ Homework Problems

Core Exercises: 3, 10, 23, 30, 38, 45, 60, 73, 76

Sample Assignment: 3, 10, 23, 26, 30, 35, 38, 45, 51, 55, 60, 70, 73, 76, 81, 84

In this exercise, we attempt to answer the question asked by many investors: "How long is it going to take for me to double my money?"

1. Consider an investment of $100 invested at 5%, compounded continuously. How long would it take for the investor to have $200?

2. What would the doubling time be if the initial investment were $1,000? $10,000? What effect does changing the principal have on the doubling time, and why?

One of the first things that is taught in an economics class is the Rule of 72. It can be summarized thusly:

"The number of years it takes an investment to double
is equal to 72 divided by the annual percentage interest rate."

3. What would the Rule of 72 say the doubling time of a 5% investment is? Is it a good estimate?

4. Repeat Problems 1 and 3 for investments of 3%, 8%, 12% and 18%. What can you say about the accuracy of the Rule of 72?

5. Derive a precise formula for the time T to double an initial investment.

6. There is an integer that gives a more accurate answer for continuous or nearly continuous compounding than the Rule of 72. What is this number? Check your answer by using it to estimate the doubling time of a 5% investment.

7. It turns out that there is a reason that we use the number 72 in the rule. It has to do with one of the assumptions we made. Why do economists use the Rule of 72?

Johnny and Jenny had a crazy dream. They wanted to retire wealthy, or at least comfortable.

1. Johnny started saving at age 20. Every year, for simplicity assume January 1 of every year, Johnny put $2000 into a type of personal retirement savings account called an IRA. Again, for simplicity, let's assume that the IRA made 7% interest per year. Ten years later, Johnny gave up saving for retirement, and never put any money away again. How much money did Johnny have when he was 67 years old?

2. Jenny spent most of her twenties reading magazines and watching movies, and didn't start saving until she was 30. At that point she started putting $2000 a year into her IRA (again, let's assume it makes 7% per year and she put it away on January 1). When she was 40 she continued to save, and at 50 she continued to save. In fact, she put in $2000 per year until she was 67, when she also retired. How much money did Jenny have when she was 67?

3. Which of the two had more money? Is that the result you expected?

4.6 MODELING WITH EXPONENTIAL AND LOGARITHMIC FUNCTIONS

▼ Suggested Time and Emphasis

$\frac{1}{2}$–1 class. Recommended material. Can be combined with Section 4.5.

▼ Points to Stress

1. Translating verbal descriptions of problems into mathematical models, and solving the problems using the models.

2. Certain standard types of problems such as those dealing with exponential growth and decay and logarithmic scales.

▼ Sample Questions

- **Text Question:** Recall that Newton's Law of Cooling is given by

$$T(t) = T_s + D_0 e^{-kt}$$

Which of the constants in this law correspond to surrounding temperature? Which represents the initial difference between the object and its surroundings? How do you know?

Answer: T_s, D_0. There is a horizontal asymptote at T_s, which would have to correspond to the surrounding temperature, because things cool off to the surrounding temperature. Their initial difference is D_0, because when $t = 0$ we know that $T = T_s + D_0$.

- **Drill Question:** Recall that the pH of a substance is given by $- \log \left[H^+ \right]$, where H^+ is the concentration of hydrogen ions measured in moles per liter. Also recall that solutions with a pH of 7 are neutral, those with pH > 7 are basic, and those with pH < 7 are acidic.

  (a) If a sample of rebulon were measured to have hydrogen concentration of $\left[H^+ \right] = 4 \times 10^{-8}$ M, what would the pH be?

  (b) What is the hydrogen ion concentration in a neutral substance?

  Answer: (a) 7.4   **(b)** 10^{-7}

▼ In-Class Materials

- Show that the expression $y = e^{kt}$ can be written as $y = a^t$ and vice versa. Add that e^{kt+c} is equivalent to Ae^{kt}.

• One way to measure the growth of the Internet is to measure the number of Internet hosts over time. Twenty years' worth of these data are shown below. Try to determine with students whether this is an example of exponential growth. (Note: Do not show the student the third column right away. Let them come up with the idea of finding growth rates between data points.)

Month	Hosts	Growth
Aug 1981	213	—
May 1982	235	1.1404
Aug 1983	562	2.0065
Oct 1984	1024	1.6701
Oct 1985	1961	1.9150
Feb 1986	2308	1.6217
Nov 1986	5089	2.8782
Dec 1987	28,174	4.8615
Jul 1988	33,000	1.3112
Oct 1988	56,000	8.1509
Jan 1989	80,000	4.1168
Jul 1989	130,000	2.6620
Oct 1989	159,000	2.2231
Oct 1990	313,000	1.9686
Jan 1991	376,000	2.0824
Jul 1991	535,000	2.0364
Oct 1991	617,000	1.7608
Jan 1992	727,000	1.9172
Apr 1992	890,000	2.2511
Jul 1992	992,000	1.5453
Oct 1992	1,136,000	1.7122

Month	Hosts	Growth
Jan 1993	1,313,000	1.7762
Apr 1993	1,486,000	1.6520
Jul 1993	1,776,000	2.0443
Oct 1993	2,056,000	1.7875
Jan 1994	2,217,000	1.3487
Jul 1994	3,212,000	2.1120
Oct 1994	3,864,000	2.0818
Jan 1995	4,852,000	2.4618
Jul 1995	6,642,000	1.8739
Jan 1996	9,472,000	2.0357
Jul 1996	12,881,000	1.8525
Jan 1997	16,146,000	1.5654
Jul 1997	19,540,000	1.4692
Jan 1998	29,670,000	2.2900
Jul 1998	36,739,000	1.5387
Jan 1999	43,230,000	1.3809
Jul 1999	56,218,000	1.6985
Jan 2000	72,398,092	1.6516
Jul 2000	93,047,785	1.6541
Jan 2001	109,574,429	1.3831

Answer: We can graph the data, and get a curve that looks like exponential growth. We can also graph growth rate and see (except for two spikes in the late 1980s) a more-or-less constant growth rate.

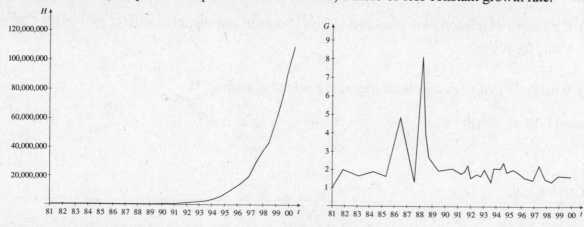

- In 1985 there were 15,948 diagnosed cases of AIDS in the United States. In 1990 there were 156,024 cases. Scientists said that if there was no research done, the disease would grow exponentially. Compute the number of cases this model predicts for the year 2000. The actual number was 774,467. Discuss possible flaws in the model with students, and point out the dangers of extrapolation.

- Discuss the logistic growth model $P = \dfrac{M}{1 + Ae^{-kt}}$. Have students graph a few of these curves with different values of M and k. This model assumes that an environment has a carrying capacity M. It assumes that when a population is much less than M, a population's growth will look like exponential growth, but that when the population approaches M, the population growth gets very slow, asymptotically approaching M. If the population starts out greater than M, then it will decay, exponentially, to M.

- Go over Examples 9 and 10, the Richter scale. Ask students the open-ended question, "How much worse is an earthquake that measures 7 on the Richter scale than an earthquake that measures 6?"

▼ Examples

Exponential decay: we know that the half-life of carbon-14 is 5,730 years. In 1988, the Vatican consented to give a few fibers to scientists to carbon date the Shroud of Turin, an ancient artifact. They found that the fibers had 92% of the original ^{14}C left. Discuss what this implies about the age of the shroud.

▼ Group Work 1: The Coffee Window

In physics and chemistry, people often refer to "Newton's Law of Cooling" and "Newton's Law of Heating". After completing this exercise, students should have discovered that these are the same law, the only difference being the relative temperatures of the substance being studied and its surroundings. The proper names have been taken from *The Hitchhiker's Guide to the Galaxy* by Douglas Adams. The temperatures were determined by painful experimentation.

This activity can also launch a discussion of how mathematical models are simplifications of reality. For example, in Newton's Law of Cooling, we assume that the temperature of the cup's surroundings is constant. But of course, that isn't exactly true. In fact, one could argue that as the coffee cools, the energy from the coffee heats up the surroundings by a fraction, and that isn't taken into account in our model. No mathematical model will ever take into account every effect on every molecule of the universe. The question to ask isn't whether a model is true or false, but whether it is accurate enough to be useful.

Answers:

1. The coffee cools down over time; it does not heat up.

2. The thermos is better. A smaller value of k corresponds to a smaller rate of change of the coffee's temperature.

3. $T = \left(118e^{-0.03t} + 42\right)^{\circ}$ 4. $t \approx 6.19$ minutes

5. $t \approx 20.92$ minutes   6. $t \approx 14.73$ minutes   7. $t \approx 34.82$ minutes

8. It will never cool down to drinking temperature.

9.

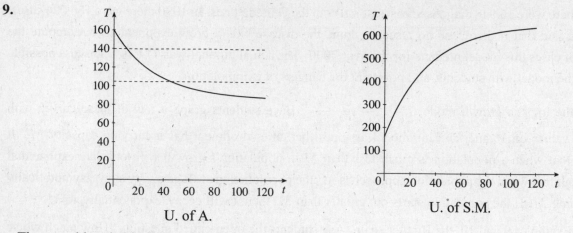

U. of A.

U. of S.M.

They would probably call it "Zaglor's Law of Heating".

▼ Group Work 2: Earthquake

This activity is based on Exercises 36 and 37 from the text.

Answers:

1. Approximately 2500 times as intense

2. Approximately twice as intense

3. When the magnitude of an earthquake increases by 0.3 on the Richter scale, its intensity doubles.

▼ Homework Problems

Core Exercises: 1, 4, 11, 16, 19, 26, 36, 40

Sample Assignment: 1, 4, 7, 11, 14, 16, 19, 21, 24, 26, 28, 31, 36, 40, 43

The Coffee Window

(Written with John Hall)

Dr. Tricia MacMillan has a problem. Every day she leaves her apartment in London at the crack of dawn and heads for Milliway's, where she purchases a delicious cup of piping hot coffee. She drinks this coffee while walking to her office. The problem is that sometimes she burns her tongue badly with her first sip, while other times she waits too long and her coffee gets cold. The latter case is the worst, because besides doing a pretty bad job of keeping you warm, cold coffee tastes terrible. As it drops below a certain temperature, coffee undergoes a chemical reaction which turns even the most expensive brand into something that tastes absolutely filthy.

Being a mathematician, Dr. MacMillan doesn't just get mad, she gets more coffee and does an experiment. She wants to figure out exactly when she can take her first sip without burning herself, and from that point, how much time she has before the coffee turns bad. Every one of her mornings for the next week is spent in Milliway's with an oven thermometer and a cup of fresh coffee.

After much painful experimentation, Dr. MacMillan determines that if the temperature of the coffee is above $140°$ F, it burns her tongue. If the temperature drops below $105°$, the coffee undergoes the reaction and becomes undrinkable (unless she's already burnt her tongue so badly in the first experiment that she can't taste a thing).

Just like every other substance in the universe, coffee obeys Newton's Law of Cooling. Its temperature as a function of time is given by

$$T(t) = T_s + D_0 e^{-kt}$$

Note that there are three parameters in this equation. One is the outside temperature, and one depends on the initial temperature of the coffee. For a typical Styrofoam cup, $k \approx 0.05$, if t is measured in minutes.

1. Why is this constant positive?

Dr. MacMillan scoffs at Styrofoam. She is the proud owner of a Sirius Cybernetics Corporation thermos (only 35% asbestos!) For this thermos the constant is $k = 0.03$.

2. Which does a better job of keeping the coffee warm, the Styrofoam cup or the thermos? How does knowing the value of k allow you to figure out the answer?

The next day, Dr. MacMillan leaves Milliway's with a thermos full of coffee at $160°$ F. It is 8:30 A.M., and the outside temperature is $42°$.

3. Find T_s and D_0, and rewrite $T(t) = T_s + D_0 e^{-kt}$ with the appropriate constants for this situation. (Let the time t be measured in minutes, and let $t = 0$ stand for 8:30 A.M.)

4. How long must she wait before she is able to drink the coffee?

5. At what time will the coffee fall below $105°$ and become undrinkable?

6. How much time does Dr. MacMillan have to drink her coffee?

7. What would the answer to Problem 6 be if Dr. MacMillan were teaching at the University of Arizona, where the outside temperature is 86°?

8. What would the answer to Problem 6 be if she were teaching at the University of Southern Mercury (outside temperature 650° in winter)?

9. Draw a graph of coffee temperature versus time for the University of Arizona and the University of Southern Mercury. Why do they look different? What would students at the University of Southern Mercury call Newton's "Law of Cooling" (if they spoke English)?

GROUP WORK 2, SECTION 4.6
Earthquake

1. The devastating 1906 earthquake in San Francisco had a magnitude of 8.3 on the Richter scale. At the same time, in Japan, an earthquake with magnitude 4.9 caused only minor damage. How many times more intense was the San Francisco earthquake than the Japanese earthquake?

2. The Alaska earthquake of 1964 had a magnitude of 8.6 on the Richter scale. How many times more intense was this than the 1906 San Francisco earthquake?

3. Fill in the blank: When the magnitude of an Earthquake goes up by _____ on the Richter scale, its intensity doubles.

5 TRIGONOMETRIC FUNCTIONS: UNIT CIRCLE APPROACH

5.1 THE UNIT CIRCLE

▼ Suggested Time and Emphasis

$\frac{1}{2}$–1 class. Essential material.

▼ Points to Stress

1. Finding the reference number for a given real number.

2. Using reference numbers to find terminal points.

▼ Sample Questions

- **Text Question:** Is it possible for two different real numbers to have the same reference number?

   Answer: Yes

- **Drill Question:** Find the reference number $\bar{t}$ for $t = \frac{17\pi}{6}$.

   Answer: $\bar{t} = \frac{\pi}{6}$

▼ In-Class Materials

- Look at the time, and then ask the class what time it will be 8 hours from now. Then ask about 12 hours from now, 13 hours from now, 25 hours from now, and 50 hours from now. Then ask what time it was 12 hours ago, 11 hours ago, and 13 hours ago. Draw the analogy of the type of arithmetic you are doing when computing future and past times to that of finding reference angles, only instead of freely adding and subtracting 12, we are freely adding and subtracting 2π.

- Figure 8 is crucial, because the way we find $\bar{t}$ depends upon the quadrant we are in. Perhaps find the reference numbers for $t = \frac{\pi}{3}, \frac{2\pi}{3}, \frac{3\pi}{3} = \pi, \frac{4\pi}{3}, \frac{5\pi}{3}$, and $\frac{6\pi}{3} = 2\pi$ all in a row to illustrate this principle.

- The text uses integer multiples of $\frac{\pi}{6}$ and $\frac{\pi}{4}$ for most of its examples of finding reference numbers. After the students understand these examples, try having them work with different rational multiples of π, such as $-\frac{121}{35}\pi$ or $\frac{10{,}001}{5}\pi$. Transition them to numbers whose terminal points lie in quadrants that are easy to figure out, such as $t = 3, 6$, or 1.5. Finally, have them try to find reference numbers of arbitrary real numbers such as 22 or -13.

- Point out that finding terminal points is much more difficult than finding reference numbers. If the reference number is not given in Table 1, they don't have a good method for finding the terminal point. Have them try to estimate a few by measurement. For example, have the students draw a circle with radius 1 inch, and have them draw arcs of length 2 and 2.5 (by "rolling" the ruler along the circle) and measuring the coordinates of the relevant terminal point. $t = 2$ should yield a terminal point at approximately $(-0.4, 0.9)$. $t = 2.5$ should yield a terminal point at approximately $(-0.8, 0.6)$.

▼ Examples

Some values of t, their reference numbers, and their terminal points.

t	$\bar{t}$	Terminal Point
$-\frac{33\pi}{2}$	$\frac{\pi}{2}$	$(0, -1)$
$\frac{55\pi}{4}$	$\frac{\pi}{4}$	$\left(\frac{\sqrt{2}}{2}, -\frac{\sqrt{2}}{2}\right)$
$\frac{48\pi}{6}$	0	$(1, 0)$
$\frac{16\pi}{3}$	$\frac{\pi}{3}$	$\left(-\frac{1}{2}, -\frac{\sqrt{3}}{2}\right)$
10	$10 - 3\pi \approx 0.57522204$	$(-0.839, -0.544)$

▼ Group Work: The Reference Number

This activity allows students to discover a speedy method for finding reference numbers for some commonly encountered angles. After they are finished, ask them to go through and identify the quadrants of the relevant terminal points.

Answers:

1.

t	$\bar{t}$	Quadrant of Terminal Point
0	0	—
$\frac{\pi}{3}$	$\frac{\pi}{3}$	I
$\frac{2\pi}{3}$	$\frac{\pi}{3}$	II
$\frac{3\pi}{3}$	0	—
$\frac{4\pi}{3}$	$\frac{\pi}{3}$	III
$\frac{5\pi}{3}$	$\frac{\pi}{3}$	IV
$\frac{6\pi}{3}$	0	—
$\frac{7\pi}{3}$	$\frac{\pi}{3}$	I
$\frac{8\pi}{3}$	$\frac{\pi}{3}$	II
$\frac{9\pi}{3}$	0	—
$\frac{10\pi}{3}$	$\frac{\pi}{3}$	III
$\frac{11\pi}{3}$	$\frac{\pi}{3}$	IV
$\frac{35\pi}{3}$	$\frac{\pi}{3}$	IV
$\frac{1000\pi}{3}$	$\frac{\pi}{3}$	I

2.

t	$\bar{t}$	Quadrant of Terminal Point
0	0	—
$\frac{\pi}{6}$	$\frac{\pi}{6}$	I
$\frac{2\pi}{6}$	$\frac{\pi}{3}$	I
$\frac{3\pi}{6}$	$\frac{\pi}{2}$	—
$\frac{4\pi}{6}$	$\frac{\pi}{3}$	II
$\frac{5\pi}{6}$	$\frac{\pi}{6}$	II
$\frac{6\pi}{6}$	0	—
$\frac{7\pi}{6}$	$\frac{\pi}{6}$	III
$\frac{8\pi}{6}$	$\frac{\pi}{3}$	III
$\frac{9\pi}{6}$	$\frac{\pi}{2}$	—
$\frac{10\pi}{6}$	$\frac{\pi}{3}$	IV
$\frac{11\pi}{6}$	$\frac{\pi}{6}$	IV
$\frac{35\pi}{6}$	$\frac{\pi}{6}$	IV
$\frac{1000\pi}{6}$	$\frac{\pi}{3}$	II

▼ Homework Problems

Core Exercises: 3, 10, 21, 26, 30, 35, 40, 44, 54

Sample Assignment: 3, 6, 10, 13, 18, 21, 26, 30, 34, 35, 37, 40, 44, 49, 54, 55, 58

GROUP WORK, SECTION 5.1

The Reference Number

1. Find the reference numbers $\bar{t}$ of the following values of t.

t	$\bar{t}$
0	
$\frac{\pi}{3}$	
$\frac{2\pi}{3}$	
$\frac{3\pi}{3}$	
$\frac{4\pi}{3}$	
$\frac{5\pi}{3}$	
$\frac{6\pi}{3}$	
$\frac{7\pi}{3}$	
$\frac{8\pi}{3}$	
$\frac{9\pi}{3}$	
$\frac{10\pi}{3}$	
$\frac{11\pi}{3}$	
$\frac{35\pi}{3}$	
$\frac{1000\pi}{3}$	

2. Find the reference numbers $\bar{t}$ of the following values of t.

t	$\bar{t}$
0	
$\frac{\pi}{6}$	
$\frac{2\pi}{6}$	
$\frac{3\pi}{6}$	
$\frac{4\pi}{6}$	
$\frac{5\pi}{6}$	
$\frac{6\pi}{6}$	
$\frac{7\pi}{6}$	
$\frac{8\pi}{6}$	
$\frac{9\pi}{6}$	
$\frac{10\pi}{6}$	
$\frac{11\pi}{6}$	
$\frac{35\pi}{6}$	
$\frac{1000\pi}{6}$	

5.2   TRIGONOMETRIC FUNCTIONS OF REAL NUMBERS

▼ Suggested Time and Emphasis

$\frac{1}{2}$–1 class. Essential material.

▼ Points to Stress

1. Computation of the trigonometric functions, given the terminal point of a real number.
2. Properties of the trigonometric functions, including their domains, and parity based on the quadrant of the terminal point.
3. The Pythagorean and reciprocal identities of the trigonometric functions.

▼ Sample Questions

- **Text Question:** If $\sin t = \frac{3}{5}$, what is the value of $\csc t$?

  Answer: $\frac{5}{3}$

- **Drill Question:** If $\sin t = \frac{3}{5}$ and the terminal point of t is in the second quadrant, what is the value of $\cos t$?

  Answer: $-\sqrt{\frac{2}{5}}$

▼ In-Class Materials

- The etymology of the word sine is fairly interesting and not that well known. It starts with the Indian word *jya*, meaning "cord of a bowstring." The Arabs translated this word as *jiba*. The written language had no vowels, so it looked like this: *jb*. In 1145, the Spanish translator Robert of Cheste had to figure out what vowels to put in. Because of the shape of the curve, he thought the word was *jaib*, which meant the opening of a garment that shows a woman's cleavage. So he used the Latin word for the cavity formed by a curve: *sinus*. (This word exists in the English language today—right behind your nose are the sinus cavities.)

- There is an inconsistency in mathematical notation that can be made explicit at this time. We say that $\frac{1}{3} = 3^{-1}$. Similarly, we say that $\frac{1}{\pi} = \pi^{-1}$. But $\dfrac{1}{\sin x}$ is written as $\csc x$. Unfortunately, there is a symbol, $\sin^{-1} x$ that means something entirely different — the arcsine of x. Even worse, as noted in the section, $\sin^2 x = (\sin x)^2$ and $\sin^3 x = (\sin x)^3$. The exponent -1 is a notational anomaly.

- Problems such as Exercises 25–28 are key when students take calculus. It is vitally important that they go beyond memorizing the answers and truly understand where they come from.

▼ Examples

- $\sin \frac{\pi}{3} = \frac{\sqrt{3}}{2}$
- $\cos \frac{7\pi}{6} = -\frac{\sqrt{3}}{2}$
- $\tan \frac{11\pi}{4} = -1$
- $\sec \frac{17\pi}{3} = 2$
- $\csc \frac{17\pi}{2} = 1$
- $\cot \frac{121\pi}{6} = \sqrt{3}$

▼ Group Work: Fun with a Calculator

This activity foreshadows Section 5.3. Instruct the class to use their calculators to approximate values, but to draw the graphs by hand. Encourage them to use their group members effectively by dividing up the work in an efficient way. Give each group a different basic trigonometric function for Problem 2. If a group finishes early, give them a different function to try.

Answers:

1. Answers will vary.

2.

x	$\sin x$	$\cos x$	$\tan x$	$\csc x$	$\sec x$	$\cot x$
0	0	1	0	—	1	—
0.5	0.4794	0.8776	0.5463	2.0858	1.1395	1.8305
1	0.8415	0.5403	1.5574	1.1884	1.8508	0.6421
1.5	0.9975	0.0707	14.1014	1.0025	14.1368	0.0709
2	0.9093	−0.4161	−2.1850	1.0998	−2.4030	−0.4577
2.5	0.5985	−0.8011	−0.7470	1.6709	−1.2482	−1.3386
3	0.1411	−0.9900	−0.1425	7.0862	−1.0101	−7.0153
3.5	−0.3508	−0.9365	0.3746	−2.8508	−1.0679	2.6696
4	−0.7568	−0.6536	1.1578	−1.3213	−1.5299	0.8637
4.5	−0.9775	−0.2108	4.6373	−1.0230	−4.7439	0.2156
5	−0.9589	0.2837	−3.3805	−1.0428	3.5253	−0.2958
5.5	−0.7055	0.7087	−0.9956	−1.4174	1.4111	−1.0044
6	−0.2794	0.9602	−0.2910	−3.5789	1.0415	−3.4364
6.5	0.2151	0.9766	0.2203	4.6486	1.0240	4.5397
7	0.6570	0.7539	0.8714	1.5221	1.3264	1.1475
7.5	0.9380	0.3466	2.7060	1.0661	2.8849	0.3695
8	0.9894	−0.1455	−6.7997	1.0108	−6.8729	−0.1471
8.5	0.7985	−0.6020	−1.3264	1.2524	−1.6611	−0.7539
9	0.4121	−0.9111	−0.4523	2.4265	−1.0975	−2.2108
9.5	−0.0752	−0.9972	0.0754	−13.3065	−1.0028	13.2689
10	−0.5440	−0.8391	0.6484	−1.8382	−1.1918	1.5424
10.5	−0.8797	−0.4755	1.8499	−1.1368	−2.1029	0.5406
11	−1.0000	0.0044	−225.9508	−1.0000	225.9531	−0.0044
11.5	−0.8755	0.4833	−1.8114	−1.1423	2.0691	−0.5521
12	−0.5366	0.8439	−0.6359	−1.8637	1.1850	−1.5727
12.5	−0.0663	0.9978	−0.0665	−15.0780	1.0022	−15.0448
13	0.4202	0.9074	0.4630	2.3800	1.1020	2.1597
13.5	0.8038	0.5949	1.3511	1.2441	1.6809	0.7401
14	0.9906	0.1367	7.2446	1.0095	7.3133	0.1380
14.5	0.9349	−0.3549	−2.6341	1.0696	−2.8175	−0.3796
15	0.6503	−0.7597	−0.8560	1.5378	−1.3163	−1.1682
15.5	0.2065	−0.9785	−0.2110	4.8434	−1.0220	−4.7390
16	−0.2879	−0.9577	0.3006	−3.4734	−1.0442	3.3263

3.

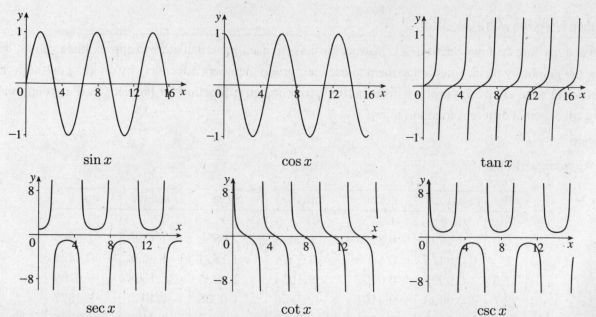

4. For $\sin x$, $\cos x$, $\sec x$, and $\csc x$, 6.25 is a good estimate (actual value: 2π); for $\tan x$ and $\cot x$, 3 is a good estimate (actual value: π).

▼ Homework Problems

Core Exercises: 3, 5, 8, 15, 20, 30, 39, 51, 58, 66, 81

Sample Assignment: 3, 5, 8, 12, 15, 20, 23, 26, 30, 33, 39, 44, 48, 51, 58, 66, 73, 80, 81

Consider the strange function graphed below:

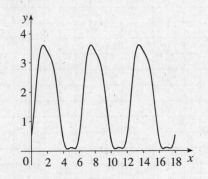

We say that the **period** of this function is 6.

1. In your own words, what is the period of a function?

2. Let $f(x) =$ _____ . Fill in the following table of values:

x	$f(x)$
0	
0.5	
1	
1.5	
2	
2.5	
3	
3.5	
4	
4.5	
5	

x	$f(x)$
5.5	
6	
6.5	
7	
7.5	
8	
8.5	
9	
9.5	
10	
10.5	

x	$f(x)$
11	
11.5	
12	
12.5	
13	
13.5	
14	
14.5	
15	
15.5	
16	

3. Plot these points, and try to sketch the graph by connecting your points.

4. Estimate the period of your graph.

5.3 TRIGONOMETRIC GRAPHS

▼ **Suggested Time and Emphasis**

1 class. Essential material.

▼ **Points to Stress**

1. The graphs of sine and cosine, their periodicity, and their transformations.

2. Sine and cosine curves with variable amplitudes.

▼ **Sample Questions**

• **Text Question:** Sketch $y = \sin x$.

  Answer:

  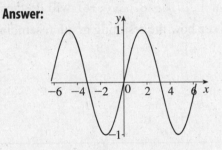

• **Drill Question:** Sketch $y = 2 \sin \pi x$.

  Answer:

  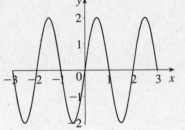

▼ **In-Class Materials**

• Let $f(x) = \sin x + \frac{1}{100} \cos x$. Have students graph this function with their calculators. In the default viewing window, the graph will be indistinguishable from that of $\sin x$. Show that when they zoom in they can see the "bumps" in the function.

• Demonstrate simple harmonic motion by bringing a spring (like a slinky, or another kind of spring, perhaps with a weight attached at the end) and letting it oscillate. Notice how the graph of the height of the end of the spring versus time is a sine (or cosine) curve. Similarly, if you chart the height with respect to time of a point on a spinning disk whose axis is parallel to the floor, you will get a sine or cosine curve.

• Ask the class if it is true that the sum of two periodic curves is always periodic. It turns out that although this seems a reasonable proposition, it is actually false. It is a true statement if you add the stipulation that the periods of the two curves are rational multiples of each other.

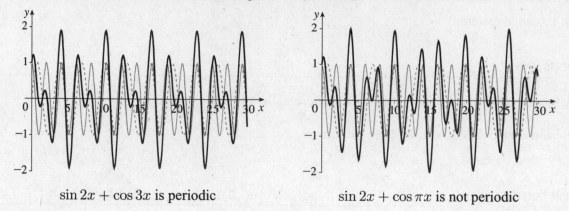

$\sin 2x + \cos 3x$ is periodic $\sin 2x + \cos \pi x$ is not periodic

• Have students obtain a table of time of sunrise versus date for your city. Perhaps have each student write down the information for a given month. (Websites such as `http://usno.navy.mil` will do these calculations for you.) Have the students pool and plot the data, and see how the resulting graph resembles a sine or cosine curve.

▼ Examples

Graphs of variants of sine and cosine curves:

• $y = 3 \sin 2x + 1$ has amplitude 3, period π, and vertical shift 1.

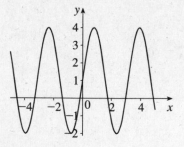

• $y = \frac{1}{2} \cos \left(\frac{\pi}{3} (x - 1) \right)$ has amplitude $\frac{1}{2}$, period 6, and horizontal shift 1.

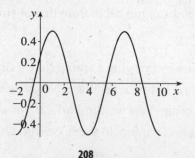

▼ Group Work 1: Pushing the Envelope

This is an extension of Examples 8 and 9. Start the activity by discussing these examples with students. This activity serves as a review of earlier sections, requiring students to recall what the graphs of exponential, logarithmic and polynomial functions look like. It should be done without a calculator.

Answers:

1. I = (b), II = (a), III = (d), IV = (c), V = (h), VI = (e), VII = (f), VIII = (g)
2. I = (c), II = (h), III = (a), IV = (f), V = (e), VI = (d), VII = (b), VIII = (g)

▼ Group Work 2: Which is the Original?

This activity allows students to experiment with such concepts as amplitude, period, and shifts of the graph of the sine function. If a group finishes early, ask them to sketch the graphs of $f(x) + 2$, $f(x) - 2$, $f(x + 2)$, and $f(x - 2)$.

Answers:

1. $2f(x)$ 2. $\frac{1}{2}f(2(x-3))$ 3. $f(x)$ 4. $\frac{1}{2}f(x)$ 5. $f(x-1)$ 6. $f\left(\frac{1}{2}x\right)$ 7. $2f\left(\frac{1}{2}x\right)$ 8. $f(2x)$

▼ Group Work 3: Fun with Fourier

This activity should be given before Fourier series are discussed in class. This activity will get students looking at combinations of sine curves, while at the same time foreshadowing the concepts of infinite series and Fourier series.

Answers:

1. No

2. $S(x) = \begin{cases} 1 & \text{if } -2\pi \leq x < -\pi \text{ or } 0 \leq x < \pi \\ -1 & \text{if } -\pi \leq x < 0 \text{ or } \pi \leq x \leq 2\pi \end{cases}$

3. $\sin x$, because at least it is an odd function, like the square wave.

4. $\frac{4}{\pi}\sin x$

5. $\frac{4}{\pi}\left(\sin x + \frac{1}{3}\sin 3x + \frac{1}{5}\sin 5x\right)$

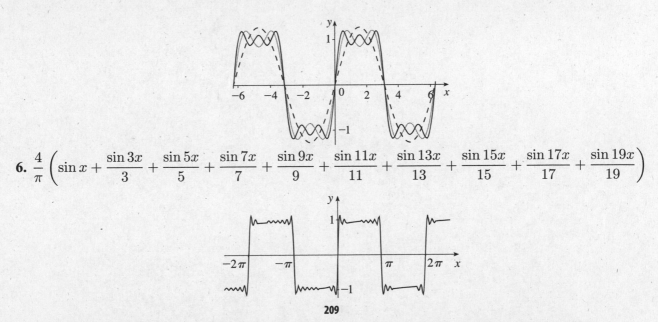

6. $\frac{4}{\pi}\left(\sin x + \frac{\sin 3x}{3} + \frac{\sin 5x}{5} + \frac{\sin 7x}{7} + \frac{\sin 9x}{9} + \frac{\sin 11x}{11} + \frac{\sin 13x}{13} + \frac{\sin 15x}{15} + \frac{\sin 17x}{17} + \frac{\sin 19x}{19}\right)$

7.

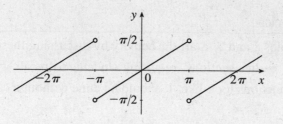

▼ Homework Problems

Core Exercises: 7, 20, 29, 46, 61, 68, 75, 78

Sample Assignment: 7, 14, 20, 27, 29, 34, 46, 50, 61, 65, 68, 74, 75, 78, 82

Match the following labels to their graphs.

1. I $e^x \sin 10x$ II $e^x \cos 10x$ III $e^{-x} \sin 10x$ IV $e^{-x} \cos 10x$
    V $e^{-2x} \sin 10x$ VI $e^{-2x} \cos 10x$ VII $e^{2x} \sin 10x$ VIII $e^{2x} \cos 10x$

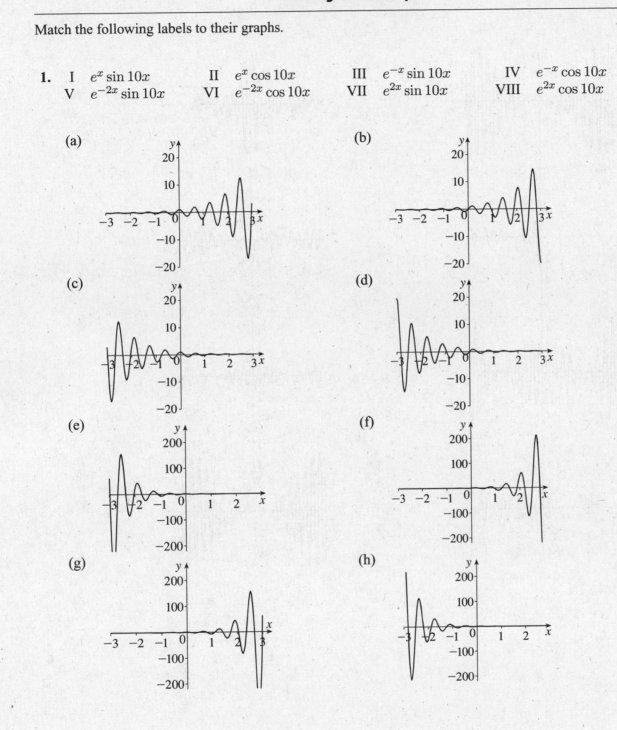

2.

I $\ln x \sin 20x$ II $x^2 \sin 20x$ III $-x^2 \sin 20x$ IV $\cos x \sin 20x$

V $(3 - x^2) \sin 20x$ VI $\sin \frac{1}{2}x \sin 20x$ VII $\frac{1}{x} \sin 20x$ VIII $\sqrt{x} \sin 20x$

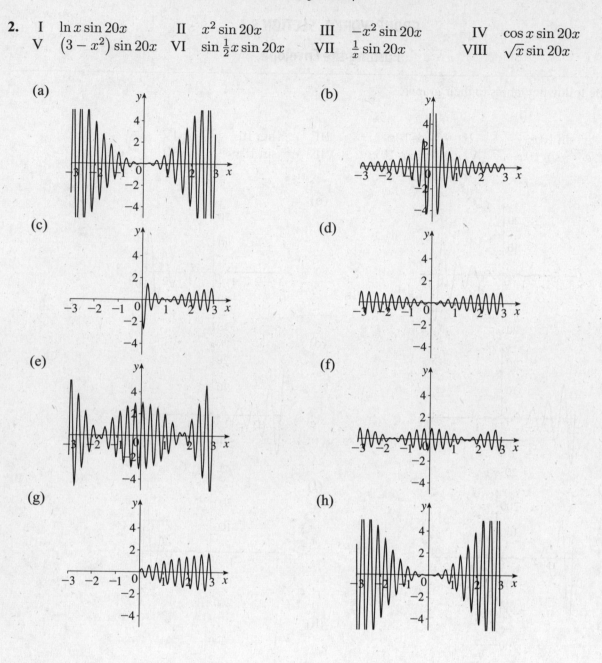

(a)   (b)   (c)   (d)   (e)   (f)   (g)   (h)

You see before you graphs of $f(x)$, $2f(x)$, $f(x-1)$, $\frac{1}{2}f(x)$, $f(2x)$, $2f\left(\frac{1}{2}x\right)$, $f\left(\frac{1}{2}x\right)$, and $\frac{1}{2}f(2(x-3))$. Give each graph the appropriate label.

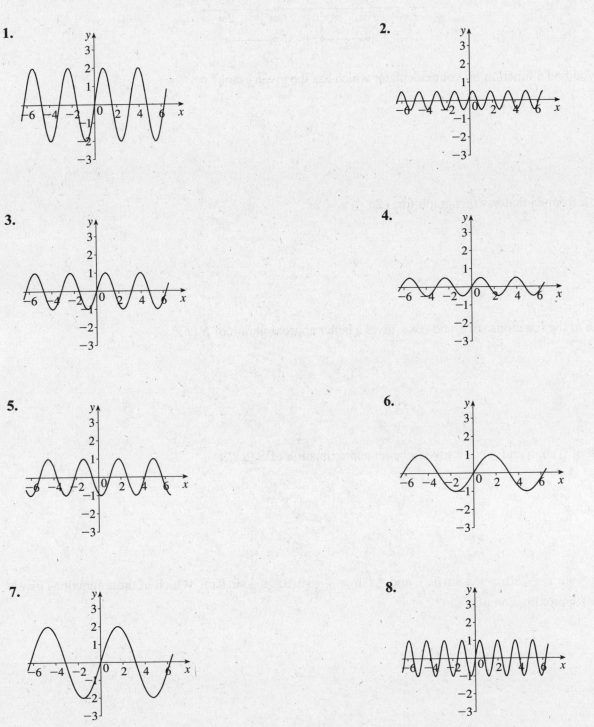

1.

2.

3.

4.

5.

6.

7.

8.

213

The following function $S(x)$ is called a **square wave**.

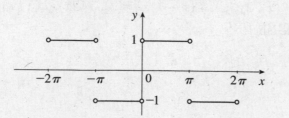

1. Can you find a function on your calculator which has the given graph?

2. Write a formula that has this graph for $-2\pi \le x \le 2\pi$.

3. Which of the functions $\sin x$ and $\cos x$ gives a better approximation of $S(x)$?

4. Which of $\frac{4}{\pi} \sin x$ and $\frac{4}{\pi} \cos x$ gives a better approximation of $S(x)$?

5. Graph $\frac{4}{\pi} \sin x$, $\frac{4}{\pi}\left(\sin x + \frac{1}{3}\sin 3x\right)$, and $\frac{4}{\pi}\left(\sin x + \frac{1}{3}\sin 3x + \frac{1}{5}\sin 5x\right)$. Which of these functions gives the best approximation of $S(x)$?

6. A **Fourier approximation** of a function is an approximation of the form

$$F(x) = a_0 + a_1 \cos x + b_1 \sin x + a_2 \cos 2x + b_2 \sin 2x + \cdots + a_n \cos nx + b_n \sin nx$$

You have just discovered the Fourier approximation to $S(x)$ with three terms. Find the Fourier approximation to $S(x)$ with ten terms, and sketch its graph.

7. The following expressions are Fourier approximations to a different function, $T(x)$:

$$T(x) \approx \sin x$$

$$T(x) \approx \sin x - \tfrac{1}{2}\sin 2x$$

$$T(x) \approx \sin x - \tfrac{1}{2}\sin 2x + \tfrac{1}{3}\sin 3x$$

$$T(x) \approx \sin x - \tfrac{1}{2}\sin 2x + \tfrac{1}{3}\sin 3x - \tfrac{1}{4}\sin 4x$$

$$T(x) \approx \sin x - \tfrac{1}{2}\sin 2x + \tfrac{1}{3}\sin 3x - \tfrac{1}{4}\sin 4x + \tfrac{1}{5}\sin 5x$$

Sketch $T(x)$.

5.4   MORE TRIGONOMETRIC GRAPHS

▼ Suggested Time and Emphasis

$\frac{1}{2}$ class. Essential material.

▼ Point to Stress

The graphs of tangent, cotangent, secant, and cosecant, their periodicity, and their transformations.

▼ Sample Questions

- **Text Question:** Sketch $y = \tan x$.

  Answer:

  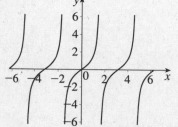

- **Drill Question:** Sketch $y = \tan \pi x$.

  Answer:

  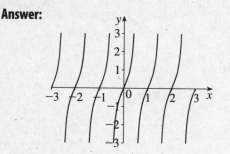

▼ In-Class Materials

- Notice that the functions $\sec x$ and $x^2 + 1$ are very different functions. ($\sec x$ has vertical asymptotes, for example, and $x^2 + 1$ does not.) When we casually sketch their graphs near $x = 0$, however, the sketches look similar:

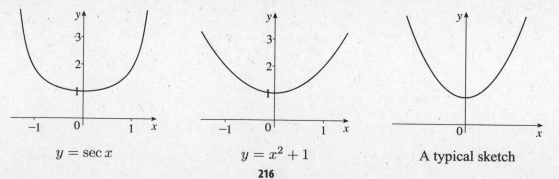

$y = \sec x$ $y = x^2 + 1$ A typical sketch

216

The problem is that a lot of curves have a "U" shape near zero. Have students try to come up with other examples. If they have calculators, they can experiment with functions they haven't learned about yet.

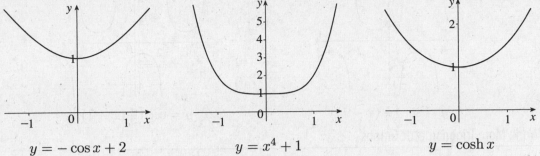

$$y = -\cos x + 2 \qquad\qquad y = x^4 + 1 \qquad\qquad y = \cosh x$$

Of course, if we look at these functions' behavior on a larger interval, their similarity decreases, but some of them would still be hard to tell apart just by looking at the shapes of the curves.

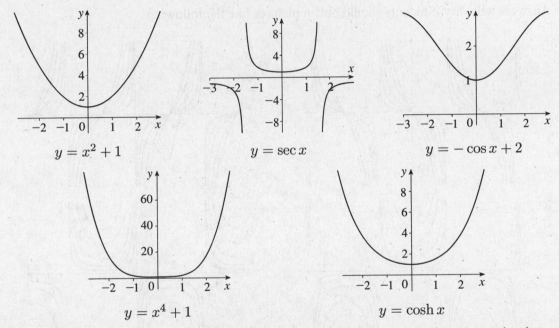

$$y = x^2 + 1 \qquad\qquad y = \sec x \qquad\qquad y = -\cos x + 2$$

$$y = x^4 + 1 \qquad\qquad\qquad y = \cosh x$$

- Similarly, discuss $\tan x$, x^3, $\sin x$, and $\sinh x$. Notice that, unlike in the previous example, these curves don't all look alike at the origin — some are flatter than others.

▼ Examples

Graphs of variants of trigonometric curves:

- $y = \tan 2x + 1$ and $y = \cot 2x + 1$ have period $\frac{\pi}{2}$ and vertical shift 1.

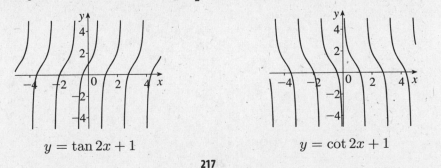

$$y = \tan 2x + 1 \qquad\qquad\qquad y = \cot 2x + 1$$

• $y = \sec\left(\frac{\pi}{3}(x-1)\right)$ and $y = \csc\left(\frac{\pi}{3}(x-1)\right)$ have period 3 and horizontal shift 1.

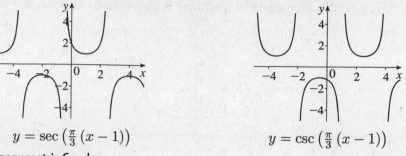

$$y = \sec\left(\frac{\pi}{3}(x-1)\right) \qquad\qquad y = \csc\left(\frac{\pi}{3}(x-1)\right)$$

▼ Group Work: More Trigonometric Graphs

This exercise assumes that students have access to graphing calculators or some other form of graphing technology.

Answers: Answers will vary. Students should obtain pictures like the following:

1.

2.

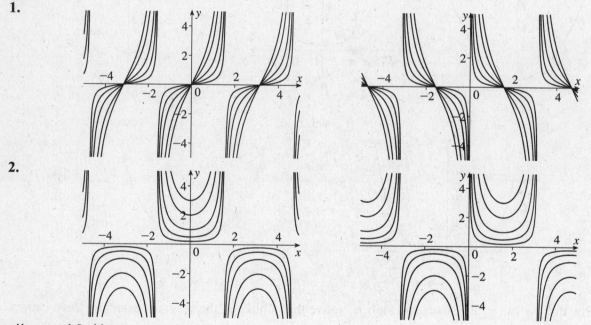

▼ Homework Problems

Core Exercises: 1, 4, 8, 13, 26, 38, 51, 55

Sample Assignment: 1, 4, 8, 13, 19, 26, 28, 38, 43, 50, 51, 55, 58

It isn't that hard to understand the amplitude of sine and cosine graphs. For example, make sure everyone in your group remembers the difference between $y = \sin x$ and $y = 2 \sin x$. Take a moment to remind each other what k does in $y = k \sin x$. Go ahead and do it. I will wait.

It is a little more difficult to see the role of k in these functions:

$$y = k \tan x$$
$$y = k \cot x$$
$$y = k \sec x$$
$$y = k \csc x$$

1. We want to understand the graph of $y = k \tan x$. You won't be able to enter that expression in your calculators, but you can enter $y = \tan x$, $y = 2 \tan x$, $y = 3 \tan x$, and so forth. Try graphing $y = k \tan x$ for various values of k, all on the same set of axes. Don't forget to play with negative values of k, values of k that are less than 1, and values of k that are much less than 1. In your own words, describe what happens to $y = k \tan x$ for various values of k.

2. Repeat Problem 1 for the other three functions mentioned above.

5.5 INVERSE TRIGONOMETRIC FUNCTIONS AND THEIR GRAPHS

▼ Suggested Time and Emphasis

1 classes. Essential material.

▼ Points to Stress

1. Defining the inverse trigonometric functions.
2. Evaluating the inverse trigonometric functions.
3. Graphing the inverse trigonometric functions.

▼ Sample Questions

- **Text Question:** We can say $\sin^{-1} y = x$ means $y = \sin x$. Given this nice definition, why does the text need to fuss with domains and ranges?

  Answer: For a given y between -1 and 1, there are infinitely many values of x such that $y = \sin x$.

- **Drill Question:** Compute $\sin^{-1}\left(-\frac{1}{2}\right)$ and $\cos^{-1}\left(-\frac{\sqrt{3}}{2}\right)$.

  Answer: $-\frac{\pi}{6}, \frac{5\pi}{6}$

▼ In-Class Materials

- It may be helpful to start by reviewing general inverse functions (Section 2.7). If $f(x) = x^3$, what is $f^{-1}(x)$? Note that $f(2) = 8$ and $f^{-1}(8) = 2$. Now move to $f(x) = \sqrt[5]{3x+2} \Rightarrow f^{-1}(x) = \dfrac{x^5 - 2}{3}$. Note that $f(5) \approx 1.762$ and $f^{-1}(1.762) \approx 5$. Now explore $f(x) = x^2$, and point out that even though there is no inverse function, we could make things work out if we were allowed to assume that x was positive. This leads to a natural segue into $f(x) = \sin x$.

- Many students may need a review of notation: $\sin^2 x = (\sin x)^2$, $\sin x^2 = \sin(x^2)$, $(\sin x)^{-1} = \dfrac{1}{\sin x} = \csc x$, $\sin x^{-1} = \sin\left(\dfrac{1}{x}\right)$, but $\sin^{-1} x$ represents the inverse sine of x, the arcsine of x, which is not the same as any of the previous functions.

- Sketch the graph of the non-function $x = \sin y$. Demonstrate how a range restriction makes this a function, and why a range restriction on this function corresponds to a domain restriction on sine.

▼ Examples

- $\sin^{-1}\left(\frac{\sqrt{2}}{2}\right) = \frac{\pi}{4}$
- $\cos^{-1}\left(-\frac{\sqrt{3}}{2}\right) = \frac{5\pi}{6}$
- $\tan^{-1}\sqrt{3} = \frac{\pi}{3}$
- $\tan^{-1}\left(-\sqrt{3}\right) = -\frac{\pi}{3}$
- $\tan\left(\sin^{-1}\frac{1}{5}\right) = \frac{\sqrt{6}}{12}$
- $\cos\left(\tan^{-1}\frac{3}{8}\right) = \frac{8\sqrt{73}}{73}$
- $\sin^{-1}\left(\sin\frac{87\pi}{4}\right) = -\frac{\pi}{4}$

▼ Group Work: The Triangle Wave

Encourage students to divide up the work in Problem 1; the calculations are fairly routine.

The triangle wave is important in waveform analysis. It is the waveform of a rich, brassy sound.

Answers:

1. $\sin^{-1}(\sin 1) = 1$
$\sin^{-1}(\sin 2) = -2 + \pi \approx 1.1415927$
$\sin^{-1}(\sin 3) = -3 + \pi \approx 0.14159265$
$\sin^{-1}(\sin 4) = -4 + \pi \approx -0.85840735$
$\sin^{-1}(\sin 5) = 5 - 2\pi \approx -1.2831853$

$\sin^{-1}(\sin 6) = 6 - 2\pi \approx -0.28318531$
$\sin^{-1}(\sin 7) = 7 - 2\pi \approx 0.71681469$
$\sin^{-1}(\sin 8) = -8 + 3\pi \approx 1.424778$
$\sin^{-1}(\sin 9) = -9 + 3\pi \approx 0.42477796$
$\sin^{-1}(\sin 10) = -10 + 3\pi \approx -0.57522204$

2.

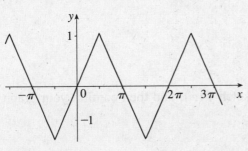

3.

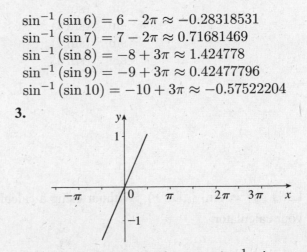

They are not the same because $\sin^{-1} x$ is defined only for $x \in [-1, 1]$.

▼ Homework Problems

Core Exercises: 2, 9, 19, 32, 44, 56, 57

Sample Assignment: 2, 4, 6, 9, 13, 19, 21, 28, 32, 38, 42, 44, 49, 56, 57, 59

GROUP WORK, SECTION 5.5

The Triangle Wave

---

1. Compute the following:

$\sin^{-1}(\sin 1)$	$\sin^{-1}(\sin 6)$
$\sin^{-1}(\sin 2)$	$\sin^{-1}(\sin 7)$
$\sin^{-1}(\sin 3)$	$\sin^{-1}(\sin 8)$
$\sin^{-1}(\sin 4)$	$\sin^{-1}(\sin 9)$
$\sin^{-1}(\sin 5)$	$\sin^{-1}(\sin 10)$

2. Let $f(x) = \sin^{-1}(\sin x)$. Without using a calculator, sketch $f(x)$, and then confirm your graph with your calculator.

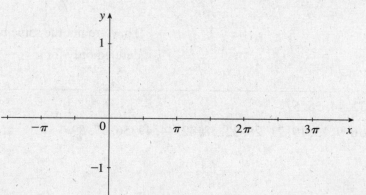

3. Let $g(x) = \sin(\sin^{-1} x)$. Sketch the graph of g. Is it the same as the graph of f? Why or why not?

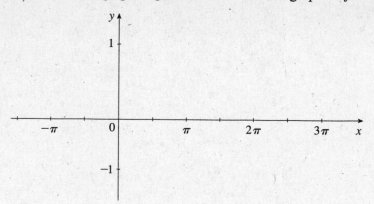

5.6 MODELING HARMONIC MOTION

▼ Suggested Time and Emphasis

1 class. Recommended material.

▼ Points to Stress

1. Understanding the meanings of amplitude, period and frequency, and determining them from the formula $y = a \sin \omega t$ or $y = a \cos \omega t$.

2. Understanding the physical meaning of a phase shift in formulas such as $y = a \sin(\omega(t-c))$ and $y = a \cos(\omega(t-c))$.

3. Damped harmonic motion ($y = ke^{-ct} \sin \omega t$, $y = ke^{-ct} \cos \omega t$).

▼ Sample Questions

- **Text Question:** What is the relationship between the period of a harmonic function and its frequency?

  Answer: They are reciprocals.

- **Drill Question:** What is the frequency of the harmonic function $y = \sin(6\pi t)$?

  Answer: 3 Hz

▼ In-Class Materials

- An easy way to graph a sine or cosine function given an amplitude and period (no phase shift) is to plot the zeros of one cycle, followed by the maximum and the minimum (between the zeros), and then draw the graph. This method also works with a phase shift, but is not as straightforward.

- Note that not all periodic functions are trigonometric functions. For example, mark a point on a car tire and plot its distance from the ground versus time as the car moves. The resulting graph is called a cycloid and looks like this:

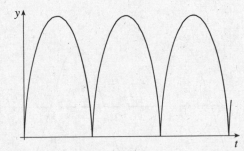

Terms such as "amplitude", "period", and "frequency" that are used in this section can be used to describe any sort of periodic function.

- Musical notes can be thought of as harmonic motion where the t-axis represents time and the y-axis represents air pressure. A sound wave is a periodic variation of air pressure. The amplitude corresponds to volume, and the frequency corresponds to the note; a higher frequency means a higher pitch. A pure sine or cosine wave sounds like a note played on a tuning fork—not a lot of character. The sound wave from a trumpet looks like this:

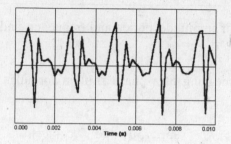

Dept. of Physics, Concordia College, Moorhead MN

- Musical instruments produce a basic sound, plus a series of overtones. We can think of the basic sound as a sine wave with a (relatively) large amplitude, and then the overtones as waves whose frequencies are rational multiples of the basic frequency, and whose amplitudes are smaller. We add the sine curves together to get a sound wave that looks something like this:

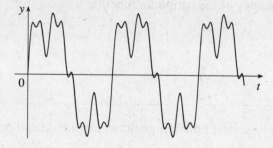

▼ Examples

- $y = 4 \sin \left(\pi \left(x - \frac{1}{4} \right) \right)$

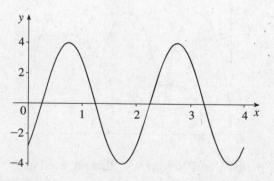

Period: 2, Frequency: $\frac{1}{2}$, Amplitude: 4

224

• $2\cos\left(\frac{1}{2}x\right)$

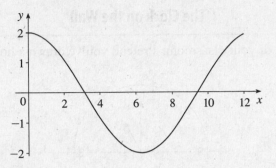

Period: 4π, Frequency: $\frac{1}{4\pi}$, Amplitude: 2

▼ Group Work: The Clock on the Wall

In this activity, students are asked to figure out physical meanings of such quantities as amplitude, frequency, and period.

Answers:

1.

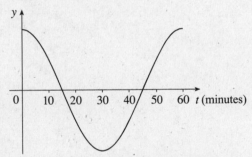

Alternatively, students can measure t in hours, in which $0 \le t \le 1$.

2. Amplitude: Length of the minute hand. Period: 60 minutes (1 hour). Frequency: $\frac{1}{60}$ cycles/minute (or 1 cycle/hour)

3.

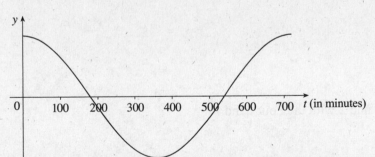

Amplitude: Length of the hour hand. Period: 720 minutes (12 hours). Frequency: $\frac{1}{720}$ cycles/minute (or $\frac{1}{12}$ cycle/hour).

▼ Homework Problems

Core Exercises: 4, 11, 16, 20, 23, 30, 37, 44

Sample Assignment: 4, 9, 11, 14, 16, 17, 20, 23, 26, 30, 34, 37, 41, 44, 46

GROUP WORK, SECTION 5.6

The Clock on the Wall

Consider the clock on the wall of your classroom. Pretend you've drawn a horizontal line between the 3 and the 9 so it looks like this:

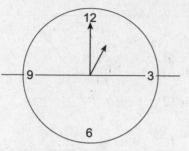

1. Sketch a graph of the height of the tip of the minute hand above this line. Make sure to include units on your graph. When the minute hand is on numbers between 3 and 9, this height will be negative. *Hint:* Your graph will be a trigonometric curve.

2. What is the amplitude of your graph? The period? The frequency?

3. Repeat Exercises 1 and 2 with the hour hand.

226

© 2012 Cengage Learning. All Rights Reserved. May not be scanned, copied or duplicated, or posted to a publicly accessible website, in whole or in part.

6 TRIGONOMETRIC FUNCTIONS: RIGHT TRIANGLE APPROACH

6.1 ANGLE MEASURE

▼ Suggested Time and Emphasis

1 class. Essential material.

▼ Points to Stress

1. Degree and radian measurements of angles.
2. Coterminal angles
3. Arc lengths
4. Linear and Angular speed

▼ Sample Questions

- **Text Question:**

  (a) Which two of the following angles (given in radian measure) are coterminal?

  $$0 \qquad \frac{\pi}{2} \qquad \pi \qquad \frac{3\pi}{2} \qquad 2\pi$$

  Answer: 0 and 2π

  (b) Which two of the following angles are coterminal?

  $$45° \qquad -45° \qquad 180° \qquad -180° \qquad 0°$$

  Answer: $180°$ and $-180°$

- **Drill Question:** Find an angle with measure (in radians) between $-\frac{\pi}{2}$ and $\frac{\pi}{2}$ that is coterminal with the angle of measure $\frac{11\pi}{3}$ in standard position.

  Answer: $-\frac{\pi}{3}$

▼ In-Class Materials

- Make an analogy between angle measurement and clock measurement. In 48 hours 15 minutes, how far will the minute hand have moved? One answer is that it will go around the clock face $48\frac{1}{4}$ times. Another answer is that it moved one quarter of the way around the clock face, relative to where it started.
- The formula for the length of a circular arc can be verified experimentally. Have students either draw circles or use trash can lids, soup cans, plastic cups, pie-tins, baking pans, or what have you. Measure arc length and radius for $90°$ angles, $45°$ angles, and so on, verifying that $s = r\theta$.
- Students often get the false impression that angles with integer measure are always in degrees, and that angles with measures that are rational multiples of π are in radians. Ask students to sketch a $1°$ angle and then a 1 radian angle. Similarly, ask students to sketch angles with measures $\frac{\pi}{2}$ radians and $\frac{\pi}{2}$ degrees.
- Show that the familiar formulas $A = \pi r^2$ and $C = 2\pi r$ are actually special cases of formulas in this section.
- One can demonstrate the relationship between linear and angular speed this way: The teacher sits in a rotating office chair, and spins at a rate of, say, 2π radians per five seconds. Now have one student stand close to the professor and one farther away, and have them both try to run in circles at that rate. Note that

227

the one farther away has to travel much faster, demonstrating that if the angular speed is held constant, and r is increased, then v is increased as well.

- If the students have taken some physics, present them with this paradox: We know that Einstein said that the speed of an object cannot exceed 186,000 miles per second, regardless of reference frame. Let the reference frame be a basketball. Have them calculate how fast the sun is moving if the basketball is spinning on a finger, relative to the frame of reference of the basketball. Then have them calculate how fast the stars are moving. These numbers will be faster than the speed of light! This "paradox" is actually a misunderstanding of relativity. The rules about the speed of light being a maximum (and most of relativity theory) apply to what is called an "inertial" reference frame — one where objects in motion remain in motion, and objects at rest remain at rest. The reference frames of a spinning basketball or an accelerating train are not inertial reference frames.

▼ Examples

- We can approximate the shape of the Earth by a sphere of radius 3960 miles. If we wanted to walk far enough to traverse exactly one degree in latitude, how far a trip would we have to take?
  Answer: $3960 \cdot 1 \cdot \frac{\pi}{180} \approx 69$ miles
- Find an angle between $0°$ and $360°$ that is coterminal with $-3624°$.
  Answer: $336°$
- Find an angle between 0 and 2π that is coterminal with $\frac{88\pi}{3}$.
  Answer: $\frac{4\pi}{3}$
- Find an angle between 0 and 2π that is coterminal with 100.
  Answer: $100 - 30\pi \approx 5.7522$

▼ Group Work

There is no group work better than Exercise 74. Ideally, if you are in contact with a teacher at another school (or if your students have willing relatives that live far away) this experiment can be duplicated. We all *believe* that the Earth is big and round, but this experiment allows us to prove it.

Answer: $500 = r (7.2) \left(\frac{\pi}{180} \right)$, so $r \approx 3978.9$ mi and $C \approx 25{,}000.0$ mi.

▼ Homework Problems

Core Exercises: 4, 7, 16, 20, 51, 56, 59, 63, 70, 74

Sample Assignment: 4, 7, 10, 16, 20, 23, 30, 34, 51, 53, 56, 59, 63, 68, 70, 74, 86 8

6.2 TRIGONOMETRY OF RIGHT TRIANGLES

▼ Suggested Time and Emphasis

$\frac{1}{2}$–1 class. Essential material.

▼ Points to Stress

1. Definition of the six trigonometric functions as ratios of sides of right triangles.

2. Special triangles: 30°-60°-90° and 45°-45°-90°.

3. Applications that involve solving right triangles.

▼ Sample Questions

- **Text Question:** Define "angle of elevation".

  Answers will vary

- **Drill Question:** Consider this triangle:

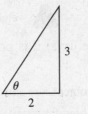

  Find $\sin \theta$, $\sec \theta$, and $\tan \theta$.

  Answer: $\frac{3}{\sqrt{13}}$, $\frac{\sqrt{13}}{2}$, $\frac{3}{2}$

▼ In-Class Materials

Note: If Chapter 5 was covered, the first two points may already have been discussed.

- The etymology of the word sine is fairly interesting and not that well known. It starts with the Indian word *jya*, meaning "cord of a bowstring". The Arabs translated this word as *jiba*. The written language had no vowels, so it looked like this: *jb*. In 1145, the Spanish translator Robert of Cheste had to figure out what vowels to put in. Because of the shape of the curve, he thought the word was *jaib*, which meant the opening of a garment that shows a woman's cleavage. So he used the Latin word for the cavity formed by a curve: *sinus*. (This word exists in the English language today — right behind your nose are the sinus cavities.)

- There is an inconsistency in mathematical notation that can be made explicit at this time. We say that $\frac{1}{3} = 3^{-1}$. Similarly, we say that $\frac{1}{\pi} = \pi^{-1}$. But $\dfrac{1}{\sin x}$ is written as $\csc x$. Unfortunately, there is a symbol, $\sin^{-1} x$ that means something entirely different—the arcsine of x. Even worse, as noted in the section, $\sin^2 x = (\sin x)^2$ and $\sin^3 x = (\sin x)^3$. The exponent -1 is a notational anomaly.

- Example 4 is a good outline for an experiment that can be done in real life. Students can estimate the height of their school, their favorite roller coaster, a flagpole, or anything else. If students measure the distance of ten of their paces, they can "pace off" the distance of shadows, which makes it easier to measure them.

229

- It is relatively easy to make a device to measure angle of elevation. Tape a soda straw to the bottom of a protractor, and tie a string with a weight to the center. When you sight an object through the straw, you can figure out the angle by noticing where the string falls.

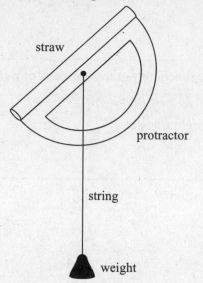

This device is called a *clinometer*. These days, it is possible to get a clinometer application for your smartphone!

- In addition to figuring out the height of an object, we can also figure out distances. If you know a building is, for example, 700 feet high, you can tell how far away you are by measuring the angle of elevation from where you are standing.

▼ Examples

- Triangles to solve:

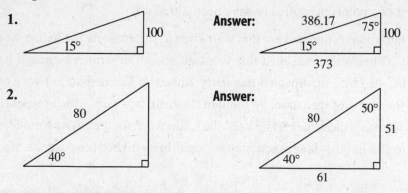

▼ Group Work: Pythagorizing

Students now have several tools to reveal sides and angles of right triangles. They know the trigonometric functions and the Pythagorean Theorem, and they know that the sum of angles in a triangle is always 180°. This activity allows them to assess what they can and can't do at this stage, and to motivate Sections 6.5 and 6.6. It will be interesting to see which students mechanically obtain solutions to Problems 5, 6, and 7, even though they have no tools to work with triangles that are not right triangles. When closing this exercise, make sure to point out that Problem 4 does not have a unique solution.

Answers:

1. $A = 55°$, $b \approx 42.012$, $c \approx 73.246$
2. $A = 55°$, $a \approx 85.689$, $c \approx 104.61$
3. $A = 55°$, $a \approx 49.149$, $b \approx 34.415$
4. The answer is not unique.
5. $A = 55°$, but we do not yet know how to find the other two sides.
6. $A = 55°$, but we do not yet know how to find the other two sides.
7. $A = 55°$, but we do not yet know how to find the other two sides.
8. $A = 90°$, $a \approx 60.926$, $b \approx 10.580$

▼ Homework Problems

Core Exercises: 1, 7, 12, 20, 25, 34, 42, 51, 54

Sample Assignment: 1, 7, 10, 12, 15, 20, 22, 25, 28, 34, 42, 46, 51, 54, 61, 65

We normally label the angles of a triangle with capital letters, and the corresponding sides with lower case letters:

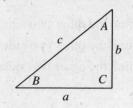

Let's summarize what we know how to do so far. For each of the questions below, solve the triangle or explain why we aren't yet able to solve it:

1. $C = 90°$, $B = 35°$, $a = 60$

2. $C = 90°$, $B = 35°$, $b = 60$

3. $C = 90°$, $B = 35°$, $c = 60$

4. $C = 90°$, $B = 35°$, $A = 55°$

5. $C = 80°$, $B = 35°$, $a = 60$

6. $C = 80°$, $B = 35°$, $b = 60$

7. $C = 80°$, $B = 35°$, $c = 60$

8. $C = 80°$, $B = 10°$, $c = 60$

6.3 TRIGONOMETRIC FUNCTIONS OF ANGLES

▼ Suggested Time and Emphasis

1 class. Essential material.

▼ Points to Stress

1. Finding the reference angle for a given angle.

2. Using the reference angle to evaluate trigonometric functions.

3. The Pythagorean and reciprocal identities of the trigonometric functions.

▼ Sample Questions

- **Text Question:** Is it possible for two different angles to have the same reference angle?
  Answer: Yes

- **Drill Question:** If $\theta = \frac{17\pi}{6}$, find its reference angle $\bar{\theta}$. In what quadrant is θ?
  Answer: $\bar{\theta} = \frac{\pi}{6}$. θ is in the second quadrant.

▼ In-Class Materials

- Students often make the mistake of assuming that the trig functions are linear functions. Since the class will probably involve computing a few trigonometric functions, one can kill two birds with one stone by computing $\sin\left(\frac{\pi}{2} + \frac{\pi}{3}\right)$, $\sin\frac{\pi}{2}$, and $\sin\frac{\pi}{3}$ to demonstrate that, for example, $\sin\left(\frac{\pi}{2} + \frac{\pi}{3}\right) \neq \sin\frac{\pi}{2} + \sin\frac{\pi}{3}$. Return to this point several times; they will be grateful when they don't make that mistake in later courses.

- Don't allow students to simply memorize the mnemonic "All Students Take Calculus" rather than learning the reason for the signs of the trigonometric functions in different quadrants. For example, make sure they are able to articulate why the cosine function is positive in quadrants I and IV and negative in quadrants II and III.

▼ Examples

- $\sin\frac{\pi}{3} = \frac{\sqrt{3}}{2}$

- $\cos\frac{7\pi}{6} = -\frac{\sqrt{3}}{2}$

- $\tan\frac{11\pi}{4} = -1$

- $\sec\frac{17\pi}{3} = 2$

- $\csc\frac{17\pi}{2} = 1$

- $\cot\frac{121\pi}{6} = \sqrt{3}$

▼ Group Work: The Reference Number

This activity allows students to discover a speedy method for finding reference angles of some commonly discussed rational multiples of π by reducing the fractions to lowest terms.

Answers:

1.

θ	Quadrant of θ	$\bar{\theta}$
0	—	0
$\frac{\pi}{3}$	I	$\frac{\pi}{3}$
$\frac{2\pi}{3}$	II	$\frac{\pi}{3}$
$\frac{3\pi}{3}$	—	0
$\frac{4\pi}{3}$	III	$\frac{\pi}{3}$
$\frac{5\pi}{3}$	IV	$\frac{\pi}{3}$
$\frac{6\pi}{3}$	—	0
$\frac{7\pi}{3}$	I	$\frac{\pi}{3}$
$\frac{8\pi}{3}$	II	$\frac{\pi}{3}$
$\frac{9\pi}{3}$	—	0
$\frac{10\pi}{3}$	III	$\frac{\pi}{3}$
$\frac{11\pi}{3}$	IV	$\frac{\pi}{3}$
$\frac{35\pi}{3}$	IV	$\frac{\pi}{3}$
$\frac{1000\pi}{3}$	I	$\frac{\pi}{3}$

2.

θ	Quadrant of θ	$\bar{\theta}$
0	—	0
$\frac{\pi}{6}$	I	$\frac{\pi}{6}$
$\frac{2\pi}{6}$	I	$\frac{\pi}{3}$
$\frac{3\pi}{6}$	—	$\frac{\pi}{2}$
$\frac{4\pi}{6}$	II	$\frac{\pi}{3}$
$\frac{5\pi}{6}$	II	$\frac{\pi}{6}$
$\frac{6\pi}{6}$	—	0
$\frac{7\pi}{6}$	III	$\frac{\pi}{6}$
$\frac{8\pi}{6}$	III	$\frac{\pi}{3}$
$\frac{9\pi}{6}$	—	$\frac{\pi}{2}$
$\frac{10\pi}{6}$	IV	$\frac{\pi}{3}$
$\frac{11\pi}{6}$	IV	$\frac{\pi}{6}$
$\frac{35\pi}{6}$	IV	$\frac{\pi}{6}$
$\frac{1000\pi}{6}$	II	$\frac{\pi}{3}$

▼ Homework Problems

Core Exercises: 5, 8, 14, 26, 35, 50, 48, 61, 67

Sample Assignment: 5, 8, 14, 26, 29, 35, 41, 45, 48, 50, 54, 61, 67, 68, 71

The Reference Number

1. For each angle θ below, identify its quadrant and find the reference angle $\bar{\theta}$.

θ	Quadrant of θ	$\bar{\theta}$
0		
$\frac{\pi}{3}$		
$\frac{2\pi}{3}$		
$\frac{3\pi}{3}$		
$\frac{4\pi}{3}$		
$\frac{5\pi}{3}$		
$\frac{6\pi}{3}$		
$\frac{7\pi}{3}$		
$\frac{8\pi}{3}$		
$\frac{9\pi}{3}$		
$\frac{10\pi}{3}$		
$\frac{11\pi}{3}$		
$\frac{35\pi}{3}$		
$\frac{1000\pi}{3}$		

2. For each angle θ below, identify its quadrant and find the reference angle $\bar{\theta}$.

t	Quadrant of θ	$\bar{\theta}$
0		
$\frac{\pi}{6}$		
$\frac{2\pi}{6}$		
$\frac{3\pi}{6}$		
$\frac{4\pi}{6}$		
$\frac{5\pi}{6}$		
$\frac{6\pi}{6}$		
$\frac{7\pi}{6}$		
$\frac{8\pi}{6}$		
$\frac{9\pi}{6}$		
$\frac{10\pi}{6}$		
$\frac{11\pi}{6}$		
$\frac{35\pi}{6}$		
$\frac{1000\pi}{6}$		

6.4   INVERSE TRIGONOMETRIC FUNCTIONS AND TRIANGLES

▼ Suggested Time and Emphasis

1 class. Essential material.

▼ Points to Stress

1. Defining and evaluating the inverse sine, cosine, and tangent functions.

2. Composing trigonometric functions with inverse trigonometric functions.

▼ Sample Questions

- **Text Question:** We can say $\sin^{-1} y = x$ means $y = \sin x$. Given this nice definition, why does the text need to fuss with domains and ranges?

  Answer: For a given y between -1 and 1, there are infinitely many values of x such that $y = \sin x$.

- **Drill Question:** Compute all angles y such that $\sin y = -\frac{1}{2}$ and $0 < y < 2\pi$.

  Answer: $\frac{7\pi}{6}, \frac{11\pi}{6}$

▼ In-Class Materials

Note: If Chapter 5 has already been covered, the first two points may have already been addressed.

- It may be helpful to start by reviewing general inverse functions (Section 2.7) or inverse trigonometric functions in a real number context (if Section 5.5 has already been covered). If $f(x) = x^3$, what is $f^{-1}(x)$? Note that $f(2) = 8$ and $f^{-1}(8) = 2$. Now move to $f(x) = \sqrt[5]{3x + 2} \;\Rightarrow\; f^{-1}(x) = \dfrac{x^5 - 2}{3}$. Note that $f(5) \approx 1.762$ and $f^{-1}(1.762) \approx 5$. Now explore $f(x) = x^2$, and point out that even though there is no inverse function, we could make things work out if we were allowed to assume that x was positive. This leads to a natural segue into $f(x) = \sin x$.

- Many students may need a review of notation: $\sin^2 x = (\sin x)^2$, $\sin x^2 = \sin(x^2)$, $(\sin x)^{-1} = \dfrac{1}{\sin x} = \csc x$, $\sin x^{-1} = \sin\left(\dfrac{1}{x}\right)$, but $\sin^{-1} x$ represents the inverse sine of x, the arcsine of x, which is not the same as any of the previous functions.

- Present students with this problem: An airplane is flying at 3000 feet, and is approaching a photographer. The photographer wants to take a picture of it when it is 4000 feet away from her. At what angle should she set the camera so that the plane will be in the shot at the right time?

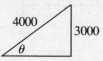

The answer is $\sin^{-1} \frac{3}{4} \approx 0.848$ radians or $48.59°$. (This problem sets up Group Work 1 in a natural way.)

- In calculus, when integrating certain functions (such as those containing terms of the form $a^2 \pm x^2$) we often obtain unwieldy answers like $\sin(\tan^{-1} x)$. The technique presented in Example 7 and Example 8 (Solution 1) is very useful in that situation.

▼ Examples

- $\sin \frac{\pi}{3} = \frac{\sqrt{3}}{2}$
- $\cos \frac{7\pi}{6} = -\frac{\sqrt{3}}{2}$
- $\tan \frac{11\pi}{4} = -1$
- $\sec \frac{17\pi}{3} = 2$
- $\csc \frac{17\pi}{2} = 1$
- $\cot \frac{121\pi}{6} = \sqrt{3}$

▼ Group Work: The Tripod

Answer: For the first picture: $\theta = \tan^{-1} \frac{150-3}{300} \approx 0.456$ radians, or about $26.1°$. For the second picture, $\theta = \tan^{-1} \frac{100-3}{200} \approx 0.452$ radians, or about $25.9°$. The first picture was taken at a steeper angle.

▼ Homework Problems

Core Exercises: 5, 8, 14, 26, 35, 50, 48, 61, 67

Sample Assignment: 5, 8, 14, 26, 29, 35, 41, 45, 48, 50, 54, 61, 67, 68, 71

A photographer is taking pictures of a 150-ft-tall roller coaster. She sets her camera up on a tripod so that the lens of the camera is 3 ft above ground and takes two pictures.

The first picture is taken from 300 feet away with the lens aimed at the top of the roller coaster. The second picture is taken from 200 feet away with the lens aimed two-thirds of the way to the top of the roller coaster.

For which picture is her camera aimed at a steeper angle?

6.5   THE LAW OF SINES

▼ Suggested Time and Emphasis

$\frac{1}{2}$–1 class. Essential material.

▼ Points to Stress

1. Using the Law of Sines to solve triangles.
2. Understanding which cases are ambiguous and which cases are unambiguous.

▼ Sample Questions

- **Text Question:** Why does the book say that SSA is the ambiguous case?

  Answer: It is possible to form two different triangles given two sides and an opposite angle.

- **Drill Question:** Find x in the following diagram:

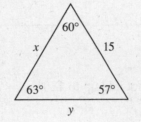

  Answer: $x \approx 14.119$

▼ In-Class Materials

- There is an interesting bit of trivia about the Mount Everest expedition described in the text: Andrew Waugh measured the peak of the mountain to be 29,000 feet exactly. He didn't want people to think his measurement was an estimate (to only two decimal places of accuracy) so he lied and said he measured it to be 29,002 feet. See also Section 1.2 of this book.

- The group work for this section asks students to solve SAS and SSS triangles. They won't be able to do this until they learn the Law of Cosines. If you are going to use this group work, then perhaps do not mention which triangles can and cannot be solved with the Law of Sines until after they have tried the group activity.

- One can demonstrate the ambiguous case physically, using two rulers, taped together to make a fixed angle, and a piece of string. See Figure 6 in the text.

- It is tempting to do all examples in degrees. Students should also be exposed to the relatively unfamiliar radian, if possible.

▼ Examples

- ASA

    1. $A = 30°$, $B = 40°$, $c = 100$

       Answer: $A = 30°$, $B = 40°$, $C = 110°$, $a \approx 53.2$, $b \approx 68.4$, $c = 100$

    2. $A = 0.75$ rad, $B = 0.8$ rad, $c = 100$

       Answer: $A = 0.75$ rad, $B = 0.8$ rad, $C \approx \pi - 1.55 \approx 1.59$ rad, $a \approx 68.18$, $b \approx 71.75$, $c = 100$

- SSA. For each of the following, have students draw triangles to try to guess how many solutions there are.

  1. $A = 80°$, $b = 100$, $a = 10$

  Answer: No solution

  2. $A = 80°$, $b = 10$, $a = 100$

  Answer: One solution: $A = 80°$, $B \approx 5.65°$, $C \approx 94.35°$, $a = 100$, $b = 10$, $c \approx 101.25$

  3. $A = 80°$, $b = 121$, $a = 120$

  Answer: Two solutions: $A = 80°$, $B \approx 83.2°$, $C \approx 16.8°$, $a = 120$, $b = 121$, $c \approx 35.2$; $A = 80°$, $B \approx 96.8°$, $C \approx 3.2°$, $a = 120$, $b = 121$, $c \approx 6.9$

  4. $A = 0.2$ rad, $b = 50$, $a = 40$

  Answer: Two solutions: $A = 0.2$ rad, $B \approx 0.25$ rad, $C \approx 2.69$ rad, $a = 40$, $b = 50$, $c \approx 87.8$; $A = 0.2$ rad, $B \approx 2.89$ rad, $C \approx 0.05$ rad, $a = 40$, $b = 50$, $c \approx 10.3$

▼ Group Work: What Can We Do So Far?

Answers:

1. $A = 50°$, $b \approx 83.91$, $c \approx 130.54$
2. No such triangle exists; the angles do not add up to $180°$.
3. The answer is not unique.
4. $A = 85°$, $c \approx 86.9$, $b \approx 57.6$
5. $B = 35°$, $c \approx 86.9$, $b \approx 57.6$
6. $A \approx 43.9°$, $B \approx 76.1°$, $b \approx 112.1$
7. We do not yet know how to solve this triangle.
8. We do not yet know how to solve this triangle.
9. We actually can figure this one out. Because $a^2 + b^2 = c^2$, we know that $C = 90°$. Then the definition of sine gives us $A \approx 53.1°$, $B \approx 36.9°$.

▼ Homework Problems

Core Exercises: 2, 3, 15, 20, 25, 30, 35, 40

Sample Assignment: 2, 3, 6, 11, 15, 17, 20, 25, 28, 30, 32, 35, 37, 40, 43

As usual, we draw and label an arbitrary triangle as follows:

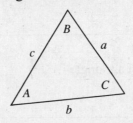

Let's summarize what we know how to do so far. For each of the questions below, solve the triangle or explain why we aren't yet able to solve it.

1. $C = 90°$, $B = 40°$, $a = 100$

2. $C = 90°$, $B = 40°$, $A = 55°$

3. $C = 50°$, $B = 30°$, $A = 100°$

4. $C = 60°$, $B = 35°$, $a = 100$

5. $C = 60°$, $A = 85°$, $a = 100$

6. $C = 60°$, $a = 80$, $c = 100$

7. $C = 60°$, $a = 120$, $b = 90$

8. $a = 40$, $b = 30$, $c = 35$

9. $a = 40$, $b = 30$, $c = 50$

6.6 THE LAW OF COSINES

▼ Suggested Time and Emphasis

$\frac{1}{2}$–1 class. Essential material.

▼ Points to Stress

1. Using the Law of Sines to solve triangles.
2. Using Heron's Formula to find the area of a triangle

▼ Sample Questions

- **Text Question:** Is it possible to find the area of a triangle if the side lengths are known, but the angles are not?

  Answer: Yes

- **Drill Question:** The sides of a triangle are $a = 5$, $b = 8$, and $c = 12$. Find the angle opposite side a.

  Answer: About $18°$ or $\frac{\pi}{10}$ radians.

▼ In-Class Materials

- Have the class apply the Law of Cosines to the special case where C is a right angle. Note that the Law of Cosines is actually a generalization of the Pythagorean theorem.

- Notice that the ability to easily find areas of triangles can be used to help find areas of polygons, because they can be decomposed into triangles.

- If the group work from Section 6.5 was assigned, students can be asked to go back and do the problems that they were not able to do previously.

▼ Examples

- **SSS:** $a = 4$, $b = 8$, $c = 11$

  Answer: $A \approx 16.2°$, $B \approx 33.9°$, $C \approx 129.8°$

- **SAS:** $A = 25°$, $b = 10$, $c = 20$

  Answer: $a \approx 11.725$, $B \approx 21.1°$, $C \approx 133.9°$

▼ Group Work: Where Do Good Friends Meet?

Answer: $6 \sin(55.77°) = 5 \sin(82.81°) \approx 4.96$ ft

▼ Homework Problems

Core Exercises: 2, 4, 7, 16, 19, 22, 27, 41, 44

Sample Assignment: 2, 4, 7, 12, 13, 16, 19, 22, 24, 27, 31, 36, 41, 43, 44, 51

GROUP WORK, SECTION 6.6

Where Do Good Friends Meet?

Every year, the Cedar Falls Chamber of Commerce sponsors a "Chat-a-thon" where happy couples stand four feet apart and compete to see who can spend the most time talking about their relationship. There are two ways that couples tend to lose — they walk away to see what is on television, or they fall asleep standing up. It is actually quite an adorable sight to see two people in love, one six feet tall, the other five feet tall, standing four feet apart, leaning against each other in sleep:

Graphic by Spencer Worobec

How far off the ground are the tops of their heads?

7 ANALYTIC TRIGONOMETRY

7.1 TRIGONOMETRIC IDENTITIES

▼ Suggested Time and Emphasis

$\frac{1}{2}$–1 class. Essential material.

▼ Points to Stress

1. The fundamental trigonometric identities.

2. Proving trigonometric identities.

▼ Sample Questions

- **Text Question:** Given that $\sin^2 x + \cos^2 x = 1$, find an identity for $\tan^2 x + 1$ and show that it is valid.

  Answer: $\dfrac{\sin^2 x}{\cos^2 x} + \dfrac{\cos^2 x}{\cos^2 x} = \dfrac{1}{\cos^2 x} \quad \Rightarrow \quad \tan^2 x + 1 = \sec^2 x$

- **Drill Question:** Prove that $\sin^3 x + \sin x \cos^2 x = \sin x$ is an identity.

  Answer: $\sin^3 x + \sin x \cos^2 x = \sin x \left(\sin^2 x + \cos^2 x \right) = \sin x$

▼ In-Class Materials

- Students often do not grasp the difference between an equation and an identity. Have students classify the following:

$$2x + x = 2x + 2 \qquad \text{(equation)}$$
$$2x + x = 3x \qquad \text{(identity)}$$
$$x + 1 = 2x + 2 \qquad \text{(equation)}$$
$$2(x + 1) = 2x + 2 \qquad \text{(identity)}$$
$$\sin 2x = 2 \sin x \cos x \qquad \text{(identity)}$$
$$2 \sin^2 2x + 2 \cos^2 2x = 2 \qquad \text{(identity)}$$
$$2 \sin^2 2x = 1 \qquad \text{(equation)}$$

- Point out the difference between a reversible operation and an irreversible one. Note the importance— reversible operations can be used to prove identities. Have students classify the following:

$$x^2 \qquad \text{(irreversible)}$$
$$x^3 \qquad \text{(reversible)}$$
$$\sqrt[3]{x} \qquad \text{(reversible)}$$
$$x + c \qquad \text{(reversible)}$$
$$cx \qquad \text{(reversible if } c \neq 0)$$

▼ Examples

- Proving an identity by combining fractions:

$$\frac{1 - \cos\theta}{\sin\theta} - \frac{\sin\theta}{1 + \cos\theta} = 0$$

Proof:

$$\frac{1 - \cos\theta}{\sin\theta} - \frac{\sin\theta}{1 + \cos\theta} = \frac{(1 + \cos\theta)(1 - \cos\theta)}{\sin\theta\,(1 + \cos\theta)} - \frac{\sin^2\theta}{\sin\theta\,(1 + \cos\theta)}$$

$$= \frac{(1 + \cos\theta)(1 - \cos\theta) - \sin^2\theta}{\sin\theta\,(1 + \cos\theta)}$$

$$= \frac{\sin^2\theta - \sin^2\theta}{\sin\theta\,(1 + \cos\theta)} = 0$$

- Proving an identity by introducing something extra:

$$\frac{\csc\theta}{\tan\theta + \cot\theta} = \cos\theta$$

Proof:

$$\frac{\csc\theta}{\tan\theta + \cot\theta} = \frac{\csc\theta}{\tan\theta + \cot\theta}\frac{\tan\theta}{\tan\theta}$$

$$= \frac{\sec\theta}{\tan^2\theta + 1}$$

$$= \frac{\sec\theta}{\sec^2\theta} = \cos\theta$$

▼ Group Work: Finding an Identity

This will allow students to come up with an identity of their own, and touch on the idea of partial fractions.

Answers:

1. $\dfrac{1}{2b\,(a - b)} - \dfrac{1}{2b\,(a + b)} = \dfrac{a + b}{2b\,(a - b)\,(a + b)} - \dfrac{a - b}{2b\,(a - b)\,(a + b)}$

$\qquad\qquad\qquad\qquad\qquad\; = \dfrac{2b}{2b\,(a^2 - b^2)} = \dfrac{1}{a^2 - b^2}$

2. Let $a = 1$ and $b = \sin\theta$ to obtain $\dfrac{1}{2\sin\theta\,(1 - \sin\theta)} - \dfrac{1}{2\sin\theta\,(1 + \sin\theta)} = \sec^2\theta$.

▼ Homework Problems

Core Exercises: 6, 13, 25, 32, 38, 45, 54, 65, 77, 82, 90, 91

Sample Assignment: 6, 12, 13, 20, 25, 32, 37, 38, 43, 45, 54, 60, 65, 72, 77, 79, 82, 88, 90, 91, 96, 97

Finding an Identity

1. Verify the following identity:

$$\frac{1}{a^2 - b^2} = \frac{1}{2b\,(a - b)} - \frac{1}{2b\,(a + b)}$$

2. Use the identity in Problem 1 to find a nice identity whose left-hand side is

$$\frac{1}{2\sin\theta\,(1 - \sin\theta)} - \frac{1}{2\sin\theta\,(1 + \sin\theta)}$$

7.2 ADDITION AND SUBTRACTION FORMULAS

▼ **Suggested Time and Emphasis**

$\frac{1}{2}$–1 class. Recommended material.

▼ **Points to Stress**

1. Addition formulas for sine and cosine.
2. The idea that $a \sin x + b \cos x$ is a phase-shifted sine wave.

▼ **Sample Questions**

- **Text Question:** The text has an example in which $\cos 75°$ is calculated. How is this done?

  Answer: Write $\cos 75° = \cos(30° + 45°)$ and use an addition formula.

- **Drill Question:** Find $\sin\left(\frac{\pi}{3} + x\right)$ if $\sin x \approx 0.42264$ and $\cos x \approx -0.75984$.

  Answer: $\sin\left(\frac{\pi}{3} + x\right) = \sin\frac{\pi}{3}\cos x + \cos\frac{\pi}{3}\sin x \approx \frac{\sqrt{3}}{2}(-0.75984) + \frac{1}{2}(0.42264) \approx -0.44672$

▼ **In-Class Materials**

- It might be a good idea for the class to work together to come up with some mnemonics to help them remember the addition formulas. The very act of trying to invent such a mnemonic forces students to look at the formulas carefully, and think about them, which is a memory aid in itself. Students might come up with such things as "the sign of the sine doesn't change" or "the *c*osine *k*eeps like functions together, while the *s*ine *s*witches them".

- Students can test the formulas by seeing if they work for values of sine and cosine that they know. For example, they can look at $\sin(2 - 2)$ and $\cos(\beta - \beta)$ to make sure they get 0 and 1, respectively. They can look at $\sin(60° + 30°)$ and $\cos\left(\frac{\pi}{4} + \frac{\pi}{2}\right)$ to make sure things work out as they should.

- Section 7.3 can be foreshadowed here. Students can be asked to compute $\sin(x + x)$, $\cos(x + x)$, and $\tan(x + x)$. Group Work 1 foreshadows the product-to-sum formulas.

- Graph $\sin x$, $4\cos x$, $2.5\sin x$, and $2.5\cos x$ like so:

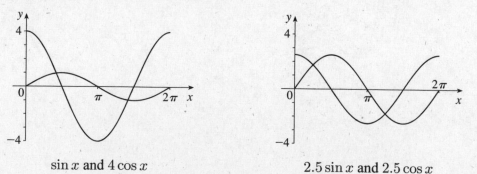

sin x and $4\cos x$ $2.5\sin x$ and $2.5\cos x$

Have students predict which will be bigger, the sum of the first two graphs or the sum of the second two. Note that the sum of the amplitudes of each pair of graphs is 5. Then use the formula from this section to show that the first sum has an amplitude of $\sqrt{17}$ and the second has an amplitude of $\sqrt{12.5}$. Finally, show them the graphs of the sums.

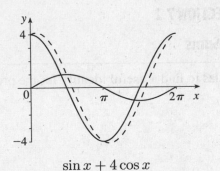

$\sin x + 4 \cos x$

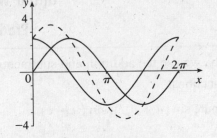

$2.5 \sin x + 2.5 \cos x$

▼ Examples

- Given that $\sin \frac{\pi}{5} \approx 0.587\,79$, find $\cos \frac{11}{30}\pi$.

  Answer: We verify that $\frac{\pi}{5} + \frac{\pi}{6} = \frac{11}{30}\pi$ and calculate $\cos \frac{11}{30}\pi = \cos \frac{\pi}{5} \cos \frac{\pi}{6} - \sin \frac{\pi}{5} \sin \frac{\pi}{6}$. Since $\frac{\pi}{5}$ is in the first quadrant, we have $\cos \frac{\pi}{5} \approx 0.80902$. Therefore, $\cos \frac{11}{30}\pi \approx 0.40674$.

- Compute $\tan \left(\frac{\pi}{3} + \frac{\pi}{4} \right)$.

  Answer: $\tan \left(\frac{\pi}{3} + \frac{\pi}{4} \right) = -\sqrt{3} - 2$

▼ Group Work: Products to Sums

This allows students to derive the Product-Sum Formulas from Section 7.3.

A good hint for Problem 2 is that we can write $\cos u \sin v$ as $\sin v \cos u$ and then modify the result from Problem 1.

Answers:

1. (a) $\sin (u + v) + \sin (u - v) = 2 \sin u \cos v$

   (b) $\sin u \cos v = \frac{1}{2} \left[\sin (u + v) + \sin (u - v) \right]$

2. $\frac{1}{2} \left[\sin (v + u) + \sin (v - u) \right]$ or $\frac{1}{2} \left[\sin (u + v) - \sin (u - v) \right]$

3. $\cos u \cos v = \frac{1}{2} \left[\cos (v + u) + \cos (v - u) \right]$, $\sin u \sin v = \frac{1}{2} \left[\cos (u - v) - \cos (u + v) \right]$

▼ Homework Problems

Core Exercises: 5, 16, 22, 27, 32, 35, 42, 52, 61, 70

Sample Assignment: 5, 12, 16, 19, 22, 27, 31, 32, 35, 38, 42, 43, 48, 52, 56, 61, 70

GROUP WORK, SECTION 7.2

Products to Sums

In this activity, we use the addition and subtraction formulas to find a useful identity for the products of sine and cosine functions.

1. (a) Compute $\sin(u+v) + \sin(u-v)$.

(b) Use your answer from part (a) to find a formula for $\sin u \cos v$.

2. Use your answer from Problem 1 to find an identity for $\cos u \sin v$.

3. Now use a similar technique to the one you used in Problems 1 and 2 to find formulas for $\cos u \cos v$ and $\sin u \sin v$.

7.3 DOUBLE-ANGLE, HALF-ANGLE, AND PRODUCT-SUM FORMULAS

▼ Suggested Time and Emphasis

$\frac{1}{2}$–1 class. Recommended material.

▼ Points to Stress

1. Double-angle formulas for sine and cosine.
2. Power reduction formulas for sine and cosine.

▼ Sample Questions

- **Text Question:** How did we obtain the formula $\sin 2x = 2 \sin x \cos x$?

  Answer: We wrote $\sin 2x = \sin (x + x)$ and used an addition formula.

- **Drill Question:** Use product-to-sum formulas to compute $\sin 15° \cos 15°$.

  Answer: $\sin 15° \cos 15° = \frac{1}{2} (\sin 30° + \sin 0°) = \frac{1}{4}$

▼ In-Class Materials

- One fun way to verify the formulas in this section is to compute $\sin x = \sin \left(2 \cdot \frac{1}{2}x\right)$ "the long way". (An even more fun method is to have your students do it.)

- One can illustrate many of the formulas in this section graphically. For example, this is how you can illustrate $\sin^2 x = \dfrac{1 - \cos 2x}{2}$:

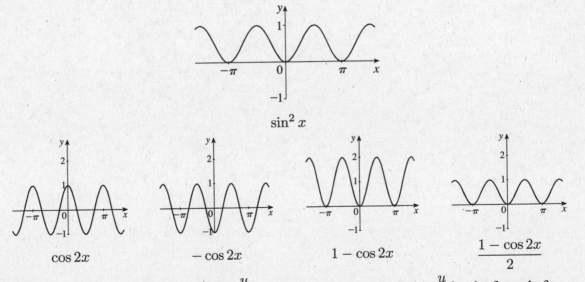

- Note that we can derive the formula for $\tan \dfrac{u}{2}$ by dividing the formula for $\sin \dfrac{u}{2}$ by the formula for $\cos \dfrac{u}{2}$.

▼ Examples

- $\sin 15° \cos 45° = \frac{1}{2} [\sin 60° + \sin (-30°)] = \dfrac{\sqrt{3} - 1}{4}$

- $\tan^2 22.5° = \dfrac{1 - \cos 45°}{1 + \cos 45°} = \dfrac{2 - \sqrt{2}}{2 + \sqrt{2}}$

▼ Group Work: Pushing Our Luck

This activity gives students practice working with identities, and helps them to understand the derivation of the double angle formulas. Students can check their answers to question 2 by graphing $\cos(3x)$ and then their proposed solution.

Answers:

1. Answers will vary. One correct answer:

$$
\begin{aligned}
\sin 3x &= \sin(x + 2x) \\
&= \sin x \cos 2x + \cos x \sin 2x \\
&= \sin x \left(2 \cos^2 x - 1\right) + 2 \cos^2 x \sin x \\
&= \sin x \left(2 \cos^2 x - 1 + 2 \cos^2 x\right) \\
&= \sin x \left(4 \cos^2 x - 1\right)
\end{aligned}
$$

2. Answers will vary. One good answer: $\cos 3x = \cos x \left(1 - 4 \sin^2 x\right)$.

▼ Homework Problems

Core Exercises: 3, 12, 20, 31, 38, 52, 59, 75, 84, 103

Sample Assignment: 3, 8, 12, 15, 20, 25, 31, 34, 38, 46, 52, 59, 61, 75, 84, 88, 96, 103

We were able to use the simple facts that $\sin 2x = \sin(x+x)$ and $\cos 2x = \cos(x+x)$ to derive the handy double angle formulas:

$$\sin 2x = 2\sin x \cos x$$
$$\cos 2x = \cos^2 x - \sin^2 x$$
$$= 1 - 2\sin^2 x$$
$$= 2\cos^2 x - 1$$

However, it isn't as easy to get nice results for $\sin 3x$ and $\cos 3x$.

1. Show that $\sin 3x = \sin x \left(4\cos^2 x - 1\right)$.

2. Find the cleanest identity you can for $\cos 3x$.

7.4   BASIC TRIGONOMETRIC EQUATIONS

▼ Suggested Time and Emphasis

1–2 classes. Essential material.

▼ Points to Stress

1. Solving linear and quadratic trigonometric equations.
2. Using identities to put trigonometric equations into linear or quadratic form.

▼ Sample Questions

- **Text Question:** In the text, the equation $2\cos^2 x - 7\cos x + 3 = 0$ is solved. The authors wrote it this way: $(2\cos x - 1)(\cos x - 3) = 0$. They then dealt with the first of the two terms, but ignored the second. Why?

  Answer: There is no x such that $\cos x = 3$.

- **Drill Question:** Solve $x\sin 3x + \frac{1}{2}x = 0$.

  Answer: $x = 0$ or $x = \frac{7\pi}{18} + \frac{2}{3}\pi k$

▼ In-Class Materials

- Assume we want to solve $\sin x = \frac{1}{3}$. We want our students to enter $\sin^{-1}\frac{1}{3}$ into a calculator, obtaining 0.33983691, then write down one answer $(0.33983691 + 2\pi k)$, and then *figure out* another $(2.8017557 + 2\pi k)$. It is easy for us to forget that the idea of having to work to find an answer *after* the calculator has spoken is antithetical to everything some students believe about technology. Most of their mathematical experiences with technology involve a problem that ends when the "=" key is pressed, save for (perhaps) checking their answer or interpreting the result. This time, the "=" key signals only the beginning of their thinking. Some students flat-out don't believe that they have to go through this process, and wait for the teacher to show them a shortcut or "the real way." If you can disabuse them of this notion, you will have performed a true service to mathematics.

- When we solve trigonometric equations, we often have to deal with restricted domains. Solve $\sin 3x = 0.15$ with the condition that $5\pi \leq x \leq 7\pi$.

  Answer: $x \approx 19.000$ or 21.840

- Solve an equation in quadratic form, such as $25\cos^2\theta - 5\cos\theta - 2 = 0$.

  Answer: The left-hand side factors, giving $\cos\theta = \frac{2}{5}$ or $\cos\theta = -\frac{1}{5}$. Thus, $\theta \approx 1.15928 \pm 2k\pi$ or $\theta \approx 1.77215 \pm 2k\pi$.

▼ Examples

- Solve $\cos x \tan x + \frac{1}{2}\tan x = 0$.

  Answer: $x = \pi k$ or $\pm\frac{2\pi}{3} + 2\pi k$

- Solve $\dfrac{\sec 5x}{2} = \cos 5x$.

  Answer: $x = \pm\frac{\pi}{20} + \frac{2}{5}\pi k$

254

▼ Group Work: Critical Days

In the 1970s, biorhythms were a big deal for some people. There were newspaper columns, special machines in grocery stores and bars, books, etc. These days, biorhythms are often used as an example of a pseudo-science. This activity starts out using techniques from this section, then foreshadows ideas from number theory.

Answers:

1. 78

2. $\frac{7}{3} + 28k$, $\frac{35}{3} + 28k$. The fractions result from the fact that you hit the halfway mark at some point *during* the day.

3. 644 days, or a little over 1 year and 9 months

4. 21,252 days, or a little over 58 years and 2 months

▼ Homework Problems

Core Exercises: 2, 9, 19, 32, 44, 56, 57

Sample Assignment: 2, 4, 6, 9, 13, 19, 21, 28, 32, 38, 42, 44, 49, 56, 57, 59

GROUP WORK, SECTION 7.4

Critical Days

Back in the 1970s, there was a fad called "biorhythms". People believed that their physical, emotional, and intellectual abilities could be modeled by the following equations:

$$\text{Physical} \ : \ \sin\frac{2\pi t}{23}$$

$$\text{Emotional} \ : \ \sin\frac{2\pi t}{28}$$

$$\text{Intellectual} \ : \ \sin\frac{2\pi t}{33}$$

In these equations, t represents the number of days a person has been alive. Biorhythm believers feared "critical days" on which one or more of the functions was equal to 0.

1. How many emotional critical days do people experience in their first three years of life?

2. Find an expression that gives all the days where a person's physical function is equal to $\frac{1}{2}$.

3. A "double critical day" occurs when two functions cross the x-axis on the same day. On what day of your life did you experience your first double critical day?

4. Believers lived in special fear of "triple critical days". On which day of your life will you experience your first triple critical day?

7.5 MORE TRIGONOMETRIC EQUATIONS

▼ Suggested Time and Emphasis

$\frac{1}{2}$–1 class. Recommended material.

▼ Points to Stress

1. Solving trigonometric equations using identities.
2. Finding intersection points.
3. Equations of trigonometric functions with multiple angles.

▼ Sample Questions

- **Text Question:** Why do we need to use an identity to solve $1 + \sin\theta = 2\cos^2\theta$, but not $1 + \sin\theta = 2\sin^2\theta$?

  Answer: The second equation can be put into quadratic form with $\sin\theta$ as the variable. The first one is tricky because it has both sine and cosine in it, so our techniques from the previous section do not work.

- **Drill Question:** Find all solutions to $\sin\frac{\theta}{3} = \frac{\sqrt{3}}{2}$.

  Answer: $\pi + 6\pi k$, $2\pi + 6\pi k$

▼ In-Class Materials

- Before discussing this section, it is good to warm up with some problems from the previous section. The solving techniques of this section all wind up with solving a basic trigonometric equation.

- Finding the intersection of two graphs algebraically is no different than solving a trigonometric equation: We set the formulas for the two graphs equal to each other. The converse is true as well: One way to approximate the solutions to a trigonometric equation is to graph each side of the equation, then use graphical methods to approximate where the two sides are equal.

▼ Examples

- Solve $\sin\theta\cos 2 + \cos\theta\sin 2 = 0.2$.

  Answer: $\sin\theta\cos 2 + \cos\theta\sin 2 = 0.2 \Leftrightarrow \sin(\theta + 2) = 0.2 \Leftrightarrow \theta + 2 \approx 0.2014 + 2\pi k$ or $\theta + 2 \approx 2.9402 + 2\pi k \Leftrightarrow \theta \approx -1.7986 + 2\pi k$ or $\theta \approx 0.9402 + 2\pi k$.

- Solve $\cos\sqrt{\theta} = 0.4$ in the interval $0 \le \theta \le 100$.

  Answer: $\cos\sqrt{\theta} = 0.4 \Leftrightarrow \sqrt{\theta} \approx 1.1592 + 2\pi k$ or $\sqrt{\theta} \approx -1.1592 + 2\pi k \Leftrightarrow \sqrt{\theta} \approx 1.1592, 5.1240, 7.4424, 11.4072\dots$.

  Solutions in the desired interval are $\theta \approx 1.3437$, $\theta \approx 26.2553$, and $\theta \approx 55.3893$.

▼ Group Work 1: Some Unusual Equations

Answers:

1. $x = \frac{\pi}{2} + \pi k$ or equivalently $x = \pm\frac{\pi}{2} + 2\pi k$
2. $x \approx \pm 0.25493168 + \frac{\pi}{2}k$

▼ Group Work 2: A Different Periodic Function

Some students get the impression that the six trig functions are the *only* periodic functions. This activity introduces another periodic function.

Answers:

1.

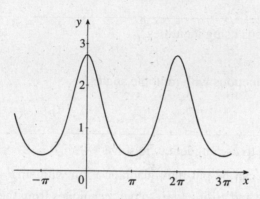

2. $x \approx 1.3457582 + 2\pi k$

3. There is no solution. The graph does not touch the line $y = 2.8$.

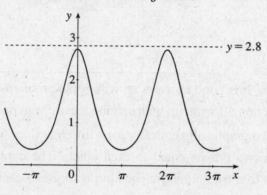

▼ Homework Problems

Core Exercises: 4, 10, 19, 32, 36, 41, 44, 52, 58, 64

Sample Assignment: 4, 10, 15, 19, 24, 32, 34, 36, 39, 41, 44, 48, 52, 55, 58, 62, 64, 65

Some Unusual Equations

1. Solve $\sin(\cos x) = 0$.

2. Solve $\sin(\cos 4x) = \frac{1}{2}$.

A Different Periodic Function

1. Graph $e^{\cos x}$.

2. Solve $e^{\cos x} = 1.25$.

3. Solve $e^{\cos x} = 2.8$. How is your solution reflected on your graph?

8 POLAR COORDINATES AND PARAMETRIC EQUATIONS

8.1 POLAR COORDINATES

▼ Suggested Time and Emphasis

1 class. Essential material.

▼ Points to Stress

1. The relationships between rectangular and polar coordinates.
2. Converting equations into different coordinate systems.

▼ Sample Questions

- **Text Question:** Where do the conversion equations $x = r \cos \theta$, $y = r \sin \theta$ come from?

  Answer: Several correct answers are possible. Anything addressing the definitions of sine and cosine, for example, should be given credit.

- **Drill Question:** Convert the equation $r \sin \theta = 3r \cos \theta + 2$ to polar form.

  Answer: $y = 3x + 2$

▼ In-Class Materials

- Begin with an intuitive definition of polar coordinates and then derive the algebraic formulas, noting that the graph of a polar function need not pass the Vertical Line Test.
- Do several examples of converting Cartesian equations into polar equations, such as $y^2 = 4x$ to $r = 4 \csc \theta \cot \theta$, and of converting polar equations into Cartesian equations (the result of which are sometimes implicit equations) such as $r = 2 \sec \theta$ to $x = 2$ and $r = 2(1 + \cos \theta)$ to $\left(x^2 + y^2 - 2x\right)^2 = 4\left(x^2 + y^2\right)$.
- Point out how some equations are simpler to consider in rectangular coordinates [$y = \ln x$ is easier than $r \sin \theta = \ln r + \ln \cos \theta$] but some equations are simpler in polar coordinates ($r = \theta$, the simple spiral, is much easier than $\pm\sqrt{x^2 + y^2} = \tan^{-1}(y/x)$). You can foreshadow Chapter 11 at this point, pointing out that there are curves called rotated ellipses, hyperbolas and parabolas, that turn out to be very nice when considered as polar equations.

▼ Examples

- Coordinate conversion:

  Rectangular $(8, 16)$ is the same as polar $\left(8\sqrt{5}, 1.107\right)$.

  Rectangular $\left(5, -5\sqrt{3}\right)$ is the same as polar $\left(10, -\frac{\pi}{3}\right)$.

  Polar $\left(4, \frac{13\pi}{6}\right)$ is the same as rectangular $\left(2\sqrt{3}, 2\right)$.

  Polar $(7, 10)$ is (approximately) the same as rectangular $(-5.8735, -3.8081)$.

- Equation conversion:

  Rectangular: $x^2 + y^2 = 9$ is the same as polar $r = 9$.

  Polar $\tan \theta = 1$ is the same as rectangular $y = x$.

▼ Group Work 1: Uniqueness of Representation

We say that one point can have several polar representations, and only one rectangular representation. This activity is designed to solidify this fact, while giving students a chance to practice converting points between coordinate systems. If students are thinking about polar coordinates entirely algebraically, they may have difficulty with Problem 1(d), because $\arctan\left(\frac{-5}{0}\right)$ is undefined. Perhaps they will need the hint that this is not a hard problem if someone just draws a picture. Problem 4 is impossible. The main point of this activity is that it can't be done. Make sure, when closing, that this is stated clearly.

Answers:

1. **(a)** $\left(\frac{5}{2}\sqrt{2}, \frac{5}{2}\sqrt{2}\right)$ **(b)** $\left(\sqrt{13}, -\arctan\frac{2}{3}\right) \approx \left(\sqrt{13}, -0.588\right)$ **(c)** $\left(4, -\frac{\pi}{3}\right)$ **(d)** $\left(5, \frac{3\pi}{2}\right)$

2. All are the point $\left(-\frac{\sqrt{2}}{2}, -\frac{\sqrt{2}}{2}\right)$.

3. Answers will vary.

4. This is impossible.

▼ Group Work 2: Some Basic Polar Graphs

This will foreshadow the next section, where polar graphs are discussed in earnest.

Answers:

1. The graph is a circle.

2. The graph is a straight line through the origin.

3. The graph is a spiral

▼ Homework Problems

Core Exercises: 2, 3, 10, 17, 30, 36, 44, 49, 54, 63

Sample Assignment: 2, 3, 6, 10, 17, 22, 23, 26, 30, 33, 36, 40, 44, 47, 49, 54, 63, 68

GROUP WORK 1, SECTION 8.1

Uniqueness of Representation

---

1. Convert these points (given in rectangular coordinates) to polar coordinates:

   (a) $(5, 5)$ **(b)** $(-3, 2)$ **(c)** $\left(2, -2\sqrt{3}\right)$ **(d)** $(0, -5)$

2. Convert these points (given in polar coordinates) to rectangular coordinates:

   (a) $\left(2, \frac{5\pi}{4}\right)$ **(b)** $\left(-2, \frac{\pi}{4}\right)$ **(c)** $\left(2, \frac{13\pi}{4}\right)$ **(d)** $\left(2, -\frac{3\pi}{4}\right)$

3. Choose a point in the first quadrant, and give three different polar representations for that point.

4. Choose a point in the first quadrant, and give three different rectangular representations for that point.

GROUP WORK 2, SECTION 8.1

Some Basic Polar Graphs

Do you remember when you first started drawing graphs? No doubt, at some point, you were given a simple formula like $y = 2x$, and were instructed to plot a bunch of points. You did so and, by Neptune's Knickerbockers, you obtained a line!

In this activity, we are going to draw some polar graphs by plotting a bunch of polar points and seeing what happens.

1. $r = 3$. Plot many points whose first polar coordinate is 3. You will probably start with $(3, 0)$, then maybe $\left(3, \frac{\pi}{6}\right)$, or whatever you like. Choose many values for θ, but make sure to keep $r = 3$. What do you get?

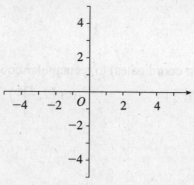

2. $\theta = \frac{5\pi}{4}$. Again, plot some points to figure out what this graph will look like. Your points can have any r-coordinate you chose, but the θ-coordinate must be $\frac{5\pi}{4}$. Make sure to include some negative values of r along with positive ones.

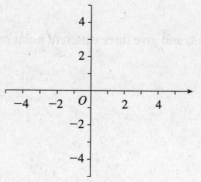

3. $r = \theta, \theta \geq 0$. In this plot, both polar coordinates will always be the same. You will probably want to plot $(0, 0)$ and $\left(\frac{\pi}{2}; \frac{\pi}{2}\right)$ and many others until you understand the shape of this curve.

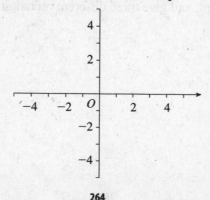

8.2   GRAPHS OF POLAR EQUATIONS

▼ Suggested Time and Emphasis

1 class. Essential material.

▼ Points to Stress

1. Graphs in polar coordinates.
2. Tests for symmetry.
3. Using graphing devices to obtain polar graphs.

▼ Sample Questions

- **Text Question:** Sketch the graph of $r = \cos\theta$.

  Answer:

  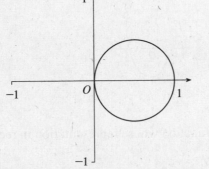

- **Drill Question:** What is the polar equation of a circle with radius 3 centered at the origin?

  Answer: $r = 3$

▼ In-Class Materials

- After showing students how to graph polar functions on a calculator, give them a chance to experiment and try to come up with interesting-looking polar graphs. Make sure they know that if their graphs appear to have a lot of cusps, it could be that their Δt is set too large.

- An interesting graph to look at is $r = \dfrac{\theta}{\theta + 1}$, $\theta \geq 0$.

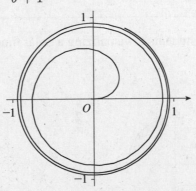

Have the class try to figure out if, as $\theta \to \infty$, the curve will get infinitely close to the curve $r = 1$, and if so, why. Ask if the curve will ever touch $r = 1$. If this curve is combined with the circle $r = 1$, the resulting set of points is what topologists call "connected, but not path-connected". The set of points is not path-connected because there is no path from the origin that touches the outer circle. It is called "connected" because (to simplify things somewhat) there is no curve that separates the two components without touching either. Dr. Shaw calls this curve "The Topologist's Hypno-Disk"

▼ Examples

- Do a problem where $r = f(\theta)$ is graphed both as a function in rectangular coordinates and as a polar function. For example, if $r = (1.5)^{\theta}$ we get the two graphs shown below.

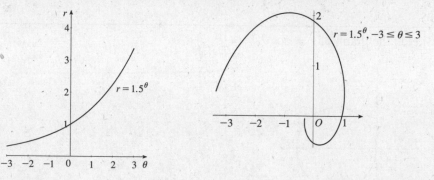

- Sketch a graph of the polar curve $r = f(\theta)$ where $f(\theta)$ is the function whose representation in rectangular coordinates is given below.

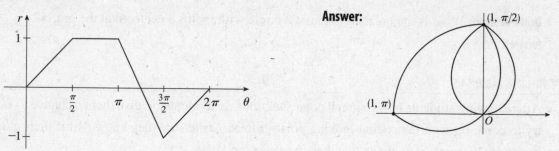

▼ Group Work 1: Picture Pages

This group work is designed to assist students in visualizing a polar function $r = f(\theta)$ graphed in rectangular coordinates.

Answers:

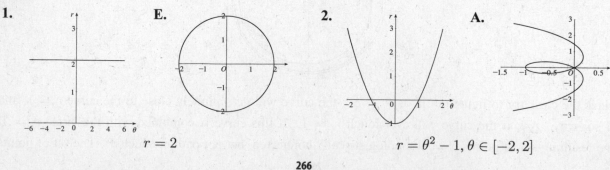

1. E. $r = 2$ 2. A. $r = \theta^2 - 1, \theta \in [-2, 2]$

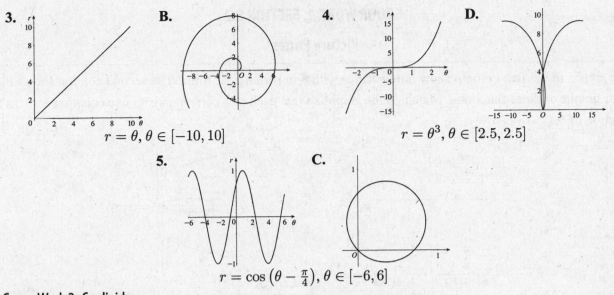

3.

B.

$r = \theta, \theta \in [-10, 10]$

4.

D.

$r = \theta^3, \theta \in [2.5, 2.5]$

5.

C.

$r = \cos\left(\theta - \frac{\pi}{4}\right), \theta \in [-6, 6]$

▼ Group Work 2: Cardioids

Answers:

1.

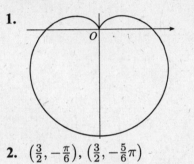

2. $\left(\frac{3}{2}, -\frac{\pi}{6}\right), \left(\frac{3}{2}, -\frac{5}{6}\pi\right)$

3. $\left(2, -\frac{\pi}{2}\right), \left(\frac{1}{2}, \frac{\pi}{6}\right), \left(\frac{1}{2}, \frac{5\pi}{6}\right)$. Note that the derivative is not defined at $\left(0, \frac{\pi}{2}\right)$.

▼ Homework Problems

Core Exercises: 3, 10, 24, 29, 36, 47, 50, 51, 55

Sample Assignment: 3, 8, 10, 13, 19, 24, 29, 36, 42, 47, 49, 50, 51, 52, 55, 57

The graphs in the first column show how r varies with θ in rectangular form. The second column shows the polar graphs of these functions. Match up the graphs so that each pair corresponds to one equation for r as a function of θ.

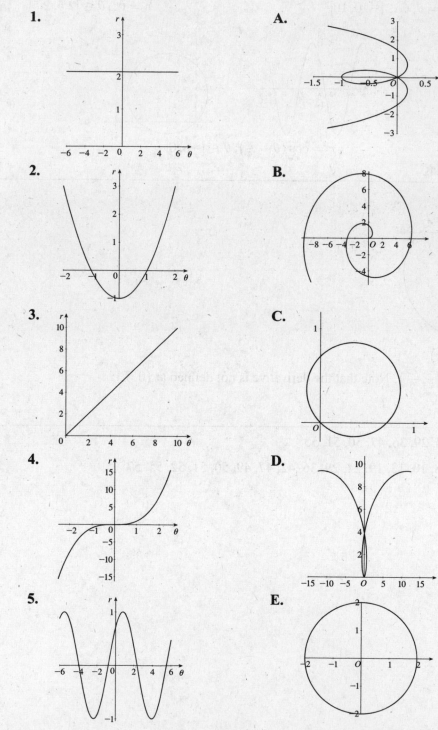

GROUP WORK 2, SECTION 8.2

Cardioids

Consider the polar curve $r = 1 - \sin\theta$

1. Carefully sketch a graph of this curve on the polar graph paper provided, by computing at least 10 points on the curve and connecting the dots.

2. Find polar coordinates for the points on the curve where the tangent line is *vertical*. Find exact values if you can, but if this is impossible, a good estimate will do.

3. Find polar coordinates for the points where the tangent line is *horizontal*. Again, find exact values where possible.

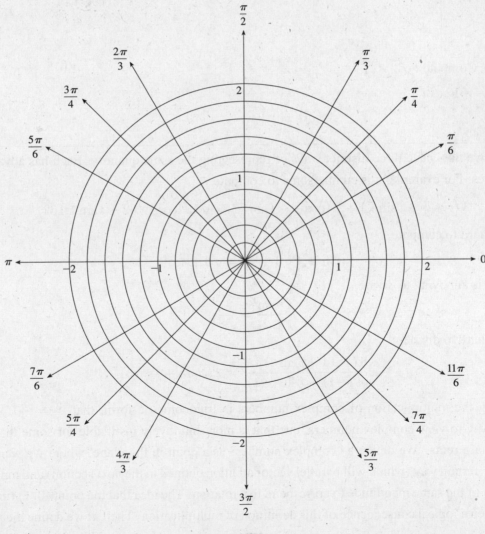

8.3 POLAR FORM OF COMPLEX NUMBERS; DE MOIVRE'S THEOREM

▼ Suggested Time and Emphasis

$\frac{1}{2}$–1 class. Recommended material.

▼ Points to Stress

1. Three representations of a complex number: as a point, as a number $a + bi$, and in trigonometric form.
2. Multiplication and division of complex numbers in trigonometric form.
3. DeMoivre's Theorem

▼ Sample Questions

- **Text Question:** Graph the following set of complex numbers: $\{z \mid |z| = 1\}$

  Answer:

  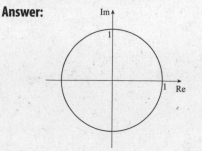

- **Drill Question:** Compute $\left(\sqrt{3} - i\right)^{10}$.

  Answer: $512 + 512\sqrt{3}i$

▼ In-Class Materials

- Notice that we now have three distinct ways of representing the same quantity. Each has advantages and disadvantages. For example, it is cumbersome to compute

$$3\left(\cos \tfrac{\pi}{2} + i \sin \tfrac{\pi}{2}\right) + 2\left(\cos \tfrac{\pi}{6} + i \sin \tfrac{\pi}{6}\right) = \sqrt{19}\left(\cos 1.162 + i \sin 1.162\right)$$

but not too hard to compute

$$3i + \left(\sqrt{3} + i\right) = \sqrt{3} + 4i$$

Similarly, it is annoying to divide

$$\frac{3 - 6i}{4 + 2i} = -\tfrac{3}{2}i$$

but it is not hard to divide

$$\frac{8\left(\cos 4 + i \sin 4\right)}{4\left[\cos\left(-1\right) + i \sin\left(-1\right)\right]} = 2\left(\cos 5 + i \sin 5\right)$$

- Verify, using the multiplication of complex numbers in trigonometric form, that $i^2 = -1$. This leads to another way to view complex numbers, one that is more intuitively justifiable for some than allowing negative square roots. We define a "complex number" as a point in the plane, where we want to define addition in a certain way (which will parallel vector addition defined in the next section) and multiplication of quantities of the same magnitude to correspond to a rotation. The idea that the point $(0, 1)$ times itself is $(-1, 0)$ is then a logical consequence of this definition of multiplication. Then, if we define the point $(1, 0)$

to be "1" and the point $(0, 1)$ to be "i" we obtain $i^2 = -1$. This is not violating the laws of conventional mathematics; it is simply a result of our definitions of operations on these point quantities. In the real world, it turns out there are quantities (such as waveforms, impedance of an AC circuit, etc.) that are most usefully represented in this way.

- Ask the class, "What are the square roots of 1?" Elicit the answers ± 1, and draw them this way:

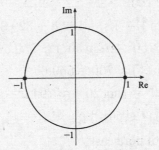

Ask about the fourth roots of 1, obtaining ± 1 and $\pm i$, and draw them as well:

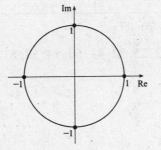

Now ask about the third roots of 1 and fifth roots of 1. you will probably have to do these as an example on the board. Draw them, and point out that the nth roots of one are always equally spaced around the unit circle.

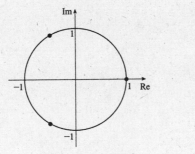

Third roots of 1

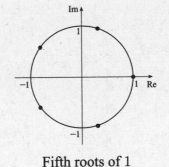

Fifth roots of 1

▼ Examples

- Switching between forms:

  - $4 \left(\cos \frac{5\pi}{4} + i \sin \frac{5\pi}{4} \right) = -2\sqrt{2} - 2\sqrt{2}i$

  - $4 \left(\cos 1 + i \sin 1 \right) \approx 2.161 + 3.366i$

  - $3 \left(\cos 20° + i \sin 20° \right) \approx 2.81907786 + 1.02606043i$

- $(4 - 3i)^5 = -3116 + 237i$

271

▼ Group Work: The Complex Pirates

This whimsical activity allows the students to practice adding and subtracting complex numbers in various forms.

Answer:

After step 3: $100\,(\cos 90° + i \sin 90°) = 100i$

After step 5: $100i + (300\cos 130° + i \sin 130°) \approx -192.8 + 329.8i$

After step 7: $-192.8 + 329.8i + 300\,(\cos 50° + i \sin 50°) \approx 559.6i$

After step 9: $559.6i + 700\,(\cos 0° + i \sin 0°) \approx 700 + 559.6i$

After step 11: $700 + 559.6i + 100\,(\cos 20° + i \sin 20°) \approx 794.0 + 594.0i$

Distance from the old skull: $\sqrt{794^2 + 594^2} \approx 991.5$ ft

Direction: $\arctan \frac{594}{794} \approx 36.8°$, just east of northeast

▼ Homework Problems

Core Exercises: 4, 9, 16, 22, 25, 32, 54, 61, 70, 87

Sample Assignment: 4, 9, 12, 16, 18, 19, 22, 25, 32, 43, 50, 54, 58, 61, 67, 70, 73, 87, 94

The fearsome pirate Rob Rackham has given you his treasure map for safekeeping. Ha ha ha! Silly Rob Rackham!

You get to Bulbous Island and find your way to the old skull, and then unroll the map to take it from there:

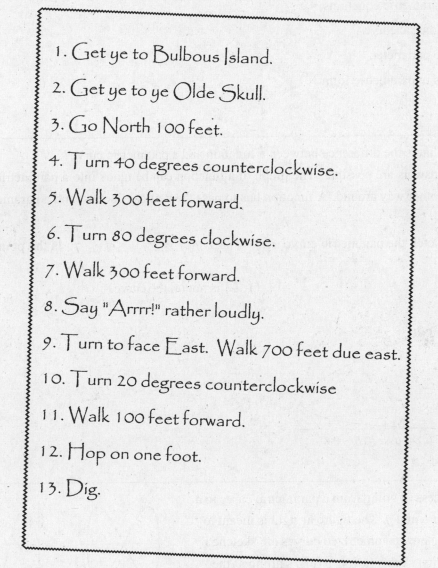

1. Get ye to Bulbous Island.
2. Get ye to ye Olde Skull.
3. Go North 100 feet.
4. Turn 40 degrees counterclockwise.
5. Walk 300 feet forward.
6. Turn 80 degrees clockwise.
7. Walk 300 feet forward.
8. Say "Arrrr!" rather loudly.
9. Turn to face East. Walk 700 feet due east.
10. Turn 20 degrees counterclockwise
11. Walk 100 feet forward.
12. Hop on one foot.
13. Dig.

How far away is the treasure from the old skull, and in what direction does it lie?

8.4 PLANE CURVES AND PARAMETRIC EQUATIONS

▼ Suggested Time and Emphasis

1 class. Recommended material.

▼ Points to Stress

1. Definition of parametric equations.

2. Sketching parametric curves.

3. Eliminating the parameter.

4. Polar equations in parametric form.

▼ Sample Questions

- **Text Question:** What is the difference between a function and a parametric curve?

  Answer: Many answers are possible. The graph of a function can be made into a parametric curve, but not necessarily the other way around. A function has to pass the vertical line test and a parametric curve does not.

- **Drill Question:** Sketch the parametric curve $x(t) = \sin t \; y(t) = t^2$, $0 \leq t \leq \pi$. Is the point $\left(1, \frac{\pi}{4}\right)$ on this curve?

  Answer: $\left(1, \frac{\pi}{4}\right)$ is not on the curve.

  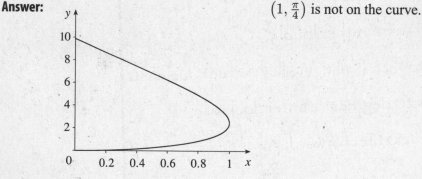

▼ In-Class Materials

- Discuss the process of going from a parametric curve to a relation between x and y. The figure at right is meant to help students see how parametrized curves are sketched out over time. First sketch $(x(t), y(t))$, starting at the initial point (the origin), and moving up and to the right. (Try to keep your speed constant.) Stop when the cycle is about to repeat. Then, to the right of the figure, graph the motion in the y-direction only. Then, below the figure, graph the motion in the x-direction. That graph is sideways because the x-axis is horizontal.

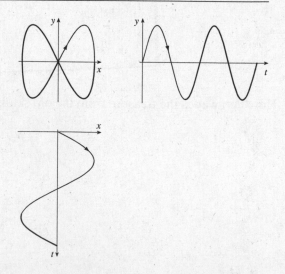

274

- Show how reversing the functions $x(t)$ and $y(t)$ yields the inverse of a given relation. For example, $\begin{cases} x(t) = t \\ y(t) = \sin t \end{cases}$ is the sine function, so $\begin{cases} x(t) = \sin t \\ y(t) = t \end{cases}$ is the general arcsine function. Display an inverse for $f(x) = x^3 + x + 2$ graphically using parametric equations. Explain the difficulties with the algebraic approach.

- Have the students get into groups, and have each group try to come up with the most interesting looking parametric curve. After displaying their best ones, perhaps show them the following examples:

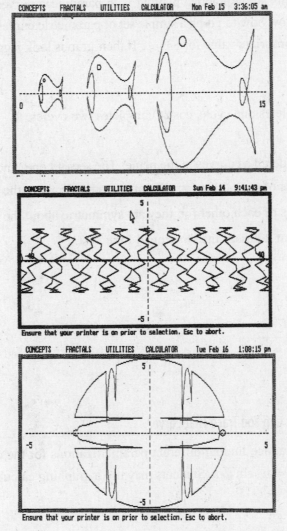

- Give an example of a curve such as $x(t) = \cos et$, $y(t) = \sin \sqrt{3}t$. This curve essentially fills the square $-1 \le x \le 1$, $-1 \le y \le 1$ in that the curve gets arbitrarily close to any point in the square. (It is not what mathematicians call a "space filling curve", because it does not actually hit every point in the square.) It can be simulated using a graphing calculator with the approximations $e \approx 2.7183$ and $\sqrt{3} \approx 1.7321$. The range $0 \le t \le 200$ should be sufficient to convey this property to the students. Next, describe the family of functions $x(t) = a \cos et$, $y(t) = b \sin \sqrt{3}t$. If the students are following well, perhaps consider the family $x(t) = \cos at$, $y(t) = \sin \sqrt{3}t$. The students might be tempted to conclude that this is always space-filling, but it is not for some values of a, such as $a = 2\sqrt{3}$.

275

▼ Examples

- Construction of an ellipse with center $(-1, -2)$ and axis lengths 2 and 3: We start with the circle $x = \cos\theta$, $y = \sin\theta$. We stretch it into shape: $x = 2\cos\theta$, $y = 3\sin\theta$. Then we move it into position: $x = 2\cos\theta - 1$, $y = 3\sin\theta - 2$.

▼ Group Work 1: Name that Parametrization

This exercise gives the students some practice playing with parametric curves. Before starting the activity, make sure that the students know how to graph a simple set of parametric curves using their technology. Make sure the students chose an appropriate value for `tstep`. If their graphs look jagged, there is a chance that their `tstep` is too large.

Answers:

1. **(a)** Every time $\sin t$ completes one cycle, $\cos 2t$ completes two cycles.

   (b) $y = \left(1 - x^2\right) - x^2 = 1 - 2x^2$

3. They are the same if considered as curves in the plane. The second one "moves" twice as fast as the first.

4. **(a)** The curves are inverses of each other (or, they are symmetric about the line $y = x$).

   (b) The curves are inverses of each other (or, they are symmetric about the line $y = x$).

5. **(a)** We graph f and see that it passes the Horizontal Line Test.

   (b)

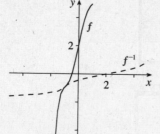

▼ Group Work 2: How Many Ways Can You Trace That Curve?

This exercise gives students practice finding different parametrizations for the circle $x^2 + y^2 = 4$, using the forms $x(t) = a_1 \cos a_2 t$, $y(t) = a_3 \sin a_4 t$. Students may use a graphing calculator.

Answers:

1. Each of a_1 and a_3 must be ± 2.

2. Once around counterclockwise, starting at $(1, 0)$.

3. $a_2 = a_4 = 2$, $a_2 = a_4 = 3$

4. Once around clockwise, starting at $(1, 0)$.

5. $a_2 = 3$, $a_4 = -3$; $a_2 = 5$, $a_4 = -5$

▼ Homework Problems

Core Exercises: 3, 14, 27, 30, 34, 37, 54, 55, 66

Sample Assignment: 3, 8, 14, 23, 27, 30, 32, 34, 37, 39, 50, 53, 54, 55, 56, 66

Name that Parametrization

1. Consider the graph of the following set of parametric equations:

$$x(t) = \sin t \qquad y(t) = \cos 2t \qquad 0 < t < \infty$$

   (a) Graph this curve with your calculator. Why does it look the way it does?

   (b) Write this equation in the form $y = f(x)$. (*Hint:* Use the formula $\cos 2\theta = \cos^2 \theta - \sin^2 \theta$.)

2. Try to guess what the graph of the following set of parametric equations looks like, and then see if you are right.

$$x(t) = \sin 2t \qquad y(t) = \cos 6t \qquad 0 \leq t \leq 4\pi$$

   These curves are called Lissajous figures, and are used in electrical engineering to see if two signals are "in sync".

3. Consider these two sets of parametric equations:

$$x(t) = t \qquad y(t) = \sin t \qquad 0 < t < \infty$$
$$x(t) = 2t \qquad y(t) = \sin 2t \qquad 0 < t < \infty$$

   What is the relationship between their associated curves?

4. (a) Consider these two sets of parametric equations:

$$x(t) = t \qquad y(t) = \sin t \qquad 0 < t < \infty$$

$$x(t) = \sin t \qquad y(t) = t \qquad 0 < t < \infty$$

What is the difference between their associated curves?

(b) Given any set of equations of the form

$$x(t) = t \qquad y(t) = f(t) \qquad 0 < t < \infty$$

What does the graph of the set of equations

$$y(t) = t \qquad x(t) = f(t) \qquad 0 < t < \infty$$

look like?

5. (a) Use a graphing calculator to check that $f(x) = x^5 - 3x^3 + 5x + 2$ is one-to-one.

(b) Graph its inverse function f^{-1}.

How Many Ways Can You Trace That Curve?

Consider the circle $x^2 + y^2 = 4$. We want to construct parametric curves $x(t) = a_1 \cos a_2 t$, $y(t) = a_3 \sin a_4 t$, with a_1, $a_2 > 0$, which will trace this circle in different ways.

1. What must be the values of a_1 and a_3 so that $(x(t), y(t))$ lies on the circle $x^2 + y^2 = 4$?

2. Describe the motion of the particle if you set $a_2 = a_4 = 1$ and let $0 \le t \le 2\pi$. What is the starting point?

3. What choice of a_2 and a_4 will trace the circle twice in a counterclockwise direction starting at $(1, 0)$? What choice will trace the circle three times in a counterclockwise direction?

4. Describe the motion if you set $a_2 = 1$, $a_4 = -1$ and let $0 \le t \le 2\pi$.

5. What choice of a_2 and a_4 will trace the circle three times in a clockwise direction starting at $(1, 0)$? What choice will trace the circle five times in a clockwise direction?

9 VECTORS IN TWO AND THREE DIMENSIONS

9.1 VECTORS IN TWO DIMENSIONS

▼ Suggested Time and Emphasis

1 class. Essential material.

▼ Points to Stress

1. The difference between a vector and a scalar.

2. Translational invariance of vectors, including the concept of standard position.

3. The geometric interpretation of vector addition and scalar multiplication.

4. The magnitude of a vector, its direction, and the resolution of a vector into its components.

▼ Sample Questions

- **Text Question:** What are the components of the vector from $(3, 3)$ to $(4, 4)$?

  Answer: 1 and 1

- **Drill Question:** What are the magnitude and direction of the vector $3\mathbf{i} + 3\mathbf{j}$?

  Answer: Magnitude $\sqrt{2}$, direction $\frac{\pi}{4}$

▼ In-Class Materials

- Assume $\mathbf{v}_1$ and $\mathbf{v}_2$ are in standard position. Demonstrate that the vector $\mathbf{v}_3 = \mathbf{v}_1 - \mathbf{v}_2$ can be viewed as the vector with initial point $\mathbf{v}_2$ and terminal point $\mathbf{v}_1$. Draw this picture in $\mathbb{R}^2$ and (if you can) in $\mathbb{R}^3$.

- Ask students to find r and s such that $\langle 3, 2 \rangle = r \langle 1, 1 \rangle + s \langle 0, 4 \rangle$. Repeat for $\langle 3, 2 \rangle = r \langle 1, 1 \rangle - s \langle 0, 4 \rangle$. Ask students if there is a vector $\langle x, y \rangle$ such that we cannot find r and s with $\langle x, y \rangle = r \langle 1, 1 \rangle + s \langle 0, 4 \rangle$. Note that this kind of question becomes very important in linear algebra.

- Go over the properties of vectors from both algebraic and geometric perspectives.

▼ Examples

- Geometric and algebraic addition and subtraction:

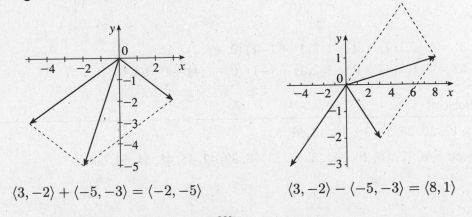

$$\langle 3, -2 \rangle + \langle -5, -3 \rangle = \langle -2, -5 \rangle \qquad \langle 3, -2 \rangle - \langle -5, -3 \rangle = \langle 8, 1 \rangle$$

▼ Group Work 1: Vector or Scalar?

This activity can be done with the whole class simultaneously. Allow some time to work individually, and then have them vote on one question at a time.

Answers:

Quantity	Vector?	Scalar?
Speed		×
Force	×	
Debt		×
Velocity	×	
Acceleration	×	×
Momentum	×	

Quantity	Vector?	Scalar?
Energy		×
Temperature		×
Work	×	
Friction	×	
Current		×

▼ Group Work 2: Where Do They Point?

This group work extends the idea of adding several vectors without coordinates. For Problem 1, consider giving the hint to first try computing $\mathbf{a} + \mathbf{b} + \mathbf{c} + \mathbf{d} + \mathbf{e}$.

Answers:

1. $-2\mathbf{e}$

2. (a) $\left\langle -\frac{1}{2}r, -\frac{\sqrt{3}}{2}r \right\rangle$ **(b)** Since $\mathbf{a} + \mathbf{b} = \langle r, 0 \rangle$, we have $\mathbf{a} + \mathbf{b} + \mathbf{c} + \mathbf{d} = -(\mathbf{a} + \mathbf{d}) = \langle -r, 0 \rangle$.

▼ Group Work 3: Cones in General

This activity will introduce students to the concept of the cone of a set of vectors. You might want to stop after the first question and make sure everyone understands the definition, or give a different example to do all together before setting them loose.

Answers

1.
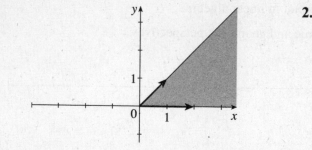

2.
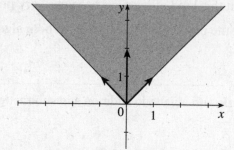

3. Yes. $\langle 0, 7, 3 \rangle = 2\langle 1, 1, 1 \rangle + 2\langle -1, 2, 1 \rangle + (-1)\langle 0, -1, 1 \rangle$

4. Yes. $\langle 0, 7, 3 \rangle = 2\langle 1, 1, 1 \rangle + 2\langle -1, 2, 1 \rangle + (-1)\langle 0, -1, 1 \rangle + 0\langle 0, 1, 0 \rangle$

▼ Homework Problems

Core Exercises: 5, 12, 20, 28, 31, 38, 39, 42, 51, 53

Sample Assignment: 5, 6, 12, 16, 20, 23, 28, 31, 34, 38, 39, 42, 45, 48, 51, 53, 60

GROUP WORK 1, SECTION 9.1

Vector or Scalar?

Some of the following quantities are vectors, and some are scalars. Classify them all by checking the appropriate box, and then come up with two or three with which to stump your classmates, and hopefully your instructor.

Quantity	Vector?	Scalar?
Speed		
Force		
Debt		
Velocity		
Acceleration		
Momentum		
Energy		
Temperature		
Work		
Friction		
Current		

1. Compute $\mathbf{a} + \mathbf{b} + \mathbf{c} + \mathbf{d} - \mathbf{e}$ for the following diagram.

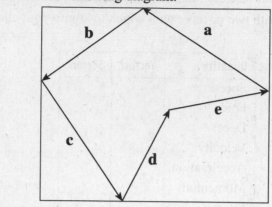

2. (a) Compute the position representation $\overrightarrow{OP}$ for $\mathbf{a} + \mathbf{b}$ in the following diagram. Give the coordinates of the point P.

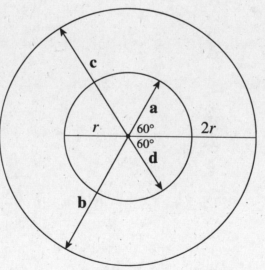

(b) Compute $\mathbf{a} + \mathbf{b} + \mathbf{c} + \mathbf{d}$.

GROUP WORK 3, SECTION 9.1

Cones in General

The **cone** in $\mathbb{R}^n$ generated by a collection of vectors $v_1, v_2, v_3, \ldots, v_k$ is the set of all nonnegative linear combinations of these vectors, drawn in standard position. (A nonnegative linear combination is of the form $\sum_{i=1}^{k} c_i v_i$, where $c_i \geq 0$, that is, a linear combination where all of the coefficients are nonnegative.)

1. Cones in $\mathbb{R}^2$ are easy to identify. Shade in the cone generated by $v_1 = \langle 1, 1 \rangle$ and $v_2 = \langle 2, 0 \rangle$.

2. Shade in the cone generated by $v_1 = \langle -1, 1 \rangle$, $v_2 = \langle 0, 2 \rangle$, and $v_3 = \langle 1, 1 \rangle$.

3. Does the vector $\langle 0, 7, 3 \rangle$ belong to the cone generated by $\langle 1, 1, 1 \rangle$, $\langle -1, 2, 1 \rangle$, and $\langle 0, -1, 1 \rangle$? Why or why not?

4. Does the vector $\langle 0, 7, 3 \rangle$ belong to the cone generated by $\langle 1, 1, 1 \rangle$, $\langle -1, 2, 1 \rangle$, $\langle 0, -1, 1 \rangle$, and $\langle 0, 1, 0 \rangle$? Why or why not?

9.2   THE DOT PRODUCT

▼ Suggested Time and Emphasis

$\frac{1}{2}$–1 class. Essential material.

▼ Points to Stress

1. The dot product and its properties.

2. Definition of orthogonality.

3. Length of a vector.

4. Projections and their applications to computer science.

▼ Sample Questions

- **Text Question:** Compute $\langle 3, 4 \rangle \cdot \langle -1, 2 \rangle$.

  Answer: 5

- **Drill Question:** Consider the following pairs of vectors, all of which have length 1:

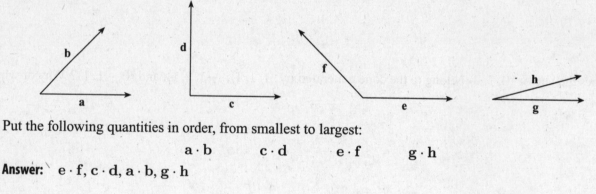

  Put the following quantities in order, from smallest to largest:

  $$\mathbf{a} \cdot \mathbf{b} \qquad \mathbf{c} \cdot \mathbf{d} \qquad \mathbf{e} \cdot \mathbf{f} \qquad \mathbf{g} \cdot \mathbf{h}$$

  Answer: $\mathbf{e} \cdot \mathbf{f}, \mathbf{c} \cdot \mathbf{d}, \mathbf{a} \cdot \mathbf{b}, \mathbf{g} \cdot \mathbf{h}$

▼ In-Class Materials

- Assume that $\mathbf{a} \cdot \mathbf{b} = \mathbf{a} \cdot \mathbf{c}$ and $\mathbf{a} \neq 0$. Pose the question, "Is it necessarily true that $\mathbf{b} = \mathbf{c}$?" When you've convinced them (perhaps by example) that the answer is "no", the next logical question to ask is, "What can we say about $\mathbf{b}$ and $\mathbf{c}$?" It can be shown that $\mathbf{b}$ and $\mathbf{c}$ have the same projection onto $\mathbf{a}$, since $\mathbf{a} \perp (\mathbf{b} - \mathbf{c})$.

- Demonstrate the distributive property in general. Note that while the dot product is commutative and distributive, the associative property makes no sense, as it is not possible to take the dot product of three vectors.

- Demonstrate the proper formation of statements involving dot products. For example, the statement $c (\mathbf{a} \cdot \mathbf{b})$ makes sense, while the statements $\mathbf{d} \cdot (\mathbf{a} \cdot \mathbf{b})$ and $c \cdot \mathbf{a}$ do not.

- This is a nice, direct application of vector projections: It is clear that a weight will slide more quickly down ramp 2 than down ramp 1:

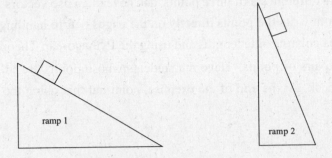

Gravity is the same in both cases, yet there is a definite difference in speed. The reason behind this is interesting. Gravity is doing two things at once: it is letting the weight slide down, and it is also preventing the weight from floating off the ramp and flying into outer space. We can draw a "free body diagram" that shows how the gravity available to let the weight slide down is affected by the angle of the ramp.

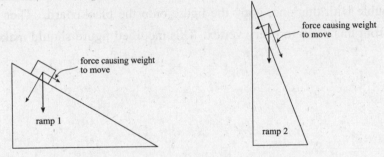

A block slides faster on a steeper slope because the projection of the gravitational force in the direction of the slope is larger. There is more force pushing the block down the slope, and less of a force holding it to the surface of the slope.

▼ Examples

- $\langle 5, 6, 2 \rangle \cdot \langle -3, 1, 0 \rangle = -9$
- Two vectors that are orthogonal: $\mathbf{a} = \langle 5, 6, 2 \rangle$, $\mathbf{b} = \langle 1, -1, \frac{1}{2} \rangle$
- Projections: If $\mathbf{a} = \langle 2, 1, -1 \rangle$ and $\mathbf{b} = \langle 3, 2, 7 \rangle$, then $\text{proj}_{\mathbf{a}} \mathbf{b} = \langle \frac{1}{3}, \frac{1}{6}, -\frac{1}{6} \rangle$, $\text{proj}_{\mathbf{b}} \mathbf{a} = \langle \frac{3}{62}, \frac{1}{31}, \frac{7}{62} \rangle$, and $|\mathbf{a}| = \sqrt{6}$.

▼ Group Work 1: Orthogonal Projections Rule

This worksheet extends what the students know about orthogonal projections to $\mathbb{R}^3$. If they have a strong conceptual knowledge of projections, this should come easily.

Answers:

1. P is a plane through the origin.
2. Answers will vary.
3. $\langle u_1 - c_1 - c_2, u_2 - c_1, u_3 - c_1 \rangle$
4. $-3c_1 - c_2 + u_1 + u_2 + u_3 = 0$, $u_1 - c_1 - c_2 = 0$
5. $c_1 = \frac{1}{2}(u_1 + u_2)$, $c_2 = \frac{1}{2}(2u_1 - u_2 - u_3)$

▼ Group Work 2: The Right Stuff

Give each group of students a different set of three points, and have them use vectors to determine if they form a right triangle. (It is easiest to write the points directly on the pages before handing them out.) They can do this using dot products, by calculating side lengths and using the Pythagorean Theorem, or by calculating the slopes of lines between the pairs of points. Have the students whose points are in $\mathbb{R}^2$ carefully graph their points to provide a visual check. At the end of the exercise, point out that using the dot product is the easier method.

Sample Answers:

$(-2, -1), (-2, 8), (8, -1)$	Right	$(3, 4), (3, 12), (6, 5)$	Not right
$(0, 0), (10, 7), (-14, 20)$	Right	$(2, 1, 2), (3, 3, 1), (2, 2, 4)$	Right
$(-1, -2, -3), (0, 0, -4), (-1, -1, -1)$	Right	$(2, 3, 6), (3, 4, 7), (3, 3, 6)$	Right

▼ Group Work 3: The Regular Hexagon

If the students have trouble with this one, copy the figure onto the blackboard. Then draw a point at its center, and draw lines from this point to every vertex. This modified figure should make the exercise more straightforward.

Answers:

1. $1, 1, 1$
2. $120°$
3. $\cos 60° = \frac{1}{2}$
4. $-\frac{1}{2}$
5. $\left\langle -\frac{1}{2}, 0 \right\rangle, \left\langle -\frac{1}{4}, \frac{\sqrt{3}}{4} \right\rangle$
6. 1

▼ Homework Problems

Core Exercises: 1, 6, 9, 17, 22, 26, 31, 35, 42, 46

Sample Assignment: 1, 6, 9, 12, 14, 17, 19, 22, 26, 28, 31, 33, 35, 38, 42, 44, 46, 49

We know how to orthogonally project one vector onto another. Let's try to extend this procedure in the setting of $\mathbb{R}^3$.

1. Let $v_1 = \langle 1, 1, 1 \rangle$ and $v_2 = \langle 1, 0, 0 \rangle$ be vectors (in standard position) in $\mathbb{R}^3$ and let P denote the set of all linear combinations of v_1 and v_2. Describe what P looks like.

2. With P fixed, we want to orthogonally project a given vector u onto P. That is, we want the orthogonal component of u that belongs to P. Sketch P and orthogonal projections for a couple of different u's. Let's let $\text{proj}_P u$ denote the projection.

3. Now since $\text{proj}_P u$ belongs to P, we can write $\text{proj}_P u = c_1 v_1 + c_2 v_2$ for some constants c_1 and c_2. Our goal is to obtain formulas for c_1 and c_2. Expressing u using coordinates, we write $u = \langle u_1, u_2, u_3 \rangle$. Now express, in coordinate form, the vector $u - \text{proj}_P u$. Make sure to use the equation for $\text{proj}_P u$ and the coordinates of v_1 and v_2 above.

4. From our work in Problem 2, we know that $u - \text{proj}_P u$ is orthogonal to both v_1 and v_2. Combine this fact with your work from Problem 3. to find 2 equations involving the unknowns c_1 and c_2.

5. Finally, solve the above equations to give formulas for c_1 and c_2.

Consider the points (,   ), (,   ), and (,   ). These three points form a triangle. Is this triangle a right triangle? Justify your answer.

Consider the following regular hexagon:

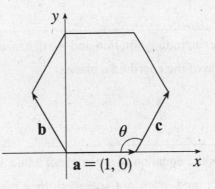

1. Compute $|\mathbf{a}|$, $|\mathbf{b}|$, and $|\mathbf{c}|$.

2. What is the angle θ?

3. What is $\mathbf{a} \cdot \mathbf{c}$?

4. What is $\mathbf{a} \cdot \mathbf{b}$?

5. Compute $\text{proj}_{\mathbf{a}} \mathbf{b}$ and $\text{proj}_{\mathbf{b}} \mathbf{c}$.

6. Compute the x-component of $\mathbf{a} + \mathbf{b} + \mathbf{c}$.

9.3 THREE-DIMENSIONAL COORDINATE GEOMETRY

▼ Suggested Time and Emphasis

$\frac{1}{2}$–1 class. Essential material.

▼ Points to Stress

1. Points in three-dimensional space, including notation and the distance formula.
2. Equations of planes parallel to one of the coordinate planes.
3. The equation of a sphere.

▼ Sample Questions

- **Text Question:** Explain why $x = 3$ is the equation of a plane, not a line, in three-dimensional space.

  Answer: Because the coordinates y and z are not specified, they can take on any value, extending the two-dimensional line $x = 3$ into a three-dimensional plane.

- **Drill Question:** What is the distance between the points $(-1, -1, -1)$ and $(-4, -1, 3)$?

  Answer: $\sqrt{[-1 - (-4)]^2 + [-1 - (-1)]^2 + (-1 - 3)^2} = 5$

▼ In-Class Materials

- If possible, mark off one corner of the lecture room with electrical tape. Determine the coordinates of various objects in the room and/or find the equation of the plane of the chalkboard.

- Explain why the equation $z = \sqrt{R^2 - (x^2 + y^2)}$ represents the hemisphere $z \geq 0$, whereas the equation $x^2 + y^2 + z^2 = R^2$ represents a full sphere, perhaps making a two-dimensional analogy.

- Introduce the equation of a circular cylinder as an extension to $\mathbb{R}^3$ of the equation of the circle $x^2 + y^2 = r^2$. Then describe some cylindrical surfaces such as $y = x^2$, $x^2 - y^2 = 1$ and $z = \sin y$.

- Describe the set of points whose distance from each of $(0, 0, 1)$ and $(0, 0, -1)$ is 1. Then similarly discuss the set of points whose distance from these points is 2, and then 0.5. Have the students explain why the set of all points equidistant in space from two given points is a plane.

▼ Examples

- One sphere in three forms:

  1. The sphere with center $(1, 2, 3)$ and radius 4.
  2. The sphere with equation $(x - 1)^2 + (y - 2)^2 + (z - 3)^2 = 16$.
  3. The sphere with equation $x^2 - 2x + y^2 - 4y + z^2 - 6z - 2 = 0$.

▼ Group Work 1: Working with Surfaces in Three-Dimensional Space

Visualizing and sketching surfaces in three-dimensional space can be difficult for students. It is recommended that the answer key (included following the question sheet) be distributed after the students have had time to work.

▼ Group Work 2: Lines, Lines, Everywhere Lines

The idea is to help students visualize the triangular surface $x + y + z = 1$, $x, y, z \geq 0$. Note that at this stage, the students have not yet learned about the general equations of lines and planes. Part 3 is ambitious, and requires some formal thinking. Depending on the mathematical maturity of your class, you may want to either give a hint to the students, or perhaps do that part as a class. Parts 3 and 4 are printed on a separate page, so you can decide what to do based upon how the students are doing on the first two parts.

Answers:

1. In the xy-plane, we have $z = 0$. If $x + y = 1$ then
   $x + y + 0 = 1$.

2. As in Problem 1, *mutatis mutandis*.

3. Adding the equations $x_1 + y_1 + z_1 = 1$ and
   $x_2 + y_2 + z_2 = 1$, we have
   $(x_1 + x_2) + (y_1 + y_2) + (z_1 + z_2) = 2$, so
   $\dfrac{(x_1 + x_2)}{2} + \dfrac{(y_1 + y_2)}{2} + \dfrac{(z_1 + z_2)}{2} = 1$, showing that
   the midpoint is in S.

4.

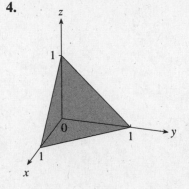

▼ Group Work 3: Fun with Visualization

Ask the students to turn off their calculators and put down their pencils. Start by asking them to picture a plane in $\mathbb{R}^3$. Ask them how many regions in space are formed by a plane. (Answer: Two regions)

Then ask them how many regions are formed by *two* planes. Notice that there are two possible answers here. If the planes are parallel, they divide space into three regions, like a layer cake. If they cross, then four regions are formed. Put the students into groups and hand out the activity. Give them time to argue with each other, and perhaps foster inter-group discussion as well. After the activity is over, discuss the analogy between dividing space by planes and dividing a plane by lines. This activity can be shortened by cutting out Problems 4 and 5.

Answers:

1. 2   **2.** 3 or 4   **3.** 8   **4.** 4, 6, 7, or 8   **5.** 15

▼ Homework Problems

Core Exercises: 1, 4, 8, 12, 15, 21, 23

Sample Assignment: 1, 4, 5, 8, 9, 12, 15, 18, 20, 21, 22, 23

GROUP WORK 1, SECTION 9.3

Working with Surfaces in Three-Dimensional Space

Draw (or describe in words) the surfaces described by the following five equations. The best way to do this exercise is to think first about the surfaces, before you calculate anything.

1. $x^2 + y^2 = 3^2$

2. $y^2 + z^2 = 1$

3. $z = y^2$

4. $xy = 1$

5. $x^2 + y^2 = z$

Working with Surfaces in Three-Dimensional Space (Solutions)

1. $x^2 + y^2 = 3^2$

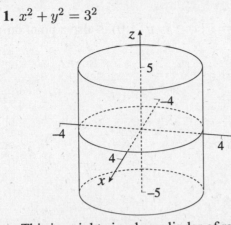

This is a right circular cylinder of radius 3 with axis the z-axis.

2. $y^2 + z^2 = 1$

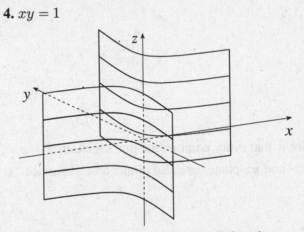

This is a right circular cylinder of radius 1 with axis the x-axis.

3. $z = y^2$

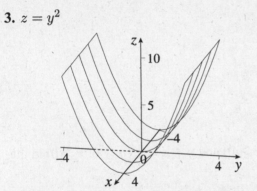

This is a parabolic cylinder parallel to the x-axis.

4. $xy = 1$

This is a hyperbolic cylinder parallel to the z-axis.

5. $x^2 + y^2 = z$

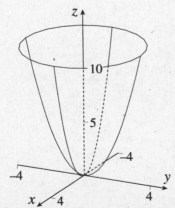

This is a paraboloid opening upward.

Lines, Lines, Everywhere Lines

Consider the surface S: $x + y + z = 1$, $x \geq 0$, $y \geq 0$, $z \geq 0$.

1. Show that every point on the line segment in the xy-plane, $x + y = 1$ ($x \geq 0$, $y \geq 0$) is also a point on this surface.

2. Show that every point on the line segments $x + z = 1$ ($x \geq 0$, $z \geq 0$) and $y + z = 1$ ($y \geq 0$, $z \geq 0$) in the xz- and yz-planes are also points on this surface.

3. Given that two points $P_1(x_1, y_1, z_1)$ and $P_2(x_2, y_2, z_2)$ are on the surface S, show that their midpoint $P\left(\dfrac{x_1 + x_2}{2}, \dfrac{y_1 + y_2}{2}, \dfrac{z_1 + z_2}{2}\right)$ must also be a point in S.

4. Draw a picture of S.

1. Picture a plane in $\mathbb{R}^3$. This plane divides space into how many regions?

2. How many regions can be formed by two planes?

3. What is the maximum number of regions that can be formed by three planes?

4. What are the other possible numbers of regions that can be formed by three planes?

5. What is the maximum number of regions that can be formed by four planes?

9.4   VECTORS IN THREE DIMENSIONS

▼ Suggested Time and Emphasis

$\frac{1}{2}$–1 class. Essential material.

▼ Points to Stress

1. The extension of vectors into three dimensions, including magnitude, vector addition, scalar multiplication, and the dot product.
2. The direction cosines of a vector in space.

▼ Sample Questions

- **Text Question:** If $\mathbf{a} = \langle a_1, a_2, a_3 \rangle$ has $a_2 > 0$ and $a_3 > 0$, then is the z-component of $-3\mathbf{a}$ positive or negative?

  Answer: Negative

- **Drill Question:** Compute the magnitude of $\langle 4, 13, 16 \rangle$.

  Answer: $\sqrt{4^2 + 13^2 + 16^2} = 21$

▼ In-Class Materials

- Picture two students standing on opposite sides of a giant cube, eight feet on a side, pushing towards the center. Have the students describe in what direction the cube will probably move. (Toward one of the two students, or not at all if the students have the same strength.) Now have them picture the students standing on adjacent sides, "kitty corner". Now have them describe the resultant motion, and try to get them to justify their answers. Lead into how vectors give us a natural way of describing the situation, and predicting the outcome.

- Show that it is tough to determine by inspection whether a three-dimensional triangle is a right triangle, but that three-dimensional vectors make it simple. For example, consider the triangle with vertices $(2, 1, 2)$, $(3, 3, 1)$, and $(2, 2, 4)$. Taking dot products of pairs of vectors between vertices, we find that one of these dot products is zero.

- Point out that although it is not easy to picture four-dimensional space, it is simple to generalize all our three-dimensional formulas and results. Write the four-dimensional vectors $\mathbf{u} = \langle 1, 2, -2, 6 \rangle$ and $\mathbf{v} = \langle 2, 1, 3, 0 \rangle$ on the board and have students figure out that the dot product is -2 without formally defining a four-dimensional dot product. Similarly, we can determine the magnitudes of four-dimensional vectors, their sums, differences, and scalar multiples.

- Find unit vectors in the directions of $\langle 8, 0, 0 \rangle$, $\langle 5, 5, 0 \rangle$ and $\langle 1, 2, 3 \rangle$, and explain what is happening geometrically. Then find a unit vector in the direction opposite that of $\langle -1, 1, 1 \rangle$.

▼ Examples

- Two perpendicular three-dimensional vectors: $\langle -2, 5, 1 \rangle$ and $\langle 5, 4, -10 \rangle$.

▼ Group Work: A Rectangular Solid

This activity foreshadows the process of resolving vectors into components and gives the students practice in working with vectors in three dimensions.

Answer: $\mathbf{a} = \langle -3, 4, 5 \rangle$, $\mathbf{b} = \langle 0, -4, 5 \rangle$, $\mathbf{c} = \langle -3, -4, 5 \rangle$

▼ Homework Problems

Core Exercises: 4, 7, 12, 13, 16, 26, 28, 29, 34, 42

Sample Assignment: 4, 5, 7, 9, 12, 13, 16, 17, 20, 24, 26, 28, 29, 34, 36, 39, 42, 43

Consider the rectangular solid with one corner at $(0, 0, 0)$ and another at $(3, 4, 5)$, as shown below.

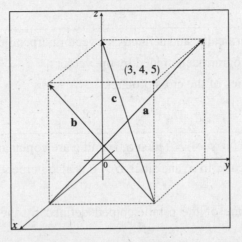

Find the component representations of each of the vectors labeled **a**, **b**, and **c**.

9.5 THE CROSS PRODUCT

▼ Suggested Time and Emphasis

1 class. Essential material.

▼ Points to Stress

1. The cross product defined algebraically, and defined as a vector perpendicular to two given vectors, whose length is the area of the parallelogram determined by the vectors

2. The right-hand rule and properties of the cross product.

▼ Sample Questions

- **Text Question:** Why is it that if $\mathbf{a} \cdot (\mathbf{b} \times \mathbf{c}) = 0$ then $\mathbf{a}$, $\mathbf{b}$ and $\mathbf{c}$ are coplanar?

  Answer: $\mathbf{b} \times \mathbf{c}$ must be perpendicular to $\mathbf{a}$, and since $\mathbf{b} \times \mathbf{c}$ is also perpendicular to $\mathbf{b}$ and $\mathbf{c}$, we see that $\mathbf{a}$, $\mathbf{b}$, and $\mathbf{c}$ are coplanar.

- **Drill Question:** What is the volume of the parallelepiped defined by the vectors $\langle 1, 1, 1 \rangle$, $\langle 0, 1, 1 \rangle$, and $\langle 1, 2, 0 \rangle$?

  Answer: 2

▼ In-Class Materials

- Pose the problem of finding a vector perpendicular to two given vectors (without considering the length of the resultant vector). Show that there is an obvious solution for $\langle 1, 0, 0 \rangle$ and $\langle 0, 1, 0 \rangle$. Then look at the two vectors $\langle 1, 0, 1 \rangle$ and $\langle 0, 1, 1 \rangle$. Repeat for $\langle -3, 1, -7 \rangle$ and $\langle 0, -5, -5 \rangle$. Point out that in this case an alternate algebraic solution using dot products gives $-3x + y - 7z = -5y - 5z$, $y = -z$, $x = -\frac{8}{3}z$, and so $\mathbf{c} = \langle -\frac{8}{3}, -1, 1 \rangle$ works. Note that $\mathbf{c}$ is a scalar multiple of $\mathbf{a} \times \mathbf{b} = \langle -40, -15, -15 \rangle$.

- Explain the geometry involved in computing the volume of a parallelepiped spanned by vectors $\mathbf{a}$, $\mathbf{b}$, and $\mathbf{c}$:

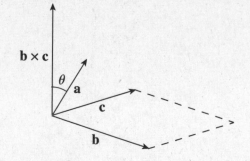

$$V = (\text{area of the base}) \times (\text{height}) = |\mathbf{b} \times \mathbf{c}| \, |\text{proj}_{\mathbf{b} \times \mathbf{c}} \, \mathbf{a}|$$
$$= |\mathbf{b} \times \mathbf{c}| \, |\mathbf{a}| \, |\cos \theta| = \mathbf{a} \cdot (\mathbf{b} \times \mathbf{c})$$

Conclude that $\mathbf{a}$, $\mathbf{b}$, and $\mathbf{c}$ are coplanar if and only if the triple product $\mathbf{a} \cdot (\mathbf{b} \times \mathbf{c}) = 0$.

- Note that the correct pronunciation of the solid discussed above is parallelEPiped, a shortening of the original *parallelepipedon*, from the Greek words *para* (beside), *allele* (other), *epi* (upon), and *pedon* (ground). This reflects the fact that the solid always has a face parallel to the one on the ground.

- A common mistake made by right-handed students can be avoided if they are reminded to *put down their pencil* before using the right hand rule!

- Point out that while $\mathbf{a} \times \mathbf{b}$ and $\mathbf{b} \times \mathbf{a}$ have the same length, $\mathbf{b} \times \mathbf{a}$ points in the opposite direction to that of $\mathbf{a} \times \mathbf{b}$, by the right-hand rule. Thus, $\mathbf{b} \times \mathbf{a} = -(\mathbf{a} \times \mathbf{b})$.

▼ Examples

- A nonzero cross product: $\langle 4, 5, 2 \rangle \times \langle 1, 3, 6 \rangle = \langle 24, -22, 7 \rangle$
- A zero cross product: $\langle 1, -2, 5 \rangle \times \langle -3, 6, -15 \rangle = \langle 0, 0, 0 \rangle$

▼ Group Work 1: Messing with the Cross Product

Four different problems are given for the group work. Give each group one problem to solve. If a group finishes early, give them another one to work out. After every group has finished their original problem, give them a few minutes to practice, and then have them come up and state their problem and demonstrate their solution.

Answers:

1. $\mathbf{c} \perp \mathbf{a}$ because $\mathbf{c}$ is the cross product of $\mathbf{a}$ and another vector. $\mathbf{c}$ is not perpendicular to $\mathbf{b}$. For example take $\mathbf{a} = \langle 1, 0, 0 \rangle$ and $\mathbf{b} = \langle 0, 1, 0 \rangle$.

2. Any vector of the form $\langle 0, t, 1 \rangle$ works.

3. The collection is a straight line; all vectors have the form $\left\langle \dfrac{4+k}{3}, \dfrac{2k-1}{3}, k \right\rangle$. (Other forms of this answer are acceptable.)

4. $\mathbf{a}$ is in the same plane as $\mathbf{a} - \mathbf{b}$ and in the same plane as $\mathbf{a} + \mathbf{b}$. Therefore, it is perpendicular to their cross product.

▼ Group Work 2: A Matter of Shading

This activity gives a nice application of cross products. Students will practice taking a wordy description of a problem, and converting it to some straightforward mathematics.

Answers:

Notice that, as suggested by the given illustration, the angles must always be between $90°$ and $180°$, so the normals must be chosen accordingly.

1. 2.265 radians or $129.76°$ 2. 2.678 radians or $154.43°$ 3. The second one

▼ Homework Problems

Core Exercises: 3, 6, 10, 14, 15, 23, 26, 31, 35

Sample Assignment: 3, 6, 7, 10, 12, 14, 15, 19, 23, 24, 26, 28, 31, 33, 35

GROUP WORK 1, SECTION 9.5

Messing with the Cross Product

1. Consider the vector $c = a \times (a \times b)$. Is $c \perp a$? Is $c \perp b$? Either prove or give a counterexample.

2. Suppose that $j \times a = i$. Give two possible solutions for a, and discuss other possible solutions.

3. Given $a = \langle 1, 2, 3 \rangle$ and $b = \langle 1, -1, -1 \rangle$, sketch the collection of all position vectors c satisfying $a \times b = a \times c$.

4. Show that a is perpendicular to $(a - b) \times (a + b)$.

A Matter of Shading

One way to accurately render three-dimensional objects on a computer screen involves using the dot and cross products. In order to determine how to shade a piece of a surface we need to determine the angle at which rays from the light source hit the surface. To determine this angle, we compute the dot product of the light vector with the vector perpendicular to the surface at the particular point, called the normal vector.

If the light ray hits the surface straight on, that is, has an angle of $180°$ with the normal, then this piece of the surface will appear bright. On the other hand, if the light comes in on an angle, this piece of the surface will not appear as bright.

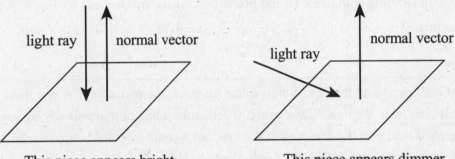

This piece appears bright.   This piece appears dimmer.

1. Suppose the light source is placed directly above the xy-plane, so that the light rays come in parallel to the vector $\langle 0, 0, -1 \rangle$. At what angle (to the normal) do the light rays hit a triangle bounded by the points $(3, 2, 4)$, $(2, 5, 3)$, and $(1, 2, 6)$?

   Note that your answer will be an obtuse angle (greater than $90°$) because the vertex of the angle is formed by the tails of the two vectors.

2. Repeat Problem 1, this time using the region bounded by $(3, 5, 2)$, $(3, 3, 1)$, and $(1, 3, 1)$.

3. Suppose we are standing above the light source looking down on the xy-plane. Which of these two regions will appear brighter to us?

9.6 EQUATIONS OF LINES AND PLANES

▼ Suggested Time and Emphasis

1 class. Essential material.

▼ Points to Stress

1. Two ways to describe a line:
   - Vector equations (starting with point P_0 on the line and direction vector $\mathbf{d}$): $\mathbf{r} = \mathbf{r}_0 + t\mathbf{d}$.
   - Parametric equations: $x = x_0 + at$, $y = y_0 + bt$, $z = z_0 + ct$

2. Two ways to describe a plane:
   - Vector equation (starting with point P_0 and normal vector $\mathbf{n}$): $\mathbf{n} \cdot (\mathbf{r} - \mathbf{r}_0) = 0$.
   - Scalar equation: $a(x - x_0) + b(y - y_0) + c(z - z_0) = 0$ or $ax + by + cz + d = 0$.

▼ Sample Questions

- **Text Question:** When specifying the equation of a line in space, the text says that you need a point on the line and a vector parallel to the line. Why can't you determine a line in space simply by using one vector?
  Answer: One vector would give the direction of the line, but it could be placed anywhere in space. It would be analogous to trying to specify a line in $\mathbb{R}^2$ using only a slope.

- **Drill Question:** Find parametric equations of the line going through the points $(1, 2, 1)$ and $(-1, 3, 5)$.
  One Possible Answer: $x = 1 - 2t$, $y = 2 + t$, $z = 1 + 4t$

- **Drill Question:** A plane has normal vector $\mathbf{n} = \langle 1, 1, 0 \rangle$ and passes through the point $P(3, 1, 9)$. Find an equation for the plane.
  One Possible Answer: $x + y = 4$. Note that this is a plane perpendicular to the xy-plane, because z can be anything.

▼ In-Class Materials

- An overall theme for this section could be that a line is determined by a point and a direction, and a plane is determined by a point and a normal vector, or a point and two directions.

- Review parametric representation of lines in $\mathbb{R}^2$, and then generalize to $\mathbb{R}^3$. Recall that in two dimensions, a line can be determined by a point and a slope. Ask for the slope of the line between the points $(0, 0)$ and $(1, 2)$. Start with the line $y = mx + b$ and write it parametrically as $x = t, y = mt + b$. Then write the vector equation with $\mathbf{r}_0 = \langle 0, b \rangle$ and $\mathbf{d} = \langle 1, m \rangle$, a vector whose direction has slope m. Next ask for the slope of the line between $(0, 0, 0)$ and $(1, 2, 3)$. Note that there is no answer — we lose the idea of "slope" when going from two to three dimensions. So a vector is our only way of specifying direction in three dimensions.

- Discuss how to find the equation of a plane containing three non-collinear points P, Q, and R. We form the normal vector $\mathbf{n} = \mathbf{a} \times \mathbf{b}$, where $\mathbf{a} = \overrightarrow{PQ}$ and $\mathbf{b} = \overrightarrow{PR}$, and use the vector equation.

- Review lines in two dimensions. For example, ask the students to draw the line passing through $(1, 2)$ in the direction of $\mathbf{i} - 2\mathbf{j}$ and then write parametric equations for this line. Stress that these equations are not unique.

▼ Examples

- A plane that is relatively easy to sketch: $10x + 5y + 5z = 10$. (The intercepts are $x = 1$, $y = 2$, and $z = 2$.)

▼ Group Work 1: The Match Game

This is a pandemonium-inducing game. Each group is given three index cards. One has two points on a straight line, the second has parametric equations for a different line, and the last has a vector equation for a third line. The groups now are allowed to trade index cards with other groups. The first group to possess three descriptions for the same line wins a prize.

For the convenience of the teacher, each row below contains a winning combination. Make sure that each team starts with descriptions from different rows.

Category A	Category B	Category C
The line between $(0, 0, 1)$ and $(1, 2, 1)$	$\mathbf{r} = \langle 2, 4, 1 \rangle + t \langle 1, 2, 0 \rangle$	$x = 2t$ $y = 4t$ $z = 1$
The line between $(0, -3, 3)$ and $(3, 3, 0)$	$\mathbf{r} = \langle 1, -1, 2 \rangle + t \langle 1, 2, -1 \rangle$	$x = 2 + t$ $y = 1 + 2t$ $z = 1 - t$
The line between $(1, 3, 2)$ and $(1, -1, 6)$	$\mathbf{r} = \langle 1, 2, 3 \rangle + t \langle 0, -1, 1 \rangle$	$x = 1$ $y = -t$ $z = 5 + t$
The line between $(0, 0, 4)$ and $(12, 8, 8)$	$\mathbf{r} = \langle 9, 6, 7 \rangle + t \langle -3, -2, -1 \rangle$	$x = 6 - 6t$ $y = 4 - 4t$ $z = 6 - 2t$
The line between $(5, 0, 7)$ and $(-2, -7, 0)$	$\mathbf{r} = \langle 3, -2, 5 \rangle + t \langle -1, -1, -1 \rangle$	$x = 2 - 2t$ $y = -3 - 2t$ $z = 4 - 2t$
The line between $(-3, 3, -9)$ and $(3, -3, 9)$	$\mathbf{r} = \langle 0, 0, 0 \rangle + t \langle -1, 1, -3 \rangle$	$x = -1 + t$ $y = 1 - t$ $z = -3 + 3t$
The line between $(-4, 2, 1)$ and $(-11, 1, -1)$	$\mathbf{r} = \langle 3, 3, 3 \rangle + t \langle 7, 1, 2 \rangle$	$x = 10 + 7t$ $y = 4 + t$ $z = 5 + 2t$

▼ Group Work 2: Planes from Points

Give each group two sets of three points each, one noncollinear set and one collinear set. Ask the students to give an equation of the unique plane containing the points. For the second set of points this is a trick question, since collinear points do not determine a plane. Sample sets of points are given below.

$(0, 0, 0)$	$(-1, 4, 2)$	$(0, -5, 5)$	$(0, 0, 0)$	$(-1, 4, 2)$	$(0, -5, 5)$
$(1, 2, 3)$	$(3, 1, 1)$	$(0, 1, 1)$	$(1, 2, 3)$	$(3, 1, 1)$	$(0, 1, 1)$
$(2, 5, 9)$	$(7, 2, 0)$	$(0, 3, 4)$	$\left(\frac{3}{2}, 3, \frac{9}{2}\right)$	$(7, -2, 0)$	$(0, 3, 7)$

▼ Group Work 3: The Spanning Set

The purpose of this activity is to give the students a sense of how two non-parallel vectors in two dimensions span the entire xy-plane.

Start by giving each student or group of students a sheet of regular graph paper and a transparent grid of parallelograms formed by two vectors **u** and **v**.

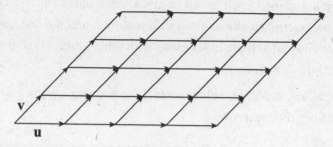

Next give each student a point (x, y) in the plane. By placing the grid over the graph paper they should estimate values of r and s such that $\langle x, y \rangle = r\mathbf{u} + s\mathbf{v}$. Repeat for several other points (including some for which one or both of r and s will be negative) until the students have convinced themselves that every point in the plane can be expressed in this manner.

Now repeat the activity with different vectors **u** and **v**, perhaps using the same points as before.

As a wrap-up, give the students specific vectors **u** and **v**, such as $\mathbf{u} = \langle 3, 1 \rangle$ and $\mathbf{v} = \langle -1, -2 \rangle$, and have them determine values of r and s for several points. See if they can find general formulas for r and s in terms of the point (x, y). What goes wrong algebraically if **u** and **v** are parallel?

▼ Homework Problems

Core Exercises: 5, 6, 11, 16, 18, 21, 24, 32

Sample Assignment: 5, 6, 8, 11, 14, 16, 18, 20, 21, 24, 25, 27, 32, 34, 36

The Match Game

Your teacher has just handed you three index cards, each with an equation of a different line. Your task is, by clever trading with other groups, to wind up with three different descriptions of the *same line*. The winning team gets a boffo prize, so go for it!

GROUP WORK 2, SECTION 9.6

Planes from Points

1. Consider the following set of three points:

                    POINT 1: _____

                    POINT 2: _____

                    POINT 3: _____

Find an equation of the unique plane containing these points.

2. Repeat Part 1 using these points:

                    POINT 1: _____

                    POINT 2: _____

                    POINT 3: _____

10 SYSTEMS OF EQUATIONS AND INEQUALITIES

10.1 SYSTEMS OF LINEAR EQUATIONS IN TWO VARIABLES

▼ Suggested Time and Emphasis

$1\frac{1}{2}$–2 classes. Essential material.

▼ Point to Stress

Solving systems of equations with two variables, using the methods of substitution, elimination, and graphing.

▼ Sample Questions

- **Text Question:** The textbook says that given the system

$$3x + 2y = 14$$
$$x - 2y = 2$$

we can add the equations to eliminate y, obtaining $4x = 16$, and thus determining $x = 4$ and $y = 1$. Could this system be solved using the substitution method? If not, why not? If so, would the answers be the same?

Answer: It could, and the answers would be the same.

- **Drill Question:** Solve this system of equations

$$x + y = 2$$
$$4x - 2y = -1$$

Answer: $x = \frac{1}{2}, y = \frac{3}{2}$

▼ In-Class Materials

- This may be a good time to point out that a linear system of equations can have zero, one, or infinitely many solutions. Examples:

$$\begin{array}{ccc} 2x + 7y = 10 & 2x + y = 3 & x + 5y = 2 \\ 20x + 70y = 50 & -2x + 3y = 3 & 2x + 10y = 4 \end{array}$$

When demonstrating these systems, it is important to show the graphical solution as well as an analytic solution. Point out that in Section 10.8 we will see that *non*linear systems can have *any number* of solutions—not just zero, one, or infinitely many.

▼ Examples

- A linear system with integer solutions:

$$x - 2y = 11$$
$$2x + y = 2$$

Answer: $x = 3, y = -4$

- A straightforward word problem:

  Retaining bricks for gardens are usually either 6 inches or 12 inches long. A 6-inch brick costs eighty cents and a 12-inch brick costs $1.20. Assume we have a garden with an 8-foot perimeter and we spend $10.80. How many bricks of each type did we buy?

  Answer: 6 small bricks, and 5 large ones

▼ Group Work: The Entertainer

This is a straightforward word problem. Notice that the question asks for the value of only one of the variables. This is to give the students practice in reading a question carefully, and answering the specific question that was asked.

Answer:

The entertainer has given 62 three-hour shows.

▼ Homework Problems

Core Exercises: 3, 7, 10, 18, 22, 31, 40, 54, 58, 69

Sample Assignment: 3, 7, 10, 13, 18, 20, 22, 26, 31, 32, 40, 47, 54, 56, 58, 61, 69, 74

An entertainer performs at weddings. He can do a two-hour show or a three-hour show. He has performed at 100 weddings for a total of 262 hours. How many three-hour shows has he given?

10.2 SYSTEMS OF LINEAR EQUATIONS IN SEVERAL VARIABLES

▼ Suggested Time and Emphasis

1 class. Essential material.

▼ Points to Stress

1. Solving systems of linear equations using Gaussian elimination.
2. Using linear systems to solve applied problems.

▼ Sample Questions

- **Text Question:** Consider this system of three equations:

$$x - 2y + 3z = 1$$
$$x + 2y - z = 13$$
$$3x + 2y - 5z = 3$$

Is the following system equivalent to the first one? Why or why not?

$$x - 2y + 3z = 1$$
$$100x + 200y - 100z = 1300$$
$$3x + 2y - 5z = 3$$

Answer: It is. The second equation was simply multiplied by a nonzero constant.

- **Drill Question:** Solve this system using Gaussian elimination:

$$x - 2y + z = 1$$
$$-x + y - z = 4$$
$$-x + 2y - 4z = 8$$

Answer: $x = -6$, $y = -5$, $z = -3$

▼ In-Class Materials

- If students have learned to use their calculators to solve linear systems, they may not realize the calculator's limitations. Have them attempt to solve a 5×5 system using their calculators, and record the length of time it takes. Then have them attempt a 10×10 system. It turns out that the length of time required to solve an arbitrary linear system grows quickly with the number of variables involved. When doing a system by hand, it is possible to take advantage of properties of the particular system in question. For example, show them this system:

$$
\begin{aligned}
-v \quad\quad\quad - 2y + z &= 1 \\
v \quad\quad\quad + 2y \quad\quad &= 3 \\
v + w - x + 2y \quad\quad &= 2 \\
-v \quad\quad + x - 2y \quad\quad &= 7 \\
v + w + x + y + z &= 26
\end{aligned}
$$

One can go through the traditional algorithm (or have a calculator do it), and it will take some time. (The time it takes to enter it into a calculator counts!) But, by looking at the individual equations, one can get w, x and z instantly (add equations 1 and 2, 2 and 4, and 3 and 4) and then v and y come easily as well.

- One can discuss the geometry of systems of three variables as an extension of the geometry of two variables, replacing lines with planes. Ask the class how they could think of a four-variable system. This is not a trivial question. We are looking at the intersection of three hyperplanes in four dimensional space. Even though you may not get a satisfactory answer (but then again, you may) there is value in trying to come up with visual interpretations for complex, abstract mathematical concepts.

- Have the students go over the applied problems from their homework. Ask them to try to come up with similar problems involving three or four variables. For example, Exercise 10.1.72 can be expanded this way:

> A woman keeps fit by bicycling, running, and swimming every day. On Monday she spends $\frac{1}{2}$ hour at each activity, covering a total of 14.25 mi. On Tuesday she runs for 12 minutes, cycles for 45 minutes, and swims for 30 minutes, covering a total of 15.45 miles. On Wednesday she runs for 30 minutes, cycles for 10 minutes, and swims for 30 minutes, covering a total of 9.25 miles. Assuming her running and cycling speeds don't change from day to day, find these speeds.

Make sure to point out that, for the problem to be solvable, the students now need three pieces of information instead of two (that is, if there is a Monday and a Tuesday in the problem, we now need a Wednesday). Also, they need to make sure that their problem has a solution. In two dimensions, it is easy to get a consistent system, using random numbers. In three dimensions, it is a bit tougher.

- Foreshadow Section 10.9 by reading through a few of the modeling problems in the assignments for this and the previous section. Notice that while some of them model situations where equality is appropriate (Exercise 41 in this section, dealing with animal nutrition, for example), some of them use "exactly" where most people would use "at least". (For example Exercise 60 in this section, in which an investor wants a total annual return of $6700—and not a penny more!) Try to get the students to suggest that inequalities are often more appropriate in applied problems.

▼ Examples

- A consistent 3×3 system:

$$3x + 2y + z = 4$$
$$x - y - z = 1$$
$$2x - 4y - z = -1$$

Answer: $x = 1, y = 1, z = -1$

- An inconsistent 3×3 system:

$$x - y + z = 3$$
$$2x - y + 2z = 4$$
$$3x - 2y + 3z = 8$$

- A dependent 3×3 system:

$$x + 5y - z = 4$$
$$2x + 3y + 4z = 0$$
$$3x + 8y + 3z = 4$$

Answer: $x = -\frac{23}{7}t - \frac{12}{7}, y = \frac{6}{7}t + \frac{8}{7}, z = t$

▼ Group Work 1: Curve Fitting

This activity can be extended, having students write systems that fit points to a variety of curves.

Answers:

1. $k = \ln \frac{23}{20} \approx 0.1398, A = \frac{800,000}{12,167} \approx 65.752$

2.

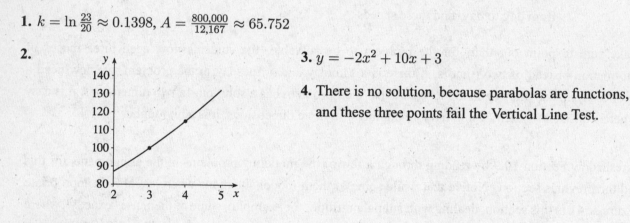

3. $y = -2x^2 + 10x + 3$

4. There is no solution, because parabolas are functions, and these three points fail the Vertical Line Test.

▼ Group Work 2: Earthquake

Although this problem seems to have two pieces of data, it actually winds up requiring students to solve three equations in three unknowns. Given the unfamiliar nature of this problem, some groups may be tempted to give up too soon. Offer words of encouragement, but try to delay giving actual hints until the class has had time to discuss the problem and try to figure out a strategy.

If you need to give a hint, tell the class that the three unknowns here are t_1, the time it took the first wave to arrive, t_2, the time it took the second wave to arrive, and s, the distance from Otisville to the epicenter.

Answer:

$$6t_1 = s$$
$$3t_2 = s$$
$$t_2 - t_1 = 4$$

So $s = 24$ km.

▼ Group Work 3: Find the Triangles

This is a exercise involves solving a nonlinear 3×3 system. Students may have the wrong idea that all systems of three equations and three unknowns are linear. This problem will disabuse them of that notion, while still being tractable.

Answers: 1. $3, 4, 5$ **2.** $4, 7, \sqrt{65}$

▼ Homework Problems

Core Exercises: 4, 9, 14, 17, 22, 34, 35, 38, 44

Sample Assignment: 4, 6, 9, 12, 14, 15, 17, 22, 28, 34, 35, 36, 38, 40, 44, 45

Curve Fitting

In science, we often know the general shape of a curve, and then find the curve by making measurements to find data points and fitting them to the curve. For example, we know that if a quantity decays exponentially (like the number of C_{14} atoms in a sample or the rate of CD sales from a one-hit wonder) its graph can be described as $y = Ae^{kt}$, where t is a variable representing time, and A and k are constants.

1. Assume that when $t = 3$, $y = 100$ and when $t = 4$, $y = 115$. Find A and k.

2. Here is another way to ask the previous question: Assume that a graph is of the form $y = Ae^{kt}$. Find A and k so that $(3, 100)$ and $(4, 115)$ are on the graph. Go ahead and graph your answer to Problem 1, and make sure that the points $(3, 100)$ and $(4, 115)$ do indeed lie on the graph.

3. Now let's assume that we know a particular graph is a parabola. (For example, if an object is thrown upward on the surface of a planet, the graph of its height versus time will be very close to a parabola). We know its equation is of the form $y = ax^2 + bx + c$. Find the equation of the parabola that goes through the points $(-1, -9)$, $(1, 11)$, and $(2, 15)$.

4. Now find the equation of the parabola that goes through the points $(-1, 9)$, $(1, 11)$, and $(1, 13)$. Explain your results.

GROUP WORK 2, SECTION 10.2

Earthquake

If you have ever been in an earthquake, you already know what an aftershock is. An earthquake causes two types of waves through the earth to be created, a primary wave and a secondary wave. (Actually, there are more than two, but these are the main types.) The primary wave travels faster than the secondary wave does. So if you are, say, thirty miles from the epicenter of an earthquake, you would first feel the primary wave shake you up, and then, a short time later, you would feel another shaking as the second wave hits. This second shake-up is called an aftershock.

Assume that, in the western United States, a primary wave travels at 6 km/s and a secondary wave travels at 3 km/s. You live in the town of Otisville, and you are awakened by a jolt. Earthquake! Four seconds later you feel an aftershock. How far are you from the epicenter of the quake?

321

1. The area of a right triangle is 6 square inches and its perimeter is 12 inches. What are the side lengths of the triangle?

2. The area of a right triangle is 14 square inches, and its perimeter is $11 + \sqrt{65}$ inches. What are the side lengths of the triangle?

10.3 MATRICES AND SYSTEMS OF LINEAR EQUATIONS

▼ Suggested Time and Emphasis

2 classes. Recommended material.

▼ Points to Stress

1. Definitions: Matrix, dimension, row, column, row-echelon form, reduced row-echelon form

2. Finding the augmented matrix of a linear system, and manipulating it using row operations.

3. Gaussian and Gauss-Jordan elimination, including inconsistent and dependent systems.

▼ Sample Questions

- **Text Question:** Which of the following matrices are in row-echelon form? Which are in reduced row echelon form?

$$\text{(a)} \begin{bmatrix} 1 & 4 & 0 & 0 & 0 \\ 0 & 0 & 1 & 0 & -5 \\ 0 & 0 & 0 & 1 & \pi \\ 0 & 0 & 0 & 0 & 0 \end{bmatrix} \quad \text{(b)} \begin{bmatrix} 1 & 0 & 0 & 0 & 0 \\ 0 & 0 & 1 & 0 & 0 \\ 0 & 1 & 0 & 1 & 0 \\ 0 & 1 & 0 & 0 & 1 \end{bmatrix} \quad \text{(c)} \begin{bmatrix} 1 & 4 & 3 & 0 & 5 \\ 0 & 0 & 1 & 2 & -5 \\ 0 & 0 & 0 & 1 & \pi \\ 0 & 0 & 0 & 0 & 0 \end{bmatrix}$$

Answer: (a) and (c) are in row-echelon form, (a) is in reduced row-echelon form.

- **Drill Question:** Consider this system of equations:

$$x + y = -1$$
$$2x - 3y = 8$$

(a) Find the augmented matrix of this system.

(b) Put the matrix in reduced row-echelon form.

Answers: $\begin{bmatrix} 1 & 1 & -1 \\ 2 & -3 & 8 \end{bmatrix}$, $\begin{bmatrix} 1 & 0 & 1 \\ 0 & 1 & -2 \end{bmatrix}$

▼ In-Class Materials

- Point out that as noted in the text, the row-echelon form of a given matrix is not unique, but the reduced row-echelon form is unique. In fact, it can be shown that if two matrices have the same reduced row-echelon form, you can transform one into the other via elementary row operations.

- It is possible to introduce the concept of homogeneous systems as a way of getting the students to think about dependent and inconsistent systems. Define a homogenous system as one where the equations are all equal to zero:

$$3x - 2y - z = 0$$
$$4x + 5y - 4z = 0$$
$$2x - 8y - z = 0$$

Start by asking the class some simple questions: Are homogeneous systems easier or harder to solve than arbitrary systems and why? Then ask them to find and solve a dependent homogenous system, a homogeneous system with a unique solution, and finally one with no solution. (Give them some time to do this—a lot of learning will take place while they go through the process of creating and solving problems both forward and backward.) When students or groups of students finish early, ask them to articulate why there cannot be an inconsistent homogeneous system.

After the students have thought about this type of system, bring them all together. Point out that it is clear that $x = 0$, $y = 0$, $z = 0$ is always a solution to a homogeneous system, and so there cannot be an inconsistent one. The only possible solutions sets are $(0,0,0)$ and a set with infinitely many points, one of which is $(0,0,0)$.

- Point out that the techniques in this section are extensible in a way that some ad hoc techniques are not. One can solve an 8×8 or even a 100×100 system (in theory) using this method. If you want to pursue this line earlier, it is interesting to estimate the complexity of using this technique. Have the students solve a 2×2 system, keeping track of every multiplication they do, and every addition, Then have them do the same for a 3×3. They can then do the same for a 4×4—not necessarily bothering to actually do all the additions and multiplications, just doing the count. Notice that the increase in complexity grows faster than a linear function.

▼ Examples

- Word problems

  1. I have $6.50 in nickels, dimes and quarters. I have twice as many nickels as dimes. That's a lot of nickels. In fact, if you add the number of dimes I have to twice the number of quarters I have, you get the number of nickels I have. How many nickels do I have?
     Answer:

     $$5n + 10d + 25q = 650$$
     $$n - 2d + 0q = 0$$
     $$-n + d + 2q = 0$$

     40 nickels, 20 dimes, 10 quarters

  2. A pet-shop has 100 puppies, kittens, and turtles. A puppy costs $30, a kitten costs $20, and a turtle costs $5. If there are twice as many kittens as puppies, and if the stock is worth $1050, how many of each type of animal is there?
     Answer:

     $$p + k + t = 100$$
     $$30p + 20k + 5t = 1050$$
     $$2p - k + 0t = 0$$

     10 puppies, 20 kittens, 70 turtles

- A system with infinitely many solutions:

$$x + 2y - 3z = 12$$
$$-2x + y + 4z = 2$$
$$x + 7y - 5z = 38$$

Answer: $x = \frac{11}{5}t + \frac{8}{5}, y = \frac{2}{5}t + \frac{26}{5}, z = t$. Note: the representation of this set of solutions is not unique.

▼ Group Work 1: Finding the k

This activity can stand on its own, or it can dovetail with a discussion of homogeneous systems, as discussed in the in-class materials. The idea is for the students to realize that, since $(0, 0, 0)$ is a solution of the system, the only way there can be another one is to make a dependent system. Once they realize this, finding $k = 9$ is straightforward. This activity can be made more challenging by using the system

$$x + 2y + 3z = 0$$
$$x + 6y + kz = 0$$
$$x + 4z = 0$$

Answer: $k = 9$ for the system in the group work, $k = 1$ for the more challenging system given above.

▼ Group Work 2: The Lemonade Trick

Students tend to find the mixture problems from Section 1.6 difficult. This will serve as a review and extension of those problems. If a group finishes early, ask them to show that, regardless of how many liters she winds up with, the proportions of the final recipe will be the same.

Answer:

1.5 liters of her father's, 2 liters of the store-bought, and 2.5 liters of Grandma's.

A table, such as the one used in Example 8, can be helpful in problems like these:

	Lemon	Sugar	Water	Amount
Father	$(0.26)\,f$	$(0.12)\,f$	$(0.62)\,f$	f
Store	$(0.10)\,s$	$(0.31)\,s$	$(0.59)\,s$	s
Grandma	$(0.10)\,g$	$(0.10)\,g$	$(0.80)\,g$	g
Total	$(0.14)\,6$	$(0.175)\,6$	$(0.685)\,6$	6

$$f + s + g = 6$$
$$0.26f + 0.1s + 0.1g = (0.14)\,6$$
$$0.12f + 0.31s + 0.1g = (0.175)\,6$$

▼ Homework Problems

Core Exercises: 3, 5, 13, 16, 22, 30, 41, 49, 56

Sample Assignment: 3, 5, 6, 13, 16, 18, 22, 27, 30, 34, 41, 45, 49, 54, 56, 60

Consider the following system:

$$x + 2y + 3z = 0$$
$$3x + 6y + kz = 0$$
$$x + 4z = 0$$

Convince yourself that, regardless of the value of k, $x = 0$, $y = 0$, $z = 0$ is a solution of this system. We call this solution the *trivial solution*.

Find a value of k to ensure that this system has a nontrivial solution.

A college student is dissatisfied with her lemonade options, and decides to mix three kinds of lemonade in her glorious quest to find the perfect cup. She mixes some of her father's sour lemonade (which turns out to be 26% lemon juice, 12% sugar, and 62% water), some store-bought supersweet lemonade (10% lemon juice, 31% sugar, 59% water) and some of her grandmothers watery lemonade (10% lemon juice, 10% sugar, 80% water with an insignificant dash of Worcestershire sauce for "color"). When she is finished, she has six liters of lemonade that contains a nice mix of 14% lemon juice and 17.5% sugar.

How many liters of each kind has she used?

10.4 THE ALGEBRA OF MATRICES

▼ Suggested Time and Emphasis

1 class. Recommended material.

▼ Points to Stress

1. Matrix addition
2. Scalar and matrix multiplication

▼ Sample Questions

- **Text Question:** True or false:

  (a) $\begin{bmatrix} 3 & 4 \\ 1 & 2 \end{bmatrix} \begin{bmatrix} -1 & 5 \\ 1 & 0 \end{bmatrix} = \begin{bmatrix} -3 & 20 \\ 1 & 0 \end{bmatrix}$

  (b) $\begin{bmatrix} 3 & 4 \\ 1 & 2 \end{bmatrix} + \begin{bmatrix} -1 & 5 \\ 1 & 0 \end{bmatrix} = \begin{bmatrix} 2 & 9 \\ 2 & 2 \end{bmatrix}$

  Answer: (a) False **(b)** True

- **Drill Question:** Compute $\begin{bmatrix} 5 & 9 & 2 \\ 6 & 5 & 3 \end{bmatrix} \begin{bmatrix} 5 \\ -1 \\ 1 \end{bmatrix}$.

  Answer: $\begin{bmatrix} 18 \\ 28 \end{bmatrix}$

▼ In-Class Materials

- The text describes which properties of real number addition and multiplication carry over to matrix addition, matrix multiplication, and scalar multiplication. Discuss how some of their consequences carry over as well. Ask the students if they believe that $(A+B)(A+B) = AA + 2AB + BB$. Let them discuss and argue. It turns out that this is false, because of commutativity. It *is* true that $(A+B)(A+B) = AA + AB + BA + BB$. Have the class look at $(A+B)(A-B)$ next.

- Let A and B be 2×2 matrices. Although AB may not be equal to BA, there are special matrices for which $AB = BA$. One necessary (but not sufficient) condition for this to happen is that $a_{12}b_{21} = a_{21}b_{12}$. It is relatively simple to show this condition by explicitly multiplying out AB and BA. After demonstrating this condition, challenge the students to find a pair of distinct matrices, without zero elements, such that $AB = BA$. The process of searching for them will give students good practice multiplying matrices. One example that works is $A = \begin{bmatrix} 1 & 2 \\ 3 & 4 \end{bmatrix}$, $B = \begin{bmatrix} -1 & 2 \\ 3 & 2 \end{bmatrix}$.

- This is a good time to discuss permutation matrices. A permutation matrix is a matrix that is all zeros except for a single 1 in each row and each column.

$$\begin{bmatrix} 0 & 0 & 1 & 0 & 0 \\ 1 & 0 & 0 & 0 & 0 \\ 0 & 0 & 0 & 1 & 0 \\ 0 & 1 & 0 & 0 & 0 \\ 0 & 0 & 0 & 0 & 1 \end{bmatrix}$$

328

Have the class figure out if the sum of two permutation matrices must always be a permutation matrix (no) and if the product of two permutation matrices must always be a permutation matrix (yes). Finally, have the students multiply arbitrary matrices by permutation matrices, to see what happens to them (the rows or columns get rearranged, depending on whether the permutation matrix was multiplied on the left or on the right). There is a group work about this topic in the next section.

- Foreshadow the next section by having students compute $\begin{bmatrix} 2 & 5 & 1 \\ 4 & 2 & 1 \\ 5 & 3 & 1 \end{bmatrix} \begin{bmatrix} x \\ y \\ z \end{bmatrix}$.

▼ Examples

Let $A = \begin{bmatrix} 3 & 1 \\ -1 & 0 \\ 3 & 2 \end{bmatrix}$, $B = \begin{bmatrix} 5 & 1 \\ 1 & 2 \\ -6 & -1 \end{bmatrix}$, and $C = \begin{bmatrix} 3 & 1 \\ 2 & 5 \end{bmatrix}$.

$$A + B = \begin{bmatrix} 8 & 2 \\ 0 & 2 \\ -3 & 1 \end{bmatrix} \qquad B - A = \begin{bmatrix} 2 & 0 \\ 2 & 2 \\ -9 & -3 \end{bmatrix} \qquad AC = \begin{bmatrix} 11 & 8 \\ -3 & -1 \\ 13 & 13 \end{bmatrix}$$

$$BC = \begin{bmatrix} 17 & 10 \\ 7 & 11 \\ -20 & -11 \end{bmatrix} \qquad (A + B)C = \begin{bmatrix} 28 & 18 \\ 4 & 10 \\ -7 & 2 \end{bmatrix}$$

If using these examples, occasionally throw in an undefined operation such as $A + C$ or AB.

▼ Group Work: Quest for the Unknown

This activity is a fairly straightforward chance for students to practice matrix operations.

Answers:

1. $a = 5$ **2.** $a = 2$ **3.** $a = \frac{5}{7}, b = -\frac{1}{7}, c = -\frac{3}{7}, d = \frac{2}{7}$

4. $a = \frac{5}{7}, b = -\frac{1}{7}, c = -\frac{3}{7}, d = \frac{2}{7}$ **5.** $a = -1, b = \frac{7}{2}, c = -2$

▼ Homework Problems

Core Exercises: 5, 7, 10, 17, 22, 32, 37, 40, 46

Sample Assignment: 5, 7, 10, 13, 17, 20, 22, 26, 32, 34, 37, 40, 41, 46, 49

GROUP WORK, SECTION 10.4

Quest for the Unknown

For each of the following computations, find the unknowns

1. $\begin{bmatrix} 1 & 5 & 3 & 1 \\ -2 & -5 & 0 & 1 \end{bmatrix} + 2\begin{bmatrix} -1 & 1 & -3 & 5 \\ -2 & a & 3 & 1 \end{bmatrix} = \begin{bmatrix} -1 & 7 & -3 & 11 \\ -6 & 5 & 6 & 3 \end{bmatrix}$

2. $\begin{bmatrix} 1 & -2 & 1 & -2 \\ -3 & 3 & -3 & 7 \\ 0 & -1 & 2 & -5 \\ -2 & 3 & -1 & 0 \end{bmatrix} \begin{bmatrix} 1 & 2 & 3 & 4 \\ -4 & -3 & -2 & -1 \\ 0 & 1 & 0 & -1 \\ 3 & 1 & a & 4 \end{bmatrix} = \begin{bmatrix} 3 & 7 & 3 & -3 \\ 6 & -11 & -1 & 16 \\ -11 & 0 & -8 & -21 \\ -14 & -14 & -12 & -10 \end{bmatrix}$

3. $\begin{bmatrix} 2 & 1 \\ 3 & 5 \end{bmatrix} \begin{bmatrix} a & b \\ c & d \end{bmatrix} = \begin{bmatrix} 1 & 0 \\ 0 & 1 \end{bmatrix}$

4. $\begin{bmatrix} a & b \\ c & d \end{bmatrix} \begin{bmatrix} 2 & 1 \\ 3 & 5 \end{bmatrix} = \begin{bmatrix} 1 & 0 \\ 0 & 1 \end{bmatrix}$

5. $\begin{bmatrix} -6 & 2 & 1 \\ -4 & 2 & 0 \\ -1 & 1 & -1 \end{bmatrix} \begin{bmatrix} a & \frac{3}{2} & -1 \\ -2 & b & -2 \\ -1 & 2 & c \end{bmatrix} = \begin{bmatrix} 1 & 0 & 0 \\ 0 & 1 & 0 \\ 0 & 0 & 1 \end{bmatrix}$

10.5 INVERSES OF MATRICES AND MATRIX EQUATIONS

▼ Suggested Time and Emphasis

1 class. Recommended material.

▼ Points to Stress

1. The identity matrix.

2. Definition and computation of the inverse of a matrix.

▼ Sample Questions

- **Text Question:** If $AB = I$, where I is the identity matrix, is it necessarily true that $BA = I$?

  Answer: Yes

- **Drill Question:** Find the inverse of the matrix $\begin{bmatrix} 3 & 0 \\ 0 & -\frac{5}{8} \end{bmatrix}$.

  Answer: $\begin{bmatrix} \frac{1}{3} & 0 \\ 0 & -\frac{8}{5} \end{bmatrix}$

▼ In-Class Materials

- Example 7 is particularly important, because Section 10.3 presented a straightforward method of solving an $n \times n$ system. The advantage of finding the inverse matrix really kicks in when solving a series of systems with the same coefficient matrix.

- Perhaps take this opportunity to talk about the inverse of a complex number: how do we find $\dfrac{1}{3 + 4i}$? The technique, multiplying by $\dfrac{3 - 4i}{3 - 4i}$, is not as important as the concept that given a real, complex, or matrix quantity it is often possible to find an inverse that will reduce it to unity. One can also add "inverse functions" to this discussion—in this case $f(x) = x$ is the identity function, referred to as such because it leaves inputs unchanged (analogous to multiplying by 1). Try to get the students to see the conceptual similarities in solving the three following equations:

$$3x = 2$$
$$(3 + i)\,x = 2 - 4i$$
$$\begin{bmatrix} 2 & 1 \\ 3 & -4 \end{bmatrix} \begin{bmatrix} x \\ y \end{bmatrix} = \begin{bmatrix} 3 \\ 1 \end{bmatrix}$$

- After doing a standard example or two, throw a singular matrix on the board before defining singularity. "Unexpectedly" run into trouble and thus discover, with your class, that not every matrix has an inverse. Examples of singular matrices are given in the Examples section.

331

- It is straightforward to demonstrate that $\left(A^{-1}\right)^{-1} = A$ for specific 2×2 or 3×3 matrices. Students can pick up why it should be true, given the definition of inverse. A general algebraic proof is a little messy:

$$\left(A^{-1}\right)^{-1} = \begin{bmatrix} \dfrac{d}{ad-bc} & -\dfrac{b}{ad-bc} \\ -\dfrac{c}{ad-bc} & \dfrac{a}{ad-bc} \end{bmatrix}^{-1}$$

$$= \dfrac{1}{\left(\dfrac{a}{ad-bc}\right)\left(\dfrac{d}{ad-bc}\right) - \left(\dfrac{b}{ad-bc}\right)\left(\dfrac{c}{ad-bc}\right)} \begin{bmatrix} \dfrac{a}{ad-bc} & \dfrac{b}{ad-bc} \\ \dfrac{c}{ad-bc} & \dfrac{d}{ad-bc} \end{bmatrix}$$

$$= \dfrac{1}{1/(ad-bc)} \cdot \dfrac{1}{ad-bc} \cdot \begin{bmatrix} a & b \\ c & d \end{bmatrix} = \begin{bmatrix} a & b \\ c & d \end{bmatrix} = A$$

- Note that there is a formula for 3×3 inverses, just as there is one for 2×2 inverses. Unfortunately, it is so complicated that it is easier to find 3×3 inverses manually than to use a formula.

$$\begin{bmatrix} a & b & c \\ d & e & f \\ g & h & i \end{bmatrix}^{-1} = \dfrac{1}{afh - aei + bdi - bfg + ceg - cdh} \begin{bmatrix} fh-ei & bi-ch & ce-bf \\ di-fg & cg-ai & af-cd \\ eg-dh & ah-bg & bd-ae \end{bmatrix}$$

▼ Examples

- Nonsingular real matrices

$$\begin{bmatrix} -2 & 1 \\ 3 & 3 \end{bmatrix}^{-1} = \begin{bmatrix} -\frac{1}{3} & \frac{1}{9} \\ \frac{1}{3} & \frac{2}{9} \end{bmatrix} \qquad \begin{bmatrix} -1 & 1 & 1 \\ 4 & -1 & 1 \\ 4 & 2 & 1 \end{bmatrix}^{-1} = \begin{bmatrix} -\frac{1}{5} & \frac{1}{15} & \frac{2}{15} \\ 0 & -\frac{1}{3} & \frac{1}{3} \\ \frac{4}{5} & \frac{2}{5} & -\frac{1}{5} \end{bmatrix}$$

$$\begin{bmatrix} 0 & 2 & 0 & 0 \\ 2 & 0 & 0 & 0 \\ 0 & 0 & 5 & 0 \\ 0 & 1 & 0 & 6 \end{bmatrix}^{-1} = \begin{bmatrix} 0 & \frac{1}{2} & 0 & 0 \\ \frac{1}{2} & 0 & 0 & 0 \\ 0 & 0 & \frac{1}{5} & 0 \\ -\frac{1}{12} & 0 & 0 & \frac{1}{6} \end{bmatrix}$$

- Singular real matrices

$$\begin{bmatrix} 5 & 4 \\ 15 & 12 \end{bmatrix}$$

$$\begin{bmatrix} 1 & 2 & 3 \\ -1 & 3 & -2 \\ -1 & 8 & -1 \end{bmatrix}$$

$$\begin{bmatrix} 8 & 3 & 5 & -8 \\ -7 & 6 & 0 & -6 \\ -5 & -3 & 7 & 9 \\ -4 & 6 & 12 & -5 \end{bmatrix}$$

- A complex matrix and its inverse

$$\begin{bmatrix} 1 & 2i \\ 1-i & 1 \end{bmatrix}^{-1} = \dfrac{1}{-1-2i} \begin{bmatrix} 1 & -2i \\ -1+i & 1 \end{bmatrix} = \begin{bmatrix} -\frac{1}{5}+\frac{2}{5}i & \frac{4}{5}+\frac{2}{5}i \\ -\frac{1}{5}-\frac{3}{5}i & -\frac{1}{5}+\frac{2}{5}i \end{bmatrix}$$

▼ Group Work: Some Special Kinds of Matrices

This activity uses various types of special matrices as a way of getting students to think about inverses, and to introduce them to some of the vocabulary of matrix algebra, such as the word "idempotent" meaning a matrix with the property $A^2 = A$. Before handing out the sheet, start by defining a diagonal matrix, one for which $a_{ij} = 0$ whenever $i \neq j$ such as $\begin{bmatrix} 1 & 0 & 0 \\ 0 & 2 & 0 \\ 0 & 0 & 3 \end{bmatrix}$. Ask the students to figure out the inverse of $\begin{bmatrix} 1 & 0 \\ 0 & 2 \end{bmatrix}$, $\begin{bmatrix} 1 & 0 & 0 \\ 0 & 2 & 0 \\ 0 & 0 & 3 \end{bmatrix}$,

and then an arbitrary diagonal matrix. They will find that $\begin{bmatrix} a & 0 & 0 \\ 0 & b & 0 \\ 0 & 0 & c \end{bmatrix}^{-1} = \begin{bmatrix} 1/a & 0 & 0 \\ 0 & 1/b & 0 \\ 0 & 0 & 1/c \end{bmatrix}$. Then hand out

the activity which will allow the students to explore more special types of matrices.

Problem 4 hits an important theorem in matrix algebra: that the only nonsingular idempotent matrix is the identity. If the students finish early, follow up on Problem 10 by asking how they could tell, at a glance, if a given permutation matrix is its own inverse. When everyone is done, close the activity by discussing that question. It turns out that if the permutation just swaps pairs of elements, then doing it twice will bring us back to the identity permutation. So all one does is makes sure that if $a_{ij} = 1$ then $a_{ji} = 1$ as well.

Answers:

Answers will vary.

1. $\begin{bmatrix} 1 & 0 & 0 \\ 0 & 1 & 0 \\ 0 & 0 & 0 \end{bmatrix}$

2. $\begin{bmatrix} 1 & 0 & 0 \\ 0 & \frac{1}{2} & \frac{1}{2} \\ 0 & \frac{1}{2} & \frac{1}{2} \end{bmatrix}$ or $\begin{bmatrix} 1 & 0 \\ 2 & 0 \end{bmatrix}$

3. $\begin{bmatrix} 1 & 0 \\ 0 & 1 \end{bmatrix}$

4. Another cannot exist. If $A^2 = A$, then $A^2 A^{-1} = AA^{-1}$ and $A = I$.

5. $\begin{bmatrix} 42 \\ 51 \\ 27 \end{bmatrix}$

6. $\begin{bmatrix} b \\ d \\ a \\ c \\ e \end{bmatrix}$

7. $\begin{bmatrix} c \\ d \\ e \\ a \\ b \end{bmatrix}$

8. They permute the elements of a matrix without changing them.

9. $\begin{bmatrix} 1 & 0 & 0 \\ 0 & 0 & 1 \\ 0 & 1 & 0 \end{bmatrix}$

10. $\begin{bmatrix} 0 & 1 & 0 \\ 0 & 0 & 1 \\ 1 & 0 & 0 \end{bmatrix}$

▼ Homework Problems

Core Exercises: 2, 4, 7, 12, 19, 27, 40, 43, 47

Sample Assignment: 2, 4, 6, 7, 8, 12, 16, 19, 24, 27, 31, 40, 42, 43, 47, 48

GROUP WORK, SECTION 10.5

Some Special Kinds of Matrices

A matrix A is called *idempotent* if $A^2 = A$.

1. Find a 3×3 diagonal idempotent matrix that is not the identity.

2. Find a nondiagonal idempotent matrix.

3. Find a nonsingular idempotent matrix.

4. Find a different nonsingular idempotent matrix, or show why one cannot exist.

A permutation matrix has a single 1 in each row and each column. The rest of the entries are zeros. Here are some permutation matrices:

$$
\begin{bmatrix} 0 & 1 & 0 \\ 0 & 0 & 1 \\ 1 & 0 & 0 \end{bmatrix}
\qquad
\begin{bmatrix} 0 & 1 & 0 & 0 & 0 \\ 0 & 0 & 0 & 1 & 0 \\ 1 & 0 & 0 & 0 & 0 \\ 0 & 0 & 1 & 0 & 0 \\ 0 & 0 & 0 & 0 & 1 \end{bmatrix}
\qquad
\begin{bmatrix} 0 & 0 & 1 & 0 & 0 \\ 0 & 0 & 0 & 1 & 0 \\ 0 & 0 & 0 & 0 & 1 \\ 1 & 0 & 0 & 0 & 0 \\ 0 & 1 & 0 & 0 & 0 \end{bmatrix}
$$

5. Compute $\begin{bmatrix} 0 & 1 & 0 \\ 0 & 0 & 1 \\ 1 & 0 & 0 \end{bmatrix} \begin{bmatrix} 27 \\ 42 \\ 51 \end{bmatrix}$.

6. Compute $\begin{bmatrix} 0 & 1 & 0 & 0 & 0 \\ 0 & 0 & 0 & 1 & 0 \\ 1 & 0 & 0 & 0 & 0 \\ 0 & 0 & 1 & 0 & 0 \\ 0 & 0 & 0 & 0 & 1 \end{bmatrix} \begin{bmatrix} a \\ b \\ c \\ d \\ e \end{bmatrix}$.

7. Compute $\begin{bmatrix} 0 & 0 & 1 & 0 & 0 \\ 0 & 0 & 0 & 1 & 0 \\ 0 & 0 & 0 & 0 & 1 \\ 1 & 0 & 0 & 0 & 0 \\ 0 & 1 & 0 & 0 & 0 \end{bmatrix} \begin{bmatrix} a \\ b \\ c \\ d \\ e \end{bmatrix}$.

8. Why are matrices of this type called permutation matrices?

9. Find a permutation matrix $A \neq I$ such that $A^{-1} = A$.

10. Find a permutation matrix $A \neq I$ such that $A^{-1} \neq A$.

10.6 DETERMINANTS AND CRAMER'S RULE

▼ Suggested Time and Emphasis

1 class. Recommended material: Determinants. Optional material: Cramer's Rule.

▼ Points to Stress

1. Definition and computation of determinants, including row operations.
2. The relationship between determinants and singularity.
3. Cramer's Rule.

▼ Sample Questions

- **Text Question:** Name one application of determinants.

  Answers: Determining the singularity of a matrix, solving systems with Cramer's Rule, finding the area of a triangle.

- **Drill Question:** Find $\begin{vmatrix} 2 & 1 & 3 \\ 1 & 0 & 0 \\ 0 & 2 & -1 \end{vmatrix}$.

  Answer: 7

▼ In-Class Materials

- Make sure the students see the fundamentally recursive nature of determinants. Draw a 6×6 matrix on the board and expand by a row, showing how you would then have to compute six 5×5 determinants, which would require the computation of thirty 4×4 determinants, and so forth.

- Discuss computational complexity. If a 2×2 determinant requires 3 arithmetical operations (two multiplications and a subtraction), then a 3×3 determinant requires 12, and a 4×4 requires 52. If we let $f(n)$ be the number of arithmetical operations for an $n \times n$ matrix, we get the formula $f(n) = nf(n-1) + n$: there are n determinants of $(n-1) \times (n-1)$ matrices and n extra multiplications (when expanding by a row). So we can generate the following table:

n	Number of Operations
2	3
3	12
4	52
5	265
6	1596
7	11,179
8	89,440
9	804,969
10	8,049,700
11	88,546,711
⋮	⋮
20	5,396,862,315,159,760,000

Students can observe this rapid growth on their calculators; it will take the calculator ten times as long to do a 10×10 determinant as it takes to do a 9×9. In fact, $f(n)$ grows a little more rapidly than $n!$.

337

- Determinants have many nice properties. For example, if a row or column consists of all zeros, it is trivial to prove that the determinant is zero. The row/column transformation rule given in the text then lets us conclude that if two rows of a matrix are identical, the determinant is zero. Also, the determinant of a product is the product of the determinants.

- Show the students the "basket" method of computing a 3×3 determinant. Stress that this method does not generalize to higher dimensions. One rewrites the first two columns of the matrix, and then multiplies along the diagonals, adding the top-to-bottom diagonals and subtracting the bottom-to-top ones. In the example below, we calculate the determinant of $\begin{bmatrix} 1 & 4 & 7 \\ 2 & 5 & 8 \\ 3 & 6 & 9 \end{bmatrix}$ to be $105 + 48 + 72 - (45 + 96 + 84) = 0$.

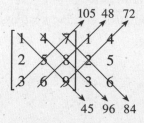

- When solving a single $n \times n$ system, Cramer's Rule doesn't have much of an advantage over Gaussian elimination. There are, however, some circumstances in which Cramer's Rule is vastly superior. One such situation is when there is a large system (say 100 equations with 100 unknowns) and we are interested in only one variable. Gaussian elimination requires us to do the work to solve the complete system. Finding the inverse of the matrix also requires us to do all the work necessary to find all the variables. Cramer's Rule, however, allows us to find two (admittedly large) determinants to get our answer.

  Another situation is when the coefficient matrix is sparse—a large proportion of the entries are zero. Determinants of sparse matrices require very few operations to compute, so in that case Cramer's rule finds answers quickly.

▼ Examples

- A 4×4 determinant:

$$\begin{vmatrix} 1 & 1 & 1 & 1 \\ 2 & -1 & 0 & 5 \\ 0 & 8 & 1 & 2 \\ 0 & 2 & 1 & 3 \end{vmatrix}$$

Expand by Row 3:

$$D = -8 \begin{vmatrix} 1 & 1 & 1 \\ 2 & 0 & 5 \\ 0 & 1 & 3 \end{vmatrix} + \begin{vmatrix} 1 & 1 & 1 \\ 2 & -1 & 5 \\ 0 & 2 & 3 \end{vmatrix} - 2 \begin{vmatrix} 1 & 1 & 1 \\ 2 & -1 & 0 \\ 0 & 2 & 1 \end{vmatrix}$$

$$= -8 (-9) + (-15) - 2 (1) = 55$$

• Cramer's Rule:

$$x - y + z = 8$$
$$-x - y - z = -9$$
$$x - 2y - 4z = 5$$

$$D = \begin{vmatrix} 1 & -1 & 1 \\ -1 & -1 & -1 \\ 1 & -2 & -4 \end{vmatrix} = 10, \ D_x = \begin{vmatrix} 8 & -1 & 1 \\ -9 & -1 & -1 \\ 5 & -2 & -4 \end{vmatrix} = 80, \ D_y = \begin{vmatrix} 1 & 8 & 1 \\ -1 & -9 & -1 \\ 1 & 5 & -4 \end{vmatrix} = 5, \text{ and}$$

$$D_z = \begin{vmatrix} 1 & -1 & 8 \\ -1 & -1 & -9 \\ 1 & -2 & 5 \end{vmatrix} = 5, \text{ so we have } x = 8, \ y = \tfrac{1}{2}, \text{ and } z = \tfrac{1}{2}.$$

▼ Group Work 1: Determinants and Row Operations

This activity can be given before or after row and column transformations of a determinant are covered. It will enable the students to discover the effect of all three row operations on the determinant of a matrix.

If students finish early, have them try to prove their answers.

Answers:

1. 16
2. Multiplying a row by a multiplies the determinant by a.
3. Oddly enough, adding a scalar multiple of one row to another row does not change the determinant, no matter what the multiple is.
4. Switching rows changes the sign of the determinant.

▼ Group Work 2: Divide and Conquer

This activity is mathematically routine. The idea here is for the students to figure out how to use their groups to do "parallel processing". In other words, if each member of the group tries to do the problem his- or herself, it will be long and boring. However, if they find a way to divide up the work, it will be quick (and boring). Put students in groups of four or five. Start by saying that each group will compute a 5×5 determinant. Give them three minutes to come up with a strategy that will enable their group to compute this determinant (a) quickly and (b) accurately. They may each want to take one of the smaller determinants, or they may want one student to be the "checker" of the others' work. Or they may want to pair up. If a group suggests trading answers with another group, allow that as well. Effective parallel processing is still a major area of research in computer science, and determinants are wonderful for illustrating this principle.

Answer: -3

▼ Homework Problems

Core Exercises: 5, 8, 16, 20, 27, 35, 48, 50, 51, 60

Sample Assignment: 5, 8, 12, 14, 16, 20, 25, 27, 31, 35, 40, 43, 48, 50, 51, 54, 56, 60

Determinants and Row Operations

1. Find $\begin{vmatrix} 1 & 0 & 1 \\ 0 & 3 & -1 \\ 2 & 4 & 6 \end{vmatrix}$.

Recall that we know three elementary row operations. They are:

   I   Multiplying a row by a nonzero scalar
  II   Adding a scalar multiple of one row to another row
 III   Switching the positions of two rows in the matrix

I would like to say that these row operations have no effect on the determinant of a matrix. I would like to say that, but it would be incorrect. Your job is to figure out the effect that each of these operations has on the matrix.

2. Start with the matrix given above. Now do an operation of type I and see what happens to the determinant. Try a few, and see if you can come up with a theory about what row operation I does.

3. Similarly, find out what effect row operation II has.

4. What effect does row operation III have?

Divide and Conquer

Find

$$
\begin{vmatrix}
1 & 1 & -1 & -1 & 1 \\
2 & -2 & 1 & 0 & 1 \\
3 & 0 & 2 & -1 & 1 \\
-1 & 1 & 0 & 2 & -1 \\
1 & 1 & 1 & 1 & 0
\end{vmatrix}
$$

by row expansion.

10.7 PARTIAL FRACTIONS

▼ Suggested Time and Emphasis

$\frac{1}{2}$–1 class. Optional material.

▼ Point to Stress

Decomposing a rational function into partial fractions.

▼ Sample Questions

- **Text Question:** What does it mean to express a rational expression as partial fractions?

  Answer: : It means to write the expression as a sum of fractions with simpler denominators.

- **Drill Question:** Express $\dfrac{2}{x^2 - 1}$ as a sum of partial fractions.

  Answer: $\dfrac{2}{x^2 - 1} = \dfrac{1}{x - 1} - \dfrac{1}{x + 1}$

▼ In-Class Materials

- It is possible to cover this section without covering every single case. For example, one might just cover the idea of linear factors (Cases 1 and 2) and mention that it is also possible to work with irreducible quadratic factors. Notice that just because every rational expression can be decomposed in theory doesn't mean it is always possible in practice, because there is no closed-form formula for factoring a polynomial of degree 5 or higher.

- Remind students of the process of polynomial division, perhaps by rewriting $\dfrac{2x^3 + 3x^2 + 7x + 4}{2x + 1}$ as $x^2 + x + 3 + \dfrac{1}{2x + 1}$. Be sure to indicate that, in order to use partial fractions, the degree of the numerator has to be less than the degree of the denominator.

- Find the coefficients for the partial fraction decomposition for $\dfrac{x + 3}{(x - 2)(x - 1)}$ in two different ways: first using two linear equations, and then using the method of creating zeros [setting $x = 1$ and then $x = -2$ in $x + 3 = A(x + 2) + B(x - 1)$].

- Point out that the quadratic in the denominator of $f(x) = \dfrac{1}{x^2 + x - 6}$ is not irreducible. It can be factored into the two linear terms $x - 2$ and $x + 3$, so the partial fraction decomposition is found by writing $\dfrac{1}{x^2 + x - 6} = \dfrac{A}{x + 2} + \dfrac{B}{x - 3}$ and solving for A and B. Therefore it is important, when factoring the denominator, to make sure all quadratics are irreducible.

- Show the class how a complicated partial fractions problem would be set up, without trying to solve it. An example is $\dfrac{5x + 3}{x^3 (x + 1)(x^2 + x + 4)(x^2 + 3)^2}$.

▼ Examples

- Case 1:

$$\frac{x-7}{(x-2)(x+3)} = \frac{-1}{x-2} + \frac{2}{x+3}$$

- Case 2:

$$\frac{3x^2 - x - 3}{x^2(x+1)} = \frac{1}{x+1} + \frac{2}{x} - \frac{3}{x^2}$$

- Case 3:

$$\frac{3}{(x-1)(x^2+2)} = \frac{1}{x-1} - \frac{x+1}{x^2+2}$$

- Case 4:

$$\frac{1}{(x^2+1)^2 x} = \frac{1}{x} - \frac{x}{x^2+1} - \frac{x}{(x^2+1)^2}$$

▼ Group Work: Partial Fraction Practice

Four problems are given, each dealing with a different case. Feel free to pick and choose which problems to assign, depending on what skills you want to emphasize. You may decide to allow the students to solve the linear systems on their calculators, or to stop at setting up the systems.

Answers:

1. (a) $x^3 - x^2 - 4x + 4 = (x-1)(x+2)(x-2)$

   (b) $\dfrac{2x^2 + 3x - 8}{(x-1)(x+2)(x-2)} = \dfrac{1}{x-1} - \dfrac{1}{2(x+2)} + \dfrac{3}{2(x-2)}$

   (c) $\dfrac{3x^5 - 3x^4 - 12x^3 + 16x^2 - 16 + 6x}{(x-1)(x+2)(x-2)} = 3x^2 + \dfrac{2}{x-1} - \dfrac{1}{x+2} + \dfrac{3}{x-2}$

2. (a) $x^3 - 3x + 2 = (x-1)^2(x+2)$

   (b) $\dfrac{5x^2 - 5x - 3}{x^3 - 3x + 2} = \dfrac{2}{x-1} - \dfrac{1}{(x-1)^2} + \dfrac{3}{x+2}$

   (c) $\dfrac{x^5 - 3x^3 + 7x^2 - 5x - 3}{(x-1)^2(x+2)} = x^2 + \dfrac{2}{x-1} - \dfrac{1}{(x-1)^2} + \dfrac{3}{x+2}$

3. (a) $x^3 + 3x^2 + 4x = x(x^2 + 3x + 4)$

   (b) $\dfrac{x^2 + 13x + 16}{x^3 + 3x^2 + 4x} = \dfrac{4}{x} - \dfrac{3x-1}{x^2 + 3x + 4}$

4. (a) $x^4 + 2x^2 + 1 = (x^2 + 1)^2$

   (b) $\dfrac{3x^3 - x^2 + 3x + 3}{x^4 + 2x^2 + 1} = \dfrac{3x-1}{(x^2+1)} + \dfrac{4}{(x^2+1)^2}$

▼ Homework Problems

Core Exercises: 1, 4, 13, 18, 26, 39, 44

Sample Assignment: 1, 4, 9, 13, 18, 24, 26, 33, 39, 42, 44, 45, 47

Partial Fraction Practice

1. (a) Factor $x^3 - x^2 - 4x + 4$.

(b) Write $\dfrac{2x^2 + 3x - 8}{x^3 - x^2 - 4x + 4}$ as a sum of partial fractions.

(c) Write $\dfrac{3x^5 - 3x^4 - 12x^3 + 16x^2 - 16 + 6x}{x^3 - x^2 - 4x + 4}$ as a sum of partial fractions.

2. (a) Factor $x^3 - 3x + 2$.

(b) Write $\dfrac{5x^2 - 5x - 3}{x^3 - 3x + 2}$ as a sum of partial fractions.

(c) Write $\dfrac{x^5 - 3x^3 + 7x^2 - 5x - 3}{x^3 - 3x + 2}$ as a sum of partial fractions.

3. (a) Factor $x^3 + 3x^2 + 4x$.

(b) Write $\dfrac{x^2 + 13x + 16}{x^3 + 3x^2 + 4x}$ as a sum of partial fractions.

4. (a) Factor $x^4 + 2x^2 + 1$.

(b) Write $\dfrac{3x^3 - x^2 + 3x + 3}{x^4 + 2x^2 + 1}$ as a sum of partial fractions.

10.8 SYSTEMS OF NONLINEAR EQUATIONS

▼ Suggested Time and Emphasis

$\frac{1}{2}$–1 class. Essential material.

▼ Point to Stress

Solving systems of equations with two variables, using the methods of substitution, elimination, and graphing.

▼ Sample Questions

- **Text Question:** Give examples of a linear system of two equations and a nonlinear system of two equations.
  Answers will vary

- **Drill Question:** Solve the system

$$x^2 + 2y = 6$$
$$3x^2 - 4y = 8$$

  Answer: $x = 2$, $y = 1$ and $x = -2$, $y = 1$

▼ In-Class Materials

- Many students will want to learn just one method of solving systems of equations, and stick with it. It is important that they become familiar with all three. One reason is that some systems are easier to solve with one method than with another. Another reason is that if they take mathematics classes in the future, their teachers will use their own favorite method in class.

  Either have the students try to come up with three sample systems, each lending itself to a different method, or use these:

$$y = 3x + 2$$
$$\sqrt{y^2 - 8x^2 - 12x - 4} = 4$$
Substitution easiest

$$3x + \tfrac{5}{11}y = 2$$
$$-3x + \tfrac{6}{11}y = 3$$
Elimination easiest

$$y = x^3 - x$$
$$y = e^x$$
Exact solution impossible—a graph can give an approximation

- Solving systems of equations is the soul of applied mathematics. Here is one example of many: Populations with an initial population P_0 grow according the logistic growth model

$$P = \frac{K}{1 + Ae^{-ct}}$$

where A, K and c are constants. $A = \dfrac{K - P_0}{P_0}$ and K is the "carrying capacity" of the environment. Draw a few sample graphs for the students:

345

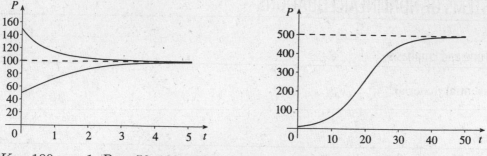

$$K = 100, c = 1, P_0 = 50, 100, 150 \qquad\qquad K = 500, c = 0.2, P_0 = 10$$

Assume that we want to find out the carrying capacity of an environment ("How many trout will Big Island Lake support?"). We can find (or estimate) P_0, and then measure the population at two times (say, at $t = 1$ and $t = 6$ months). Now we have a system of two equations with two unknowns, and we are able to find K and c.

- It was previously pointed out that a linear system of equations can have zero, one, or infinitely many solutions. Nonlinear systems can have *any number* of solutions. The following systems have one, two, three, and infinitely many solutions, respectively:

$$
\begin{array}{llll}
x^3 + 2y = 5 & x + y = 3 & y = x & x + y = 5 \\
3x^3 - y = 1 & x^3 y = 0 & y = x^3 & x^2 + 2xy + y^2 = 25
\end{array}
$$

The solutions to these systems can be demonstrated algebraically or graphically.

▼ Examples

- A nonlinear system with an integer solution:

$$
\begin{aligned}
x^3 - y^2 &= 23 \\
2x - 3y &= 0
\end{aligned}
$$

Answer: $x = 3$, $y = 2$

- A nonlinear system with a transcendental solution:

$$
\begin{aligned}
e^x + 2y &= 5 \\
-e^x + 5y &= 2
\end{aligned}
$$

Answer: $x = \ln 3$, $y = 1$

▼ Group Work 1: Area and Perimeter

Do not start out by reminding students of the relevant formulas—let them look them up. This should partially be a review of area and perimeter formulas. Notice that the rectangle referred to in Problem 1 is the very piece of paper that the students are writing on!

Answers:

1. 8.5 inches and 11 inches

2. 5 inches, 5 inches, and 6 inches

▼ Group Work 2: Intersection Points

The first three problems are routine. The fourth also involves solving a system, but requires some thought.

Answers:

1. $(1, 3)$, $(-2, -6)$, $(-3, -21)$

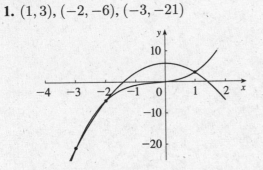

2. $(2, 4 + \ln 2) \approx (2, 4.693)$

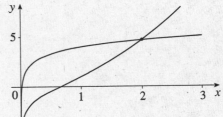

3. There is no solution.

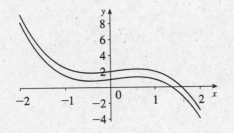

4. $\{2 = a - b + 2, 2 = a + b\}$; $a = 1$, $b = 1$

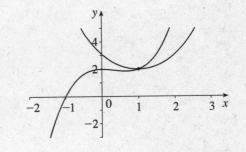

▼ Homework Problems

Core Exercises: 4, 10, 17, 19, 26, 35, 42, 46

Sample Assignment: 4, 7, 10, 14, 17, 18, 19, 21, 26, 31, 35, 40, 42, 45, 46

GROUP WORK 1, SECTION 10.8

Area and Perimeter

1. The area of a rectangle is 93.5 square inches and its perimeter is 39 inches. What are the dimensions of the rectangle?

2. The surface area of a box with a square base is 170 square inches and its volume is 150 cubic inches. What are the dimensions of the box?

Graph the following pairs of curves, and then find each pair's point(s) of intersection.

1. $y = x^3 + x^2 + x$, $y = -3x^2 + 6$

2. $y = \ln x + 4$, $y = \ln x + x^2$

3. $y = 2^x - x^3$, $y = 2^x - x^3 + 1$

4. $y = ax^3 - bx^2 + 2$, $y = ae^{x-1} + be^{-x+1}$ [Find a and b that make these curves intersect at the point $(1, 2)$.]

10.9 SYSTEMS OF INEQUALITIES

▼ Suggested Time and Emphasis

1 class. Recommended material.

▼ Point to Stress

Graphing inequalities and systems of inequalities by graphing the border and testing points in the defined regions.

▼ Sample Questions

- **Text Question:** Consider the system of inequalities

$$x^2 + y^2 < 25$$
$$x + 2y \geq 5$$

Which one of the following sentences is true?

1. The solution set of this system is all the points that satisfy at least one of these inequalities.

2. The solution set of this system is all the points that satisfy exactly one of these inequalities.

3. The solution set of this system is all the points that satisfy both of these inequalities.

Answer: Sentence 3 is true.

- **Drill Question:** Graph the solution set of the system of inequalities

$$-\tfrac{1}{2}x^2 + y \geq -2$$
$$x - y < 0$$

Answer:

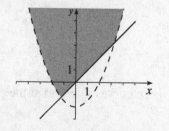

▼ In-Class Materials

- Surprisingly, many students are not able to answer this question correctly: "True or false: If $a < b$ then $a \leq b$." Perhaps take a minute or two to remind the students of the basics of inequalities. From straightforward statements involving inequalities, make the transition to some simple regions such as $x > 2$, $y \leq 3$, etc. The idea is to make sure that the students are crystal-clear on the objects they are working with before working with them.

- This section allows one to foreshadow the concept of area. For example, students should be able to compute the area of the regions defined by the following systems:

$$\{x \geq 1, x \leq 3, y \leq 2, y \geq 0\}$$
$$\{y \geq 2, x \geq 1, y + 2x \geq 0\}$$
$$\left\{y \geq 2x, (x-3)^2 + (y-6)^2 \leq 4\right\}$$

- If areas are discussed, then the idea of infinite regions with finite areas can be discussed. It is interesting that these regions have finite area:

$$x \geq 1, \quad 0 \leq y \leq e^{-x}$$
$$x \geq 1, \quad 0 \leq y \leq \frac{1}{x^2}$$
$$x \geq 1, \quad 0 \leq y \leq \frac{1}{x^{1.05}}$$

whereas these do not:

$$x \geq 1, \quad 0 \leq y \leq \frac{1}{x}$$
$$x \geq 1, \quad 0 \leq y \leq \frac{1}{x \ln(x+1)}$$
$$x \geq 1, \quad 0 \leq y \leq \frac{x}{100(x^2+x)}$$

- Have the students come up with examples of systems of two cubic inequalities with varying numbers of separate solution spaces.

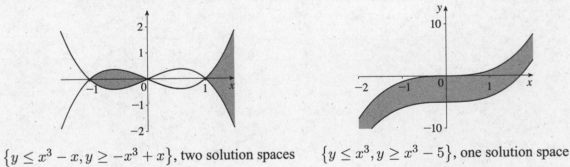

$\{y \leq x^3 - x, y \geq -x^3 + x\}$, two solution spaces

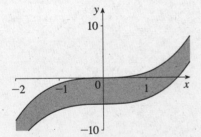

$\{y \leq x^3, y \geq x^3 - 5\}$, one solution space

▼ **Examples**

- $\{5x - 3y < 3, x - 2y > 4, x + y \leq 1\}$

- $\{y > x^2 - 4, y \leq 4 - x^2\}$

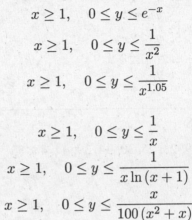

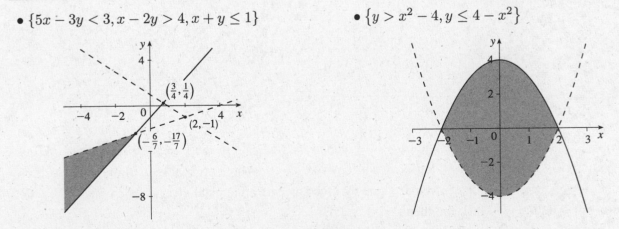

▼ Group Work: Describe the Region

The students should warm up by trying a few examples of graphing solution sets of inequalities and systems of inequalities, as in the above examples and in the homework. This activity asks them to reverse the process, to describe a region of interest. If students find this difficult, the solutions to one or two of them could be given out of order, and this could start out as a matching activity.

Answers:

1. $y < 3x + 2$

2. $y \le \sqrt[3]{x}$
$y \ge x^2$

3. $x^2 + y^2 > 1$
$x^2 + y^2 \le 9$

4. $x^2 + y^2 \ge 9$

5. $y \le 2x$
$y \ge -x + 6$
$y \ge x$

6. $y \le 3 + \sqrt{4 - x^2}$
$y \ge 0$

▼ Homework Problems

Core Exercises: 2, 3, 14, 18, 23, 30, 39, 48

Sample Assignment: 2, 3, 6, 12, 14, 18, 19, 23, 25, 30, 34, 39, 44, 48, 53

Write inequalities or systems of inequalities that describe the following regions.

1.

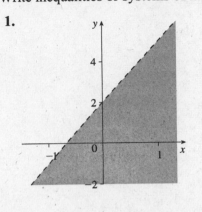

2.

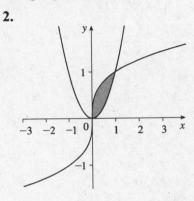

3.

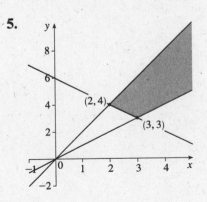

4.

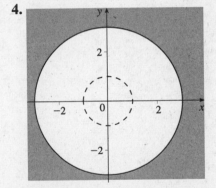

5.

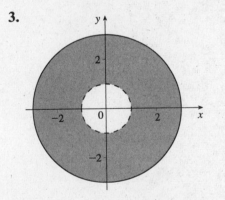

6.

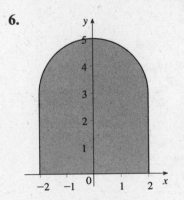

11 CONIC SECTIONS

11.1 PARABOLAS

▼ Suggested Time and Emphasis

$\frac{1}{2}$ class. Recommended material.

▼ Points to Stress

1. The definition and geometry of parabolas.
2. Using the equation of a parabola to find relevant constants.
3. Graphing a parabola given its equation.

▼ Sample Questions

- **Text Question:** How can you tell if the axis of a parabola is vertical or horizontal?

  Answer: If there is a y^2, term it is horizontal; if there is an x^2 term, it is vertical.

- **Drill Question:** Find the focus and directrix of $y = \frac{1}{16}x^2$ and sketch its graph.

  Answer: Focus $\left(0, \frac{1}{4}\right)$, directrix $y = -\frac{1}{4}$

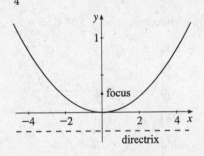

▼ In-Class Materials

- Have students sketch a parabola from scratch. Hand out a sheet of paper with focus and directrix, and hand out rulers. Get the students to plot the points from which the distance to the directrix is equal to the distance to the focus. Have them keep plotting points until a parabolic shape emerges.

- Using dental floss and modeling compound (such as clay or Play-Doh) it is easy for the students to make half a cone and slice it. Have the class attempt to do so to get a parabola. Most of them will wind up creating half of a hyperbola. Refer these students to the chapter overview. Make sure that they note a parabola is not as easy to create this way as a hyperbola or an ellipse. If the cut is at the wrong angle, even slightly, a hyperbola or an ellipse will be formed instead of a parabola.

- Discuss the reflection properties of parabolas: A beam of light originating at the origin will emerge parallel to the parabola's axis of symmetry, and a beam of light that is parallel to the parabola's axis of symmetry will reflect off of the parabola in a direction that goes through its focus. One nice project is to construct a parabolic pool table or miniature golf hole. The students accurately graph a parabola, and glue erasers or wood along its border, placing the "hole" at the focus. A golf ball or pool ball that is rolled in a direction parallel to the axis will always bounce into the hole.

355

- As of this writing, it is possible to purchase a parabolic listening device for about $40 on eBay, or about $60 new. If this is feasible, many experiments and demonstrations can be done. For example, students can whisper from a long distance away and be heard using the device.

- Make the connection between quadratic functions and parabolas explicit. Point out that any equation of the form $y = ax^2 + bx + c$ can be written as $y = n(x - h)^2 + k$ by completing the square, yielding a (possibly shifted) parabola. The constant n is often written as $4p$. Note that if $a = 0$ we have a line. So we can call a line a "degenerate parabola".

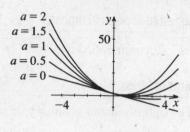

▼ Examples

A shifted parabola:

$$y = 2x^2 - 8x + 2$$
$$= 2(x^2 - 4x) + 2$$
$$= 2(x^2 - 4x + 4) - 6$$
$$= 2(x - 2)^2 - 6$$

$p = \frac{1}{2}$, focus $\left(0 + 2, \frac{1}{2} - 6\right) = \left(2, -\frac{11}{2}\right)$, directrix $y = -\frac{1}{2} - 6 = -\frac{13}{2}$

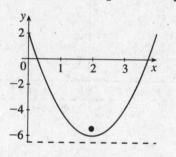

▼ Group Work: The Effect of Gravity

Demonstrate that a tossed object will trace out a parabola. A quick way to do this is, of course, to throw an eraser. A more elaborate way to do it is to darken the room and toss a glow-stick or tiny flashlight. Starting with Problem 5, this activity segues into shifting the parabola, which will be covered in more detail in Section 11.4.

Answers:

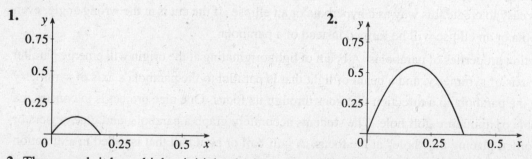

3. The second: it has a higher initial velocity, so its maximum height is greater.

4. The second: it has a higher initial velocity, so it travels upward longer.

5. $h(t) = -16t^2 + v_0 t + 100$

6. $h(t) = -16t^2 + v_0 t + s_0$

7. (a) $0 = -16t^2 + 216 \implies t \approx 3.674$ s

   (b) $0 = -16t^2 + 10t + 216 \implies t = 4$ s

   (c) $h(t) = -16t^2 + 10t + 216 = -16\left(t^2 - \frac{5}{8}t + \frac{25}{256}\right) + 216 + \frac{25}{256} = -16\left(t - \frac{5}{16}\right)^2 + \frac{55{,}321}{256}$. It reaches its maximum height at $t = \frac{5}{16}$ s.

   (d) The maximum height is $\frac{3481}{16} \approx 217.56$ ft.

▼ Homework Problems

Core Exercises: 3, 7, 14, 18, 31, 40, 42, 53

Sample Assignment: 3, 7, 10, 14, 18, 21, 31, 36, 40, 42, 46, 49, 53, 55, 56

GROUP WORK, SECTION 11.1

The Effect of Gravity

If you toss an object upward from the ground, its height at time t (in feet) is given by

$$h(t) = -16t^2 + v_0 t$$

where v_0 (pronounced "vee-naught") is the velocity of the toss in ft/s.

1. Sketch the graph of the height of a ball as a function of time if it is thrown with an initial velocity of 3 ft/s.

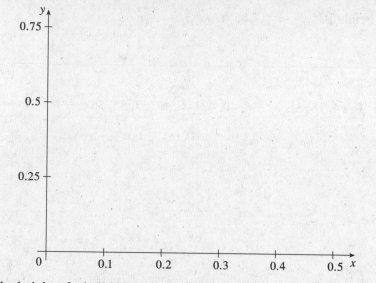

2. Sketch the graph of the height of a ball if it is thrown with an initial velocity of six feet per second.

3. Which of your two graphs has a higher vertex? Physically, why is that the case?

4. Which of your two graphs has a vertex that is farther to the right? Physically, why is that the case?

5. Now assume you are not starting at the ground, but at a height of 100 feet. Find a formula for the height of the object as a function of time.

6. Find a formula for the height of the object if you are starting s_0 feet above the ground.

7. (a) Assume now that you take a ball to the top of a 216 foot tall building and let it drop. When does it reach the ground?

(b) When would it reach the ground if you tossed it upwards with an initial velocity of 10 ft/s?

(c) In that case, when would it reach its maximum height?

(d) What would that maximum height be?

11.2 ELLIPSES

▼ Suggested Time and Emphasis

$\frac{1}{2}$–1 class. Optional material.

▼ Points to Stress

1. The definition and geometry of ellipses.

2. Using the equation of an ellipse to find relevant constants and to graph the ellipse.

3. Eccentricity.

▼ Sample Questions

- **Text Question:** Does $\dfrac{x^2}{5^2} + \dfrac{y^2}{6^2} = 1$ describe a horizontal or a vertical ellipse? How do you know?

  Answer: It is vertical because the denominator of the y^2 term is larger than that of the x^2 term.

- **Drill Question:** Find the vertices and foci of the ellipse $\frac{1}{4}x^2 + y^2 = 1$ and sketch its graph.

  Answer: Vertices $(\pm 2, 0)$, foci $(\pm\sqrt{3}, 0)$

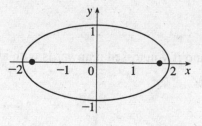

▼ In-Class Materials

- Have students sketch an ellipse with thumbtacks and string, as suggested in the text. Have some use foci that are close together, and some that are farther apart. Make sure they see the connection between this activity and the idea that the summed distance from the foci is a constant.

- As noted in Section 11.1, one can use dental floss and a modeling compound (such as clay or Play-Doh) to make half a cone and slice it. Have the class attempt to do so to get a circle. Note that if their angle is slightly off, they will get an ellipse. Make the analogy that just as a square is a particular kind of rectangle, a circle is a particular kind of ellipse.

- Many representational artists never draw circles, noting that it is rare in nature to see a circle, since we are usually looking at an angle, thus seeing an ellipse. Perhaps have the students bring in photographs of manhole covers and other "circular" objects, noting that if the camera angle is not straight on, the resultant image is elliptical. (Because of the optical illusion of perspective, it makes things easier to draw the outline of the "circle" with a marker to see that it is an ellipse.)

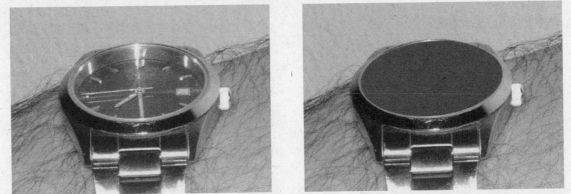

- Discuss the reflection property of an ellipse: a beam of light originating at one focus will reflect off the ellipse and pass through the other focus. One nice project is to construct an elliptical pool table. The students accurately graph an ellipse, and glue erasers or wood along its border, placing the "hole" at one focus and marking the second. A golf ball or pool ball that is placed on the mark and struck in any direction will ricochet into the hole.

- Note that if $a = b$ then we have only one focus, at $(0, 0)$. In this case, the geometric definition breaks down, but it is clear from the equation that we have a circle. This is why a circle can be thought of as a "degenerate ellipse".

▼ Examples

- A vertical ellipse: $\dfrac{x^2}{16} + \dfrac{y^2}{25} = 1$
- A horizontal ellipse: $\dfrac{x^2}{9} + 4y^2 = 1$

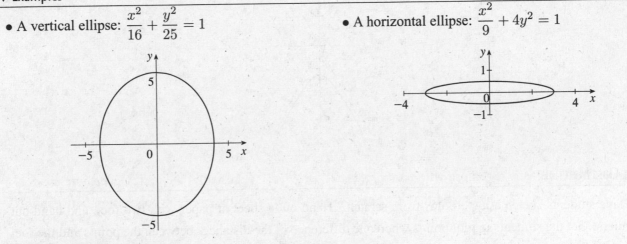

▼ Group Work: Ellipses in Nature

As suggested earlier, have the students bring in photographs of circles, either clipped out of magazines or taken by themselves. Have them use a photocopier to make the photograph sufficiently large. Using a photocopier or a transparency, instruct the students to overlay a grid on their photograph, and determine whether the shape in question is a circle or an ellipse. Have the students find the equation of their shape.

▼ Homework Problems

Core Exercises: 2, 6, 9, 20, 28, 33, 40, 48, 55

Sample Assignment: 2, 6, 8, 9, 13, 20, 24, 28, 33, 36, 40, 43, 48, 51, 54, 55

11.3   HYPERBOLAS

▼ Suggested Time and Emphasis

$\frac{1}{2}$ class. Optional material.

▼ Points to Stress

1. The definition and geometry of hyperbolas.
2. Using the equation of a hyperbola to find relevant constants.
3. Graphing a hyperbola given its equation.

▼ Sample Questions

- **Text Question:** Is $\dfrac{x^2}{5^2} - \dfrac{y^2}{6^2} = 1$ the equation of a horizontal or a vertical hyperbola? How do you know?

  Answer: It is horizontal because the x^2 term is positive.

- **Drill Question:** Find the vertices, foci, and asymptotes of the hyperbola given by $\frac{y^2}{4} - x^2 = 1$. Then graph it.

  Answer: Vertices $(0, \pm 2)$, foci $\left(0, \pm\sqrt{5}\right)$, asymptotes $y = \pm 2x$

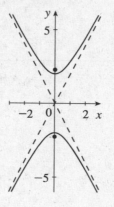

▼ In-Class Materials

- Have students sketch a hyperbola "from scratch." Hand out a sheet of paper with two foci, and hand out rulers. Get the students to plot points where the difference of the distances between the points and the foci is 1 inch. Have them keep plotting points until a hyperbolic shape emerges. There is another way to sketch a hyperbola which will be discussed in the Group Work.

- As noted in Section 11.1, one can use dental floss and a modeling compound (such as clay or Play-Doh) to make a half-cone and slice it. Have the students attempt to do so to get a hyperbola. Notice that the slice does not have to be straight up and down, as shown in the prologue to the chapter. As long as the slice would cut the other half of the cone, the resultant curve is a hyperbola.

- Discuss the reflection property of hyperbolas: Take a point between the branches, and aim a beam of light at one of the foci. It will reflect off the hyperbola, and go in a path aimed directly at the other focus. This reflection property is harder to model physically than those of the ellipse and the parabola.

▼ Examples

- A vertical hyperbola: $-\dfrac{x^2}{16} + \dfrac{y^2}{25} = 1$

  Vertices $(0, \pm 5)$, asymptotes $y = \pm\frac{5}{4}x$, foci $\left(0, \pm\sqrt{41}\right)$

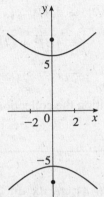

- A horizontal hyperbola: $\dfrac{x^2}{9} - 2y^2 = 1$

  Vertices $(\pm 3, 0)$, asymptotes $y = \pm\frac{1}{3\sqrt{2}}x$, foci $\left(\pm\sqrt{\frac{37}{2}}, 0\right)$

▼ Group Work: Sketching Hyperbolas

This will require students to follow directions carefully. You may have to model the process for them on an overhead projector. There is a bit of a "knack" to keeping the string in the correct position. The students will need a cardboard ruler or straightedge, a thumbtack, tape or fast-drying glue, string, scissors, a pencil, and patience.

If students finish early, there is another construction they can try: Mark two points A and B on a piece of paper. Draw a circle centered at A with a radius small enough so that B lies outside the circle. Now mark an arbitrary point on the circle and fold the paper so B touches that point. Crease the paper along the fold. Mark a different point on the circle, and crease again. If you do this enough times, the creases will form a filled-in hyperbola. As of this writing, the result of this process can be seen on the web at `http://www.cognitiohk.edu.hk/maths/math/em03con.htm`.

Answer:

Let the length of the string be s and the length of the ruler r. Call the unlabeled end of the ruler C. Consider a point on your curve — call it P. (In the figure, the tip of the pencil is at P.)

Then

$$
\begin{aligned}
\left|\overline{BP} - \overline{AP}\right| &= \left|\overline{BP} - (s - \overline{CP})\right| \\
&= \left|\overline{BP} + \overline{CP} - s\right| \\
&= |r - s|
\end{aligned}
$$

Thus $\overline{BP} - \overline{AP}$ is a constant, and so by definition the collection of points P constitutes a hyperbola.

▼ Homework Problems

Core Exercises: 2, 5, 15, 22, 32, 41, 46, 49

Sample Assignment: 2, 5, 8, 15, 20, 22, 25, 32, 36, 41, 46, 48, 49

Sketching Hyperbolas

We are going to be constructing the graph of a hyperbola. This method is going to require some patience, and mastering an unnatural motion, but it does work!

1. Mark two points A and B on a piece of paper. They will be the foci of your hyperbola.

2. Cut a piece of string, a bit longer or a bit shorter than your ruler.

3. Attach one end of the string to one end of your ruler, and the other end of the string to A. Attach it firmly—you don't want it to move about.

4. Pin the other end of the ruler to B, so that the ruler is free to rotate around B.

5. Now tighten the string with a pencil, as shown in the diagram, and rotate the ruler. Make sure that the string does not stretch.

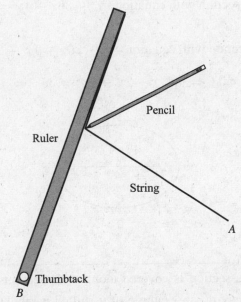

6. To get the other half of the hyperbola, perform the same trick with the end of the ruler tacked to point A and the end of the string attached to point B.

Congratulations! You are now the proud parent of a lovely little hyperbola. Now figure out why this process works.

11.4 SHIFTED CONICS

▼ Suggested Time and Emphasis

1 class. Optional material. May be combined with Sections 11.1–11.3.

▼ Points to Stress

1. Completing the square in a general equation of a conic in order to apply the techniques of Section 2.2 to graph the conic.
2. Identifying conic sections by the constants in the general equation.
3. Understanding degenerate conic sections.

▼ Sample Questions

- **Text Question:** Identify the conic section with equation $9x^2 - 36x + 4y^2 = 0$.

  Answer: Ellipse

- **Drill Question:** Graph the conic section with equation $4x^2 - 16x + 9y^2 - 20 = 0$.

  Answer: $4x^2 - 16x + 9y^2 - 20 = 0 \quad \Leftrightarrow \quad 4(x-2)^2 + 9y^2 = 36 \quad \Leftrightarrow \quad \dfrac{(x-2)^2}{9} + \dfrac{y^2}{4} = 1$

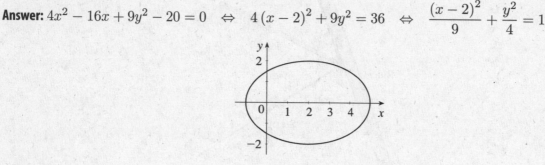

▼ In-Class Materials

- Class time can be saved if this section is covered along with Sections 11.1–11.3. For example, after discussing parabolas, immediately do an example of a shifted parabola. Teach ellipses and hyperbolas similarly.

- The text's guide to the general equation of a shifted conic is important, and students should not memorize it blindly. Point out that if they've learned the previous section, these rules of thumb should make perfect sense. Have them look at the three general formulas they have learned, generalizing them to allow for a shift:

$$y = 4p(x-h)^2$$
$$\frac{(x-h)^2}{a^2} + \frac{(y-k)^2}{b^2} = 1$$
$$\frac{(x-h)^2}{a^2} - \frac{(y-k)^2}{b^2} = 1$$

- Help the class recognize the difference between the formulas of conic sections by pointing out that the equation of a parabola has degree 2 in only one variable (which variable it is determines which type of parabola it is). Equations of ellipses and hyperbolas have degree 2 in both variables; for ellipses the second-degree terms have the same sign, and for hyperbolas they have opposite signs.

366

▼ Examples

- A nondegenerate ellipse:

$$25x^2 + 4y^2 - 150x + 40y + 324 = 0 \quad \Leftrightarrow$$

$$\frac{(x-3)^2}{4} + \frac{(y+5)^2}{25} = 1$$

- A degenerate hyperbola:

$$x^2 - y^2 - 4x - 2y + 3 = 0 \quad \Leftrightarrow$$

$$(x-2)^2 - (y+1)^2 = 0$$

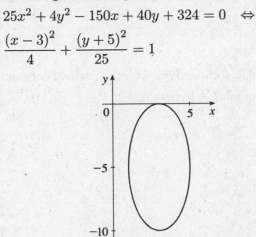

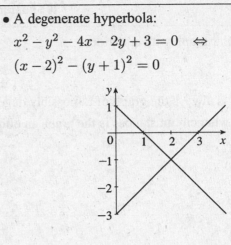

▼ Group Work: It's Easier in Polar

This activity is for classes which have covered polar coordinates.

Answer: The graph is an ellipse if $e < 1$, a hyperbola if $e > 1$, and a parabola when $e = 1$. The directrix is $x = \pm d$ or $y = \pm d$.

▼ Homework Problems

Core Exercises: 5, 10, 18, 24, 27, 42, 40

Sample Assignment: 5, 8, 10, 11, 18, 21, 24, 27, 34, 40, 42, 43

Consider the polar graph with equation

$$r = \frac{ed}{1 \pm e \sin \theta}$$

It turns out this is always the graph of a (possibly degenerate) conic section. Play with the positive constants d and e. Under what circumstances is the graph an ellipse? A parabola? A hyperbola?

11.5 ROTATION OF AXES

▼ Suggested Time and Emphasis

1 class. Optional material.

▼ Points to Stress

1. Rotation of axes formulas.
2. Graphing a general quadratic equation, including middle terms.

▼ Sample Questions

- **Text Question:** If you are presented with the equation of a conic such as $3x^2 + 5xy - 2y^2 + x - y + 4 = 0$, how would you go about finding if it is an ellipse, parabola, or hyperbola?

  Answer: Evaluate the discriminant.

- **Drill Questions:** Consider the equation $3x^2 + 5xy - 2y^2 + x - y + 4 = 0$. What shape is its graph?

  Answer: It is a hyperbola.

▼ In-Class Materials

- Point out the progression of the past few sections. Write out $Ax^2 + Bxy + Cy^2 + Dx + Ey + F = 0$. When the course started, we studied equations of lines, which was just the case in which $A = B = C = 0$. When we discussed circles, that was the case where $A = C$, $B = D = E = 0$. Shifting the center of a circle allowed D and E to take on nonzero values. Our study of conic sections removed the restriction that $A = C$, so this section really is the last step in a logical progression.

- This is a good section to teach with the aid of a CAS, or even a good place to introduce such a device. A great deal of the work in graphing an arbitrary conic section is multiplying out long algebraic expressions, which a CAS can do easily.

- If the students are going to be moving on to linear algebra in the future, Exercise 37 is an excellent one to go over in class. It addresses the idea of transformations, which will be a major topic in that course.

▼ Examples

- The rotated parabola $x^2 + 2xy + y^2 + 2x - 4y = 0$:

  $\cot(2\phi) = 0 \;\Rightarrow\; 2\phi = \frac{\pi}{2} \;\Rightarrow\; \phi = \frac{\pi}{4}$. Now we have $x = \sqrt{2}X - \sqrt{2}Y$, $y = \sqrt{2}X + \sqrt{2}Y$. After substituting, and a lot of algebra, we get $8x^2 - 2\sqrt{2}x - 6\sqrt{2}y = 0$. Completing the square, $y = \frac{2\sqrt{2}}{3}\left(x - \frac{\sqrt{2}}{8}\right)^2 - \frac{\sqrt{2}}{48} \approx 0.9\,(x - 0.2)^2$ (for sketching purposes).

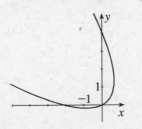

▼ Group Work

Graphing any of the conics in Exercises 15–28 makes a good group project, but be aware that these problems will take the students a significant amount of time.

▼ Homework Problems

Core Exercises: 4, 10, 18, 25, 28, 31, 35

Sample Assignment: 4, 8, 10, 14, 18, 21, 25, 28, 31, 34, 35, 36, 37

11.6 POLAR EQUATIONS OF CONICS

▼ Suggested Time and Emphasis

1 class. Optional material.

▼ Points to Stress

1. Expressing conic sections in polar form.
2. Rotating conic sections in parametric form.
3. The eccentricity of a conic.

▼ Sample Questions

- **Text Question:** State a reason that we would want to express a conic in polar form.

  Answer: Answers will vary. One reason is that they are easier to rotate when expressed in polar form.

- **Drill Question:** Identify the conic $r = \dfrac{6}{1 \pm 3\cos\theta}$

  Answer: It is a hyperbola.

▼ In-Class Materials

- It is good to go over Figure 6 with the class, having them use their calculators to vary the eccentricity e of a given conic section, and see how it affects the graph. Most graphic calculators have a mode for graphing polar functions as well.
- Notice the advantages of working with conics in polar form. They are easier to rotate, for example. It is also easier to identify a conic as an ellipse, parabola, or hyperbola by inspection. After some practice, we can even look at such an equation and have a good idea of what the graph will look like, again by inspection.
- We have called a circle a "degenerate ellipse". The text notes that when e is close to zero, the resultant ellipse is close to circular. Examine the equation of a conic when $e = 0$ to see how it is undefined for that value of e.

▼ Examples

Identifying and graphing conic sections:

- $r = \dfrac{6}{1 + 3\cos\left(\theta - \frac{\pi}{6}\right)}$ is a hyperbola, rotated 30° from standard position, with eccentricity 3.

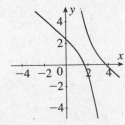

- $r = \dfrac{6}{3 + 3\cos\left(\theta - \frac{\pi}{6}\right)} = \dfrac{2}{1 + \cos\left(\theta - \frac{\pi}{6}\right)}$ is a parabola.

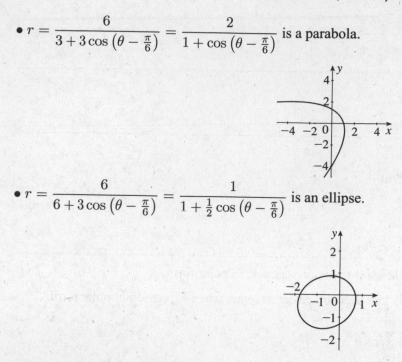

- $r = \dfrac{6}{6 + 3\cos\left(\theta - \frac{\pi}{6}\right)} = \dfrac{1}{1 + \frac{1}{2}\cos\left(\theta - \frac{\pi}{6}\right)}$ is an ellipse.

▼ Group Work: The Polar Conic

This activity allows students to discover the last topic in the section, and reinforces the formulas in the section.

Answers:

1. For $e > 1$ we have a hyperbola, for $e = 1$ we have a parabola, and for $0 < e < 1$ we have an ellipse. Also, as $e \to 0$, the ellipse becomes more circular.
2. As c changes, the ellipse rotates about the origin.
3. Technically, we are moving the directrix. The students should notice that the size of the ellipse changes.

▼ Homework Problems

Core Exercises: 3, 7, 12, 18, 23, 26, 32, 43

Sample Assignment: 3, 7, 9, 12, 14, 18, 20, 23, 26, 27, 32, 33, 38, 43, 44

1. Consider the polar equation $r = \dfrac{2e}{1 + e \sin \theta}$. Graph this equation for $e = 4, 3, 2, 1.5, 1, 0.8, \frac{1}{2}, \frac{1}{3}, \frac{1}{4}$, and $\frac{1}{5}$. What do you notice?

2. Now consider the equation $r = \dfrac{1}{1 + \frac{1}{2} \sin (\theta + c)}$. Graph this equation for various values of c, such as $c = -0.3, -0.2, -0.1, 0, 0.1, 0.2$, and 0.3. What do you notice?

3. Finally, consider the equation $r = \dfrac{\frac{1}{2}d}{1 + \frac{1}{2} \sin \theta}$. Graph this equation for various values of d. What do you notice?

12 SEQUENCES AND SERIES

12.1 SEQUENCES AND SUMMATION NOTATION

▼ Suggested Time and Emphasis

1 class. Optional material.

▼ Points to Stress

1. Definition and notation of sequences.
2. Recursively defined sequences, including the Fibonacci sequence.
3. Partial sums, including summation notation.

▼ Sample Questions

- **Text Question:** Compute $\sum_{k=1}^{5} k$.

  Answer: 15

- **Drill Question:** If we have a sequence defined by $a_1 = 4$, $a_2 = -3$ and $a_n = a_{n-2} + a_{n-1}$ for $n \geq 3$, what is a_4?

  Answer: -2

▼ In-Class Materials

- Students often confuse the ideas of a function and a sequence. Have the students graph the function $f(n) = \sin 2\pi n$, $n \in \mathbb{R}$. Then have them graph the sequence $a_n = \sin 2\pi n$, $n \in \mathbb{N}$. This should help them understand the difference.

- Note that there are many sequences that have no pattern: $1, \pi, 3, e, -27, \ldots$. Also point out that not every sequence with a pattern has a rule that is easily written as a formula. Examples:

$$3, 1, 4, 1, 5, 9, 2, 6, 5, 3, \ldots$$

$$3, 3.1, 3.14, 3.141, 3.1415, \ldots$$

$$1, 100, 1000, 2, 99, 1001, 3, 98, 1002, 4, 97, 1003, 5, 96, 1004, \ldots$$

$$0, 0.1, 0.12, 0.123, \ldots, 0.123456789, 0.12345678910, 0.1234567891011, \ldots$$

  (The limit of this last sequence is called the Champernowne constant.)

- Have the students try to figure out the pattern of this sequence:

$$3, 3, 5, 4, 4, 3, 5, 5, 4, 3, \ldots$$

  Answer: It counts the number of letters in the words 'one', 'two', 'three', ...

- Melissa Pfohl's favorite sequence is $a_n = n^2 + (-1)^n n$. Starting with $n = 0$, the sequence goes as follows: 0, 0, 6, 6, 20, 20, 42, 42, ... Note that the formula is far from obvious, and the tantalizing "doubling property" can be proved using elementary methods.

- There are several ways of making the terms of a sequence alternate. The text gives the term $(-1)^n$. Another alternating sequence is $\cos \pi n$. Ask the students to come up with a formula for the following sequence: 0, 1, 0, -1, 0, 1, 0, -1, ... There are several ways to do this, but the cleanest is $\sin\left(\frac{\pi}{2}n\right)$.

375

- The Fibonacci sequence comes up in many contexts. Group Work 1 gives students several. If this group work is not completely covered, its problems can be used as examples. They can then be called back into service when mathematical induction is covered.

- Have students compute some partial sums that converge quickly to a recognizable number, such as the one associated with $a_n = \dfrac{1}{(n-1)!}$ (with $a_1 = 1$) which converges to e, and $a_n = \left(\dfrac{3}{4}\right)^n$ which converges to 3. Then have them look at some partial sums that go off to infinity, such as the ones associated with $a_n = 10^n$ and $a_n = n$. Then have them conjecture about the fate of $a_n = \dfrac{1}{n}$, perhaps deferring the answer until Group Work 3.

▼ Examples

- A non-obvious telescoping series: Consider the sequence $\frac{1}{2}$, $\frac{1}{6}$, $\frac{1}{12}$, $\frac{1}{20}$, $\ldots$, $a_n = \dfrac{1}{n(n+1)}$. This can be rewritten as $a_n = \dfrac{1}{n} - \dfrac{1}{n+1}$. Thus $\displaystyle\sum_{n=1}^{k} a_n = 1 - \dfrac{1}{k+1}$ (as shown in the text).

- A sequence whose values look random: $a_n = \sin\left(n^2\right)$

▼ Group Work 1: Finding a Pattern

This activity involves several problems. Divide the students into groups, and give each group a different problem. If a group finishes early, you can have them try to prove their answer, or you can give them a different problem to work on. Have them save their work, because these answers can all be shown by the principle of mathematical induction, which is covered in Section 12.5.

An interesting article about human geneology, related to Form C, can be found at `http://www.msnbc.msn.com/id/13621729/`.

Answers:

All the questions boil down to finding Fibonacci numbers.

Form A: 165580141

Form B: 165580141

Form C: 1. 5   **2.** 165580141

▼ Group Work 2: Using the Notation

The idea of this activity is to familiarize the students with the notation of sequences and series. Perhaps do the first problem with the class, so they get the idea of writing out a general term.

Answers:

1. 5, n, 21
2. 0.00002, 2×10^{-n}, 0.222222
3. 0.0002, 20×10^{-n} or $2 \times 10^{-n+1}$, 2.22222
4. 12, $2 + 2n$, 54
5. $\dfrac{1}{25}$, $(-1)^{n+1}\dfrac{1}{n^2}$, $\dfrac{973}{1200}$

376

▼ Group Work 3: The Harmonic Series

This activity was suggested by the Teacher's Guide to AP Calculus published by the College Board. It will allow the students to discover the divergence of the harmonic series for themselves.

Answer:

1. $s_1 = 1$, $s_2 = 1.5$, $s_3 \approx 1.8333$, $s_4 \approx 2.08333$, $s_5 \approx 2.28333$, $s_6 = 2.45$, $s_7 \approx 2.5929$, $s_8 \approx 2.7179$, $s_9 \approx 2.8290$, $s_{10} \approx 2.9290$

2, 4.

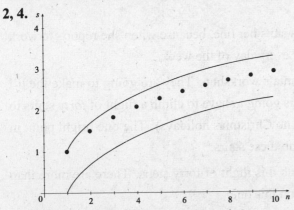

3. The partial sums appear to approach 3.

5. We know $\ln x$ goes to infinity, and the partial sum s_n seems to always be larger than $\ln n$.

6. The guesses will vary, but will almost certainly be overestimates. As of 2008, and continuing through our grandchildren's lives, the answer to five significant digits is 25.967.

▼ Homework Problems

Core Exercises: 4, 7, 14, 28, 33, 42, 57, 62, 67

Sample Assignment: 4, 7, 12, 14, 17, 28, 32, 33, 39, 42, 46, 57, 62, 65, 67, 74, 77

Finding a Pattern (Form A)

Sally the Elf likes to climb stairs. She can climb them one step or two steps at a time. The staircase in front of Santa's workshop has four steps. Every day, when she reports to work, Sally tries to climb it a different way. Sometimes she goes one step at a time $(1, 1, 1, 1)$, sometimes two steps at a time $(2, 2)$, sometimes she goes up one step, then two, then one $(1, 2, 1)$, sometimes she goes up one, another, then two $(1, 1, 2)$ or vice versa $(2, 1, 1)$.

So there are a total of five ways she can climb the steps. This suits her fine, because when she reports to work (at 9 A.M., Monday to Friday) she can go up a different way every day of the week.

This will all change in 2008, when Microdweeb acquires Santa's workshop. They are going to make the li'l toy factory into a huge manufacturing megaplex. Poor Sally is going to have to climb a flight of *forty* stairs to get to work every day (at 8 A.M., Monday to Saturday, with no Christmas holidays). The one bright point in her newly sad life is that she will have plenty of ways to climb these stairs.

Your challenge is to compute how many ways Sally can climb this flight of forty steps. There are more than 5,000 of them, so listing them is probably not the way to go on this one.

A sequence of 0s and 1s is called **successor-free** if it does not have two 1s in a row. For example, these sequences are successor-free:

$$00000$$

$$010101$$

$$0100100010001$$

These sequences are not successor-free:

$$0011$$

$$11111111$$

$$0100110001$$

There are five three-element successor-free sequences: 000, 001, 010, 100, and 101.

How many thirty-nine-element successor-free sequences are there? There are more than 5,000 of them, so listing them is probably not the way to go here.

Finding a Pattern (Form C)

A female bee, or worker, comes from a fertilized egg, laid by the Queen bee. A male bee, or drone, comes from an unfertilized egg, laid by either the Queen bee or a worker bee. In other words:

A female bee has a mother and a father, but a male bee has only a mother.

This makes life strange for bee genealogists. For example, a drone has two grandparents, but a worker has three! Check it out:

Drone Ancestry: One mommy (who has a mommy and a daddy). He has two grandparents.

Worker Ancestry: One mommy (who has a mommy and a daddy) and one daddy (who has a mommy). She has three grandparents.

1. How many great-grandparents does a worker bee have?

2. Assuming all ancestors are distinct, how many great^{37}-grandparents does a worker bee have? (37 "great"s). There are more than 5,000 of them, so listing them is probably not the way to go.

Fill in the blanks:

1. $a_1 = 1$, $a_2 = 2$, $a_3 = 3$, $a_4 = 4$, $a_5 = $ _____ , ..., $a_n = $ _____ , $\displaystyle\sum_{n=1}^{6} a_n = $ _____ .

2. $b_1 = 0.2$, $b_2 = 0.02$, $b_3 = 0.002$, $b_4 = 0.0002$, $b_5 = $ _____ , ..., $b_n = $ _____ , $\displaystyle\sum_{n=1}^{6} b_n = $ _____ .

3. $c_1 = 2$, $c_2 = 0.2$, $c_3 = 0.02$, $c_4 = 0.002$, $c_5 = $ _____ , ..., $c_n = $ _____ , $\displaystyle\sum_{n=1}^{6} c_n = $ _____ .

4. $d_1 = 4$, $d_2 = 6$, $d_3 = 8$, $d_4 = 10$, $d_5 = $ _____ , ..., $d_n = $ _____ , $\displaystyle\sum_{n=1}^{6} d_n = $ _____ .

5. $e_1 = 1$, $e_2 = -\frac{1}{4}$, $e_3 = \frac{1}{9}$, $e_4 = -\frac{1}{16}$, $e_5 = $ _____ , ..., $e_n = $ _____ , $\displaystyle\sum_{n=1}^{6} d_n = $ _____ .

In this exercise, we look at $\displaystyle\sum_{n=1}^{\infty} \frac{1}{n}$.

1. What are the first ten partial sums s_n?

$s_1 =$	$s_6 =$
$s_2 =$	$s_7 =$
$s_3 =$	$s_8 =$
$s_4 =$	$s_9 =$
$s_5 =$	$s_{10} =$

2. The way we will compute $\displaystyle\sum_{n=1}^{\infty} \frac{1}{n}$ (or prove that it goes to infinity) is to compute the limit of its partial sums. Plot the partial sums on the following graph, as accurately as you can.

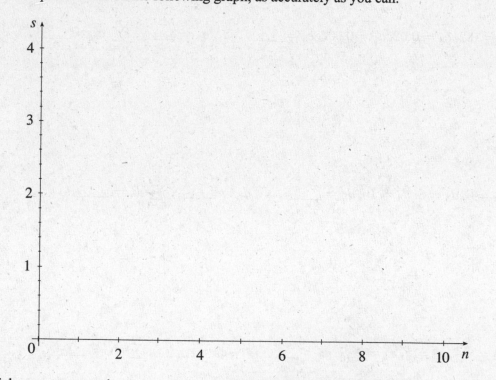

3. The partial sums appear to be approaching a number. What is that number?

4. Now, on the same axes, graph $y = \ln x$ and $y = 1 + \ln x$ for $x \geq 1$. (Both of these graphs, as you know, go to infinity as x gets arbitrarily large.)

5. Using your answer to Problem 4 and your graph, explain why it is reasonable to believe that $\sum_{n=1}^{\infty} \dfrac{1}{n}$ goes to infinity.

6. Assume that in the year 4000 B.C., you started adding up the terms of the harmonic series, at the rate of, say, one term per second. We know that the sum gets arbitrarily large, but approximately how big would your partial sum be as of now? Go ahead and make a guess, based on your best judgment and intuition.

12.2 ARITHMETIC SEQUENCES

▼ Suggested Time and Emphasis

$\frac{1}{2}$–1 class. Optional material.

▼ Points to Stress

1. Recognizing arithmetic sequences by their formula and by their graph.
2. Finding the first term a and the common difference d of a given arithmetic sequence, and using this information to compute partial sums.

▼ Sample Questions

- **Text Question:** What distinguishes an "arithmetic sequence" from a plain ol' arbitrary "sequence"?

  Answer: Successive terms in an arithmetic sequence have a common difference.
- **Drill Question:** Consider the sequence 3, 8, 13, 18, 23, 28, 33, 38, ... Find the 100th partial sum.

  Answer: 25,050

▼ In-Class Materials

- The perfect squares 1, 4, 9, 16, . . . can be represented as a square array of dots.

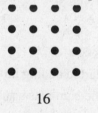

16

- The triangular numbers are those that can be represented by a triangular array of dots: 1, 3, 6, 10, 15, ...

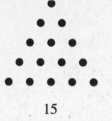

15

Note that the triangular numbers are precisely the partial sums of the sequence 1, 2, 3, 4, ...
- Examine this broader triangular array:

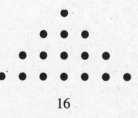

16

Notice we again run into perfect squares! This can be demonstrated by looking at the partial sums of the arithmetic sequence $1 + 2(n - 1)$, or by rearranging the dots of the broader triangle to make a square.
- Consider the classic "handshaking problem". If n people are in a room, and shake hands, we can ask the question: How many handshakes took place? If, for example, four people (Alfred, Brendel, Claude, and

384

Debussy) all shake hands, a total of 6 shakes take place:

$$A \& B \qquad B \& C \qquad C \& D$$
$$A \& C \qquad B \& D$$
$$A \& D$$

Allow the students to try to figure out how many handshakes take place if 12, or if n people shake hands. It turns out that the answer is $1 + 2 + \cdots + (n-1)$ (as illustrated above), the partial sum of an arithmetic sequence.

- Many phenomena are either linear or locally linear (they look linear when viewing them over a narrow range). For example, assume that a company earns about \$120,000 in 2011, \$140,000 in 2012, \$160,000 in 2013, etc. If it is linear growth over ten years, the total ten-year earning can be found from adding up the terms of an arithmetic sequence.

- Show the students that a constant sequence such as $5, 5, 5, 5, \ldots$ is trivially an arithmetic sequence. Notice that the formula for the partial sum is consistent with what we know about basic arithmetic.

- Have the students try to define an arithmetic sequence recursively. It can be done relatively simply as $a_n = a_{n-1} + d$, but obtaining this formula requires an understanding of arithmetic sequences and recursively defined sequences.

▼ Examples

Finding details of an arithmetic sequence given two terms: If an arithmetic sequence has $a_3 = 39$ and $a_{10} = 25$, then we can calculate $a = 43$, $d = -2$. $a_n = 43 - 2(n-1)$, so $a_{100} = -155$ and $\sum_{n=1}^{100} 43 - 2(n-1) = -5600$. Make sure to point out that this trick works only if we *know* ahead of time that this is an arithmetic sequence.

▼ Group Work: Balancing the Budget

This activity gives the students practice with partial sums of arithmetic sequences, and clarifies the differences between terms that are commonly mentioned on the news. After the students have finished the activity, you can discuss the difference between a budget deficit and the national debt.

Answers:

1. $a_n = 50,000 - 1250(n-1)$. So $a_{41} = 0$. The deficit will be zero in 2051.

2. $\sum_{n=1}^{41} (50,000 - 1250(n-1)) = \$1,025,000$

▼ Homework Problems

Core Exercises: 5, 10, 15, 24, 28, 41, 46, 62, 67 8, 19, 26, 32, 51, 57, 64

Sample Assignment: 5, 8, 10, 15, 19, 24, 26, 28, 32, 41, 46, 51, 57, 62, 64 , 67

The budget deficit of a company or country is the difference between the amount it spends in a year and the amount that it earns. If, for example, a company earns $10,000 and spends $12,000 we say that the budget deficit is $2000. (If a company or country earns more then it spends, we call that a budget surplus).

Assume a company starts out with a budget deficit of $50,000 in the year 2011. The company doesn't want to have a deficit, but it is very hard to erase a budget deficit; it is hard to suddenly reduce costs or increase income. To do this, the company enacts a program to reduce the deficit by $1250 every year. So in the year 2012, for example, the budget deficit will be $48,750.

1. In what year will the deficit be gone?

2. Just because the deficit is gone does not mean the news is all good. Recall that every year from 2011 until the year the deficit goes away, more money is going out than coming in! That amount still has to be made up, and is called (as you would think) debt. What is the total amount of debt the company owes in the year the deficit is eliminate?

12.3 GEOMETRIC SEQUENCES

▼ Suggested Time and Emphasis

$\frac{1}{2}$–1 class. Optional material.

▼ Points to Stress

1. Definition of geometric sequences and geometric series.
2. Formula for the partial sum of a geometric sequence.
3. Formula for the sum of an infinite geometric series.

▼ Sample Questions

- **Text Question:** What distinguishes a "geometric sequence" from a plain ol' arbitrary "sequence"?

  Answer: Successive terms in a geometric sequence have a common ratio.

- **Drill Question:** Find the 100th partial sum of the sequence 2, 6, 18, 54, 162, ...

  Answer: $\dfrac{2\left(1 - 3^{100}\right)}{1 - 3} \approx 5.154 \times 10^{47}$

▼ In-Class Materials

- Represent a geometric series visually. For example, a geometric view of the equation $\sum\limits_{n=1}^{\infty} 1/2^n = 1$ is given below.

An alternative geometric view is given in Group Work 1, Problem 2. If this group work is not assigned, the figure should be shown to the class at this time.

- Introduce the idea that for any two real numbers A and B, the statement $A = B$ is the same as saying that for any integer N, $|A - B| < 1/N$. Now use this idea to show that $0.9999\ldots = 0.\overline{9} = 1$, since

$$\left|1 - 0.\overline{9}\right| < \left|1 - \underbrace{0.99999\ldots99}_{N \text{ nines}}\right| = \underbrace{0.00000\ldots0001}_{N-1 \text{ zeros}} = 10^{-N} = \frac{1}{10^N}.$$ Then use the usual approach to

define $0.\overline{9}$ as $\sum\limits_{n=1}^{\infty} 9/10^n$ and show directly that $0.\overline{9} = 1$. Generalize this result by pointing out that *any* repeating decimal ($0.\overline{3}$, $0.\overline{412}$, $0.24\overline{621}$) can be written as a geometric series, and can thus be written as a fraction using the formula for a geometric series. Demonstrate with $0.\overline{412} = \frac{412}{1000}\left(\frac{1}{1 - 1/1000}\right) = \frac{412}{999}$.

- Explore the "middle third" Cantor set with the class: This set is defined as the set of points obtained by taking the interval $[0, 1]$, throwing out the middle third to obtain $\left[0, \frac{1}{3}\right] \cup \left[\frac{2}{3}, 1\right]$, throwing out the middle third of each remaining interval to obtain $\left[0, \frac{1}{9}\right] \cup \left[\frac{2}{9}, \frac{1}{3}\right] \cup \left[\frac{2}{3}, \frac{7}{9}\right] \cup \left[\frac{8}{9}, 1\right]$, and repeating this process *ad infinitum*. Point out that there are infinitely many points left after this process. (If a point winds up as the endpoint of an interval, it never gets removed, and new intervals are created with every step). Now calculate the total length of the sections that were thrown away: $\frac{1}{3} + 2 \cdot \frac{1}{9} + 4 \cdot \frac{1}{27} + \cdots = \sum\limits_{k=0}^{\infty} \frac{2^k}{3^{k+1}} = 1$.

Notice the apparent paradox: We've thrown away a total interval of length 1, but still infinitely many points remain. (See also Exercise 85.)

● **Do Exercise 79** (the "St. Ives" problem) with the students. After obtaining the partial sum solution, point out that traditionally people give the answer 1. The poem says "As *I* was going to St. Ives..." So presumably all the other people were going the other way, away from St. Ives! (The text is careful to state the assumptions clearly in order to avoid this issue.)

● **One of the consequences** of parenthood is it often causes otherwise rational adults to say things like, "If I told you once, I've told you one *hundred* times!" Assume that this was true, and a child was told something on a Friday. The parental rule means that the child was previously told that fact one hundred times, say on Thursday. Thus, on Wednesday, the child must have been told the information 100 times for every time on Thursday, or 10,000 times. Use the methods of this section to determine how many times the child has been told since Monday.

♥ Examples

Zeno's Paradox: In order to walk to a wall across the room, you have to first walk halfway to the wall, and in order to do that you have to walk halfway to the halfway point, etc. This process can be viewed as finding the sum of $\frac{1}{2} + \frac{1}{4} + \frac{1}{8} + \cdots$. The sum of this infinite series is 1.

♥ Group Work 1: Made in the Shade

Problem 1 attempts to help the students visualize geometric series. Problem 2 gives a geometric interpretation of the fact that $\frac{1}{2} + \frac{1}{4} + \frac{1}{8} + \frac{1}{16} + \cdots = 1$.

Answers:

1. (a) $a = \frac{1}{2}\pi, r = \frac{1}{4}, A = \frac{2\pi}{3}$ **(b)** $a = \frac{1}{4}, r = \frac{1}{4}, A = \frac{1}{3}$

2. (a) $a_n = \dfrac{1}{2^n}$

   (b) 1. Note that the students may use the geometric series formula to get the answer, but it should be pointed out that the answer is immediate from the diagram.

♥ Group Work 2: An Unusual Series and its Sums

The initial student reaction may be "I have no idea where to start!" One option is to start the problem on the board. Another approach may be to encourage the students to write down the length of the largest dotted line segment (b), then to figure out the length of the next one, which they can get using trigonometry, and keep going as long as they can. Many students still resist the idea of tackling a problem "one step at a time" if it seems difficult.

Answers:

1. $L = b + b\sin\theta + b\sin^2\theta + \cdots$ or $\sum_{n=1}^{\infty} b(\sin\theta)^{n-1}$. Because there are infinitely many terms, we need to write the answer as a series.

2. $L = \dfrac{b}{1 - \sin\theta}$ **3.** L approaches infinity.

4. *Geometrically:* As $\theta \to \frac{\pi}{2}$, the picture breaks down. The easiest way to see this is to have the students try to sketch what happens for θ close to $\frac{\pi}{2}$. The dotted lines become infinitely dense.

Using infinite sums: $\lim\limits_{\theta \to \pi/2} \dfrac{b}{1 - \sin\theta}$ diverges.

▼ Group Work 3: The Popular Organization

This activity dramatizes exponential growth, while at the same time exploring geometric series. After the students have done the assignment, ask them to redo Questions 2 and 4, this time using a time period of 100 years.

Answers:

1. $a_n = 1000 + 100\,(n - 1)$, $a_{10} = 1900$

2. $\sum_{n=1}^{10} (1000 + 100\,(n - 1)) = 14{,}500$

3. $a_n = 1000\,(1.1)^{n-1}$, $a_{10} \approx \$2357.95$

4. $\sum_{n=1}^{10} 1000\,(1.1)^{n-1} \approx \$15{,}937.42$

For 100 years, the arithmetic sequence gives $595,000 and the geometric sequence gives $137,796,120.

▼ Homework Problems

Core Exercises: 4, 5, 14, 28, 38, 49, 54, 61, 64, 85

Sample Assignment: 4, 5, 11, 14, 17, 23, 28, 34, 38, 44, 49, 54, 57, 61, 64, 73, 76, 85

1. Compute the sum of the shaded areas for each figure.

(a)

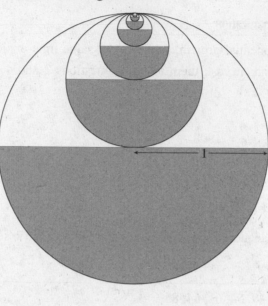

(b)

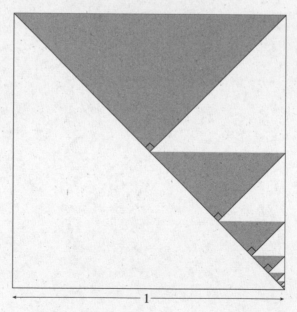

2. Consider the figure below.

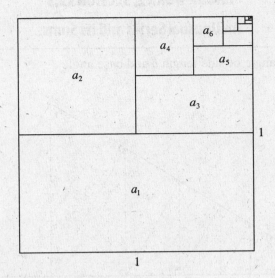

(a) Find an general expression for the area a_n.

(b) What is $\sum_{n=1}^{\infty} a_n$?

Consider the following right triangle of side length b and base angle θ.

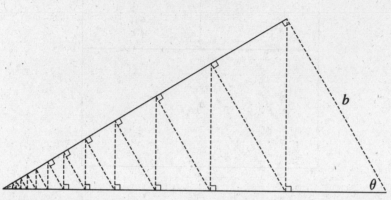

1. Express the total length of the dotted line in the triangle in terms of b and θ. Why should your answer be given in terms of a series?

2. Compute the sum of this series.

3. What happens as $\theta \to \frac{\pi}{2}$?

4. Justify this answer geometrically and using infinite sums.

GROUP WORK 3, SECTION 12.3

The Popular Organization

I have started a wonderful organization, called the Society for the Enhancement of the Lives of certain pro-Fessors (SELF). People can join for an amount of money of their choosing, and it goes to me, to enhance my life. This year hasn't been good—I made only $1100. But it is better than last year, my first year, when I made $1000.

1. Assume the annual earnings increase as an arithmetic sequence. How much money will people send SELF in year 10?

2. What will be the total earnings after 10 years?

3. Assume the annual earnings increase as a geometric sequence. How much money will people send SELF in year 10?

4. What will be the total earnings after 10 years?

12.4 MATHEMATICS OF FINANCE

▼ Suggested Time and Emphasis

$\frac{1}{2}$–1 class. Optional material.

▼ Points to Stress

1. The future and present values of an annuity.
2. Calculating the interest rate of an annuity from the size of monthly payments.

▼ Sample Questions

- **Text Question:** What is an annuity?

  Answer: An annuity is a sum of money paid in regular equal payments.
- **Drill Question:** Every year, an investor deposits $2000 in an IRA that earns an interest rate of 6% per year. How much is in the IRA after ten years?

  Answer: $2000\dfrac{(1+0.06)^{10}-1}{0.06} = 26{,}361.59$

▼ In-Class Materials

The key idea here is that there are many practical examples available to use as illustrations.

- Many states and companies hold lotteries and sweepstakes. The large ones have options where the winner can chose a large lump sum award, or a larger award paid out over a period of years. Find the data for a local lottery or sweepstakes, and decide which option is the better option from a financial standpoint. For example, in the multistate United States Powerball, five white balls are drawn from a set of 53, and one red Powerball is drawn from a set of 42. The payouts are as follows:

Numbers Matched	Payout
All five numbers + Powerball	Jackpot (use $10 million as an example)
All five numbers, without Powerball	$100,000
Four numbers + Powerball	$5000
Four numbers, without Powerball	$100
Three numbers + Powerball	$100
Three numbers without Powerball	$7
Two numbers + Powerball	$7
One number + Powerball	$4
Powerball only	$3

If the grand prize is $10 million, it will be paid over 30 years, or the winner can choose to receive a lump sum payment of $5.8 million.

- A phone call to a cooperative automobile dealership will get a sample monthly payment on a 4-year car loan. Students can figure out the interest rate on cars in their community, and see if it varies based on the cost of the car.

- Students can be assigned to contact mortgage brokers to find the size of payments (and current interest rate) on an average 30 year mortgage on a house near their home or school. They then can explore the effects of making a larger or smaller down payment on the house.

▼ **Examples**

A person borrows $20,000 to buy a car, and wants to pay it off in 4 years. If the interest rate is 8% per year, compounded monthly, what is the amount of each monthly payment?

Answer: $488.26

▼ **Group Work: The Double Payment**

It is a common myth that if you pay double your first payment on a mortgage, then you will be paid off years earlier. This fact has appeared in newspapers and is often repeated on television. In this activity, your students prove it to be false. It is true, however, that if you make one extra payment *per year* then the mortgage will be paid off significantly faster.

Answers:

1. $1197.55   **2.** $431,118.00   **3.** 29 years, 3 months

▼ **Homework Problems**

Core Exercises: 4, 9, 14, 23, 26, 31

Sample Assignment: 4, 7, 9, 10, 14, 15, 18, 23, 26, 28, 31

GROUP WORK, SECTION 12.4

The Double Payment

I **want to buy** a $200,000 home, and take a 30 year mortgage on it. My interest rate is 7%. I have saved $20,000 to make a down payment.

1. What will my monthly payment be?

2. What will be the total amount that I pay the bank?

3. If I double my first payment, my loan will be paid off before the 30 years are up. How long will it take **before the** loan is paid off?

12.5 MATHEMATICAL INDUCTION

▼ Suggested Time and Emphasis

1–2 classes. Optional material.

▼ Point to Stress

The concept and execution of a proof by mathematical induction.

▼ Sample Questions

- **Text Question:** There are two main steps to a proof by mathematical induction. What is the first one?
  Answer: Any answer getting at the idea of a base case or a "proof for $n = 1$" should be accepted, even if the latter isn't technically true.

- **Drill Question:** Use mathematical induction to prove that $1 + 2 + \cdots + n = \dfrac{n(n+1)}{2}$.

  Answer: This is Example 2 from the text.

▼ In-Class Materials

- The main thing for induction is to give the students plenty of examples to work from, and plenty of practice.

  1. We can use induction to show that $\dfrac{(2n)!}{2^n n!}$ is an integer for all positive n. The base case is trivial. The key step in the inductive case:

  $$\frac{(2n+2)!}{2^{n+1}(n+1)!} = \frac{(2n)!}{2^n n!} \cdot \frac{(2n+1)(2n+2)}{2(n+1)}$$

  and now cancellation occurs.

  2. We can use induction to show that the sum of the cubes of three consecutive integers is divisible by 9. The base case is trivial. The key inductive step:

  $$(n+1)^3 + (n+2)^3 + (n+3)^3 = n^3 + (n+1)^3 + (n+2)^3 + 9n^2 + 27n + 27$$

  3. We can use induction to show that

  $$\frac{n^3 - n}{3} = (1 \cdot 2) + (2 \cdot 3) + \ldots + (n-1)n$$

  The base step should be $n = 2$, and the inductive step uses the fact that

  $$\frac{(n+1)^3 - (n+1)}{3} = \frac{n^3 - n}{3} + \frac{3n^2 + 3n}{3}$$

- A variant on induction can be used to prove the results of Group Work 1 in Section 12.1 ("Finding a Pattern"). The students can do these, or you can write it on the blackboard.

  1. Let $F(n)$ be the number of ways to climb n steps. We want to prove $F(n) = F(n-1) + F(n-2)$.
  Base Case: $n = 3$. It is true that $F(3) = F(2) + F(1)$.
  Inductive Step: Assume that this is true for 1 through n. Consider $F(n+1)$. The first step is either a one-step or a two-step. If the first step is a one-step, there are n steps left to climb, and the number of ways to do that is $F(n)$. If the first step is a two-step then there are $n - 2$ steps left to climb, and the number of ways to do that is $F(n-1)$. So we have $F(n) = F(n-1) + F(n-2)$.

397

2. Let $F(n)$ be the number of successor-free n-element sequences. We want to prove
$$F(n) = F(n-1) + F(n-2).$$
Base Case: $n = 3$. It is true that $F(3) = F(2) + F(1)$.

Inductive Step: Assume that this is true for 1 through n. Consider $F(n+1)$. The first number in an $n+1$ sequence will be either 0 or 1. If the first number is 0, we have n left to go. So the number of ways to finish the sequence is $F(n)$. If the first number is 1, the second must be 0, or we wouldn't be successor free. Then we have $n-2$ numbers to go, so the number of ways to finish the sequence is $F(n-1)$. So $F(n) = F(n-1) + F(n-2)$.

3. Let $F(n)$ be the number of ancestors of a female bee at stage n. In other words, $n = 1$ means the number of parents, $n = 2$ means the number of grandparents, etc. We want to prove
$$F(n) = F(n-1) + F(n-2).$$
Base Case: $n = 3$. It is true that $F(3) = F(2) + F(1)$.

Inductive Step: Assume that this is true for 1 through n. Consider $F(n+1)$. The worker bee has a mommy, who has $F(n-1)$ ancestors. She also has a daddy who has a mommy who has $F(n-2)$ ancestors. So, again, $F(n) = F(n-1) + F(n-2)$.

▼ Examples

See above.

▼ Group Work 1: A Property of Matrices

This serves as a review of Section 10.4, as well as giving the students a chance to practice induction. It is more straightforward than Group Work 2. If necessary, remind the students of the definition of A^k if A is a matrix before handing out the problem. If a group finishes early, have them look at B^n, where $B = \begin{bmatrix} 1 & 1 \\ 1 & 0 \end{bmatrix}$. Notice that this is a surprisingly different problem. (It is also Exercise 33 in the text.)

Answers:

1. $A^2 = \begin{bmatrix} 1 & 2 \\ 0 & 1 \end{bmatrix}$, $A^3 = \begin{bmatrix} 1 & 3 \\ 0 & 1 \end{bmatrix}$, $A^4 = \begin{bmatrix} 1 & 4 \\ 0 & 1 \end{bmatrix}$

2. $A^{1000} = \begin{bmatrix} 1 & 1000 \\ 0 & 1 \end{bmatrix}$

3. Base Case: trivial. The inductive step boils down to
$$\begin{bmatrix} 1 & 1 \\ 0 & 1 \end{bmatrix} \begin{bmatrix} 1 & n \\ 0 & 1 \end{bmatrix} = \begin{bmatrix} 1 & n+1 \\ 0 & 1 \end{bmatrix}$$

Bonus: As stated in Exercise 33, $\begin{bmatrix} 1 & 1 \\ 1 & 0 \end{bmatrix}^n = \begin{bmatrix} F_{n+1} & F_n \\ F_n & F_{n-1} \end{bmatrix}$, where F_n is the nth Fibonacci number.

▼ Group Work 2: The Angular Triomino

This activity is a mathematical induction proof, although there are no algebraic equations involved. It helps ensure the students know what is going on in an induction proof, as opposed to learning an algebraic "hoop" to jump through.

Answer:

The base case is trivial. For the induction step, divide the $2^{n+1} \times 2^{n+1}$ checkerboard into four equal pieces as shown, then temporarily remove three squares:

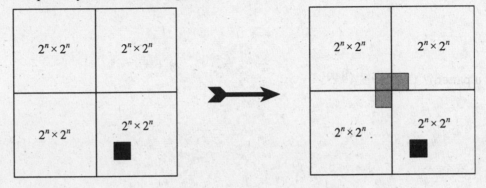

As we have four $2^n \times 2^n$ boards with one square missing in each, we can tile what is left by induction, and then we can tile the removed squares with one angular triomino.

▼ Homework Problems

Core Exercises: 1, 4, 11, 20, 27, 33

Sample Assignment: 1, 4, 7, 11, 16, 20, 22, 27, 30, 33, 37, 38

A Property of Matrices

Consider the matrix $A = \begin{pmatrix} 1 & 1 \\ 0 & 1 \end{pmatrix}$.

1. Compute A^2, A^3 and A^4.

2. Do you see a pattern? Compute A^{1000}.

3. Prove that your pattern is true using mathematical induction.

Meet the "angular triomino"

It is a useful little shape. For example, suppose I had a 4×4 chessboard, with one square missing, like this:

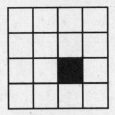

I could tile it with my friend the angular triomino, as so:

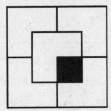

As fate would have it, I could tile the board regardless of where the missing square is. In fact, I can do it for an 8×8 chessboard, a 16×16 chessboard, etc. as long as there is one square missing. In fact, I can even *prove* that I can tile any $2^n \times 2^n$ chessboard (with one square missing) with angular triominos. But what fun would it be if *I* proved it? None, I tell you, none at all. You go ahead and prove it.

12.6   THE BINOMIAL THEOREM

▼ Suggested Time and Emphasis

$\frac{1}{2}$ class. Optional material.

▼ Points to Stress

1. The expansion of $(a + b)^n$ for a, b expressions, n a positive integer.
2. The computation of $\binom{n}{r}$ using factorials and using Pascal's triangle.

▼ Sample Questions

- **Text Question:** Compute $\binom{5}{4}$.

  Answer: 5

- **Drill Question:** Expand $(x + 2y)^6$.

  Answer: $(x + 2y)^6 = x^6 + 12x^5y + 60x^4y^2 + 160x^3y^3 + 240x^2y^4 + 192xy^5 + 64y^6$

▼ In-Class Materials

- Point out that some of the formulas previously covered are just special cases of the binomial theorem, for example the formulas for $(x + y)^2$, $(x - y)^2$, $(x + y)^3$, and $(x - y)^3$.
- Pascal's Triangle is actually full of patterns. Have the students see how many they can find. They can look along the diagonals, look down "columns", find the sum of each row, etc. Some instructors spend an entire class on patterns visible in Pascal's triangle. As of this writing, the website `http://ptri1.tripod.com` has a good discussion of patterns to be found in Pascal's triangle.
- If every odd number in Pascal's triangle is colored black, and every even number colored white, Sierpinski's triangle is revealed. Students need complete only a few rows before the recursive structure is visible.
- The binomial theorem can be extended to the real numbers, and then some interesting things happen. First we generalize the definition of $\binom{n}{r}$:

$$\binom{n}{r} = \frac{n\,(n-1)\,(n-2)\ldots(n-r+1)}{r!}$$

Notice that this is equivalent to our former definition if n and r are positive integers, even if $r > n$ (in that case the numerator will be zero). But this new definition works even if n is an arbitrary real number. Now we can say

$$(a + b)^n = \sum_{r=0}^{\infty} \binom{n}{r} a^r b^{n-r}$$

Notice again that if n is a positive integer, then we are back to the standard binomial theorem, since $\binom{n}{r}$ is 0 for $r > n$. But now we can let $n = -1$ to obtain

$$\frac{1}{x+1} = 1 - x + x^2 - x^3 + x^4 - x^5 + \cdots$$

Similarly, we can let $n = \frac{1}{2}$ to obtain

$$\sqrt{x+1} = 1 + \tfrac{1}{2}x - \tfrac{1}{8}x^2 + \tfrac{1}{16}x^3 - \tfrac{5}{128}x^4 + \cdots$$

with the general term being $(-1)^{n-1} \dfrac{1 \cdot 3 \cdot 5 \cdot 7 \cdot \ldots \cdot (2n-3)}{2^n n!} x^n$.

▼ Examples

- $(4 - \sqrt{x})^5 = 1024 - 1280\sqrt{x} + 640x - 160(\sqrt{x})^3 + 20x^2 - (\sqrt{x})^5$
- $\left(x + \dfrac{1}{x}\right)^8 = x^8 + 8x^6 + 28x^4 + 56x^2 + 70 + \dfrac{56}{x^2} + \dfrac{28}{x^4} + \dfrac{8}{x^6} + \dfrac{1}{x^8}$

▼ Group Work

Exercises 58 and 59 are particularly well suited for group work.

▼ Homework Problems

Core Exercises: 5, 12, 18, 26, 37, 43, 48, 56

Sample Assignment: 5, 12, 16, 18, 21, 26, 31, 37, 40, 43, 46, 48, 51, 56, 58

13 LIMITS: A PREVIEW OF CALCULUS

13.1 FINDING LIMITS NUMERICALLY AND GRAPHICALLY

▼ **Suggested Time and Emphasis**

2 classes. Optional material.

▼ **Points to Stress**

1. Informal definition of limit.
2. Limits that do not exist.
3. Estimating limits from numerical tables.
4. Estimating limits from graphs.
5. One-sided limits.

▼ **Sample Questions**

- **Text Question:** What is the difference between the statements "$f(a) = L$" and "$\lim_{x \to a} f(x) = L$"?

  Answer: The first is a statement about the value of f at the point $x = a$, the second is a statement about the values of f at points near, but not equal to, $x = a$.

- **Drill Question:** The graph of a function f is shown below. Are the following statements about f true or false? Why?

  (a) $x = a$ is in the domain of f **(b)** $\lim_{x \to a} f(x)$ exists   **(c)** $\lim_{x \to a^+} f(x)$ is equal to $\lim_{x \to a^-} f(x)$

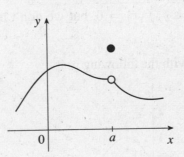

Answer:

(a) True, because f is defined at $x = a$.

(b) True, because as x gets close to a, $f(x)$ approaches a value.

(c) True, because the same value is approached from both directions.

▼ **In-Class Materials**

- Perhaps present the "graphing calculator" definition of limit: We say that $\lim_{x \to a} f(x) = L$ if for any y-range centered at L, there is an x-range centered at a such that the graph is contained in the window. This is a little closer to the formal definition of limit that will be presented in calculus, using a metaphor with which students are familiar.

405

- After discussing vertical asymptotes (graphical and numerical definitions, followed by the limit definition), ask students to describe horizontal asymptotes from the same perspective. They may come up with the concept of $\lim_{x \to \infty}$ on their own!

- Examine $\lim_{x \to 0} \dfrac{\sin x}{x}$. This limit comes up in calculus, and can be explored numerically and graphically. Once it is established that $\lim_{x \to 0} \dfrac{\sin x}{x} = 1$, you can show students that in the study of optics (or any other application where x is very small) scientists often make the approximation $\sin x \approx x$. Emphasize that they can get away with this only for $x \approx 0$.

- Explore $\lim_{x \to 0} \left(2 - 2^{1/x}\right)$, looking carefully at $2^{1/x}$ from both sides for small x. After numerical and graphical explorations, you can also discuss this from a common-sense perspective. When x is small and positive, what do we know about $1/x$? And then what do we know about $2^{1/x}$? How about $\left(2 - 2^{1/x}\right)$? Ask these questions again for small, negative values of x.

▼ Examples

- Numerical: Consider the function f about which we know the following:

x	$f(x)$
1	62
1.8	4
1.9	5.35
1.99	5.9
1.999	5.999
1.9999	5.9999

We have reason to believe that $\lim_{x \to 2^-} f(x) = 6$, but we don't have proof. We do *not* have reason to believe that $\lim_{x \to 2} f(x) = 6$.

- Graphical: Consider the function f with the following graph:

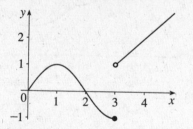

We have $f(3) = -1$, $\lim_{x \to 3^-} f(x) = -1$, $\lim_{x \to 3^+} f(x) = 1$. Also, $f(4) = 2$ and $\lim_{x \to 4} f(x) = 2$.

▼ Group Work 1: Infinite Limits

After students are finished, Part 2 can be used to initiate a discussion of left and right hand limits, and of the precise definition of a vertical asymptote, as presented in the text. In addition, Section 13.4 can be foreshadowed by asking students to explore the behavior of $\dfrac{3x^2 + 4x + 5}{\sqrt{16x^4 - 81}}$ for large positive and large negative values of x, both on the graph and numerically. If there is time, ask students to analyze the asymptotes of $f(x) = \sec x$ and the other trigonometric functions.

Answers:

1. Answers will vary. The main thing to check is that there are vertical asymptotes at $\pm\frac{\pi}{2}$ and at $\pm\frac{3\pi}{2}$.

2. 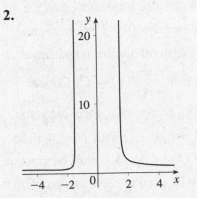 There are vertical asymptotes at $x = \pm 1.5$.

▼ Group Work 2: The Shape of Things to Come

This exercise foreshadows concepts that will be discussed later, but can be introduced now.

Answers:

1. $2^1 = 2$, $(0.6)^2 = 0.36$, $(0.8)^3 = 0.512$, $0^4 = 0$, $(1.01)^8 = 1.0829$

2.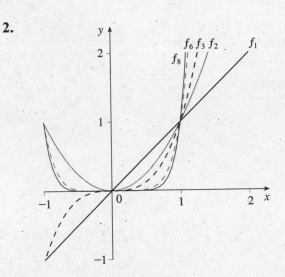

3. $f_n(1) = 1$ for all n.

4. The curves all go through the origin.

▼ Group Work 3: A Jittery Function

This exercise can be done several ways. After they have worked for a while, perhaps ask one group to try to solve it using the Squeeze Theorem, another to solve it using the "narrow range" definition of limit, and a third to solve it using the ε-δ definition of limit. They should show why their method works for Problem 2, and fails for Problem 3.

Answers:

1.

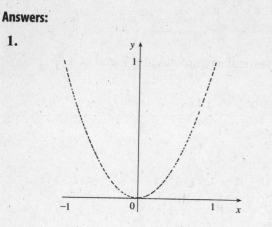

2. $\lim\limits_{x\to 0} f(x) = 0$. Choose ε with $\varepsilon > 0$. Let $\delta = \sqrt{\varepsilon}$. Now if $-\delta < x < \delta$, then $x^2 < \varepsilon$, regardless of whether x is rational or irrational. This can also be shown using the Squeeze Theorem and the fact that $0 < f(x) < x^2$, and then using the Limit Laws to compute $\lim\limits_{x\to 0} 0$ and $\lim\limits_{x\to 0} x^2$.

3. It does not exist. Assume that $\lim\limits_{x\to 1} f(x) = L$. Choose $\varepsilon = \frac{1}{10}$. Now, whatever your choice of δ, there are some x-values in the interval $(1+\delta, 1-\delta)$ with $f(x) = 0$, so L must be less than $\frac{1}{10}$. But there are also values of x in the interval with $f(x) > \frac{2}{10}$, so L must be greater than $\frac{1}{10}$. So L cannot exist. The "narrow range" definition of limit can also be used to solve this problem.

4. We can conjecture that the limit does not exist by applying the reasoning from Problem 3.

▼ **Homework Problems**

Core Exercises: 1, 3, 6, 12, 20, 22, 29, 33

Sample Assignment: 1, 2, 3, 6, 10, 12, 17, 20, 22, 28, 29, 31, 33

1. Draw an odd function which has the lines $x = \frac{\pi}{2}$ and $x = -\frac{3\pi}{2}$ among its vertical asymptotes.

2. Analyze the vertical asymptotes of $\dfrac{3x^2 + 4x + 5}{\sqrt{16x^4 - 81}}$.

The Shape of Things to Come

In this activity we are going to explore a set of functions:

$$f_1(x) = x$$
$$f_2(x) = x^2$$
$$f_3(x) = x^3$$
$$\vdots$$
$$f_n(x) = x^n, n \text{ any positive integer}$$

1. To start with, let's practice the new notation. Compute the following:

$f_1(2) =$ _____ $f_2(0.6) =$ _____ $f_3(0.8) =$ _____ $f_4(0) =$ _____ $f_8(1.01) =$ _____

2. Sketch the functions f_1, f_2, f_3, f_6, and f_8 on the set of axes below.

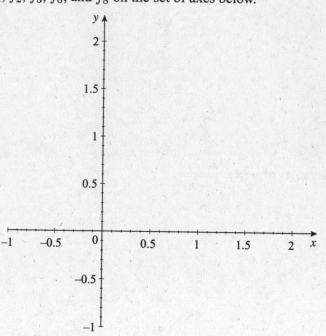

3. The number 0 plays a special role, since $f_n(0) = 0^n = 0$ for any n. Find another number $a > 0$ such that $f_n(a) = a$ for all n.

4. We know that $\lim_{x \to 0} f_n(x) = 0$ for any n. How is this fact reflected on your graphs above?

A Jittery Function

Not all functions that occur in mathematics are simple combinations of the "toolkit" functions usually seen in calculus. Consider this function:

$$f(x) = \begin{cases} 0 & \text{if } x \text{ is rational} \\ x^2 & \text{if } x \text{ is irrational} \end{cases}$$

1. It is obvious that you can't graph this function in the same literal way that you would graph $y = \cos x$, but it is useful to have some idea of what this function looks like. Try to sketch the graph of $y = f(x)$.

2. Does $\lim_{x \to 0} f(x)$ exist? If so, what is its value? If not, why not? Make sure to justify your answer carefully.

3. Does $\lim_{x \to 1} f(x)$ exist? Carefully justify your answer.

4. What do you conjecture about $\lim_{x \to a} f(x)$ if $a \neq 0$?

13.2 FINDING LIMITS ALGEBRAICALLY

▼ Suggested Time and Emphasis

1 class. Optional material.

▼ Points to Stress

1. Limit Laws.

2. Direct substitution for rational functions (within their domains).

3. Algebraic manipulation.

▼ Sample Questions

- **Text Question:** In Example 1, why isn't $\lim\limits_{x \to -2} f(x) = 2$?

  Answer: The limit has nothing to do with the function's value *at* $x = -2$. It depends only on the values of the function for x *close to* -2.

- **Drill Question:** If $a \neq 0$, find $\lim\limits_{x \to a} \dfrac{x^2 - 2ax + a^2}{x^2 - a^2}$.

  Answer: 0

▼ In-Class Materials

- Do some subtle product and quotient limits, such as $\lim\limits_{x \to 0} \left(\dfrac{x}{|x|} \sin x \right)$ and $\lim\limits_{x \to 1} \dfrac{\sqrt{x+3} - 2}{x - 1}$.

- Have students determine the existence of $\lim\limits_{x \to 0^+} \sqrt{x}$ and determine why we cannot compute $\lim\limits_{x \to 0} \sqrt{x}$.

- Compute some limits of quotients, such as $\lim\limits_{x \to 2} \dfrac{x^2 - 4}{x - 2}$, $\lim\limits_{x \to 0} \dfrac{x^3 - 8}{x - 2}$, $\lim\limits_{x \to 3} \dfrac{x^3 - 8}{x - 2}$, and $\lim\limits_{x \to 2} \dfrac{x^3 - 8}{x - 2}$, always attempting to plug in values first.

- Have students check whether $\lim\limits_{x \to -5} \dfrac{x + 5}{|x + 5|}$ exists, and then compute left- and right-hand limits. Then check $\lim\limits_{x \to -5} \dfrac{(x + 5)^2}{|x + 5|}$.

▼ Examples

- Algebraic simplification:

$$\lim_{x \to 2} \frac{x - 2}{x^2 + x - 6} = \frac{1}{5}$$

$$\lim_{x \to -3} \frac{x - 2}{x^2 + x - 6} \text{ does not exist}$$

$$\lim_{x \to 0} \frac{x - 2}{x^2 + x - 6} = \frac{1}{3} \text{ by direct substitution}$$

412

- Algebraic simplification, with variables:

  This limits will be seen again in calculus, and provides a good review of the algebra involved in working with fractions.

$$\lim_{h \to 0} \frac{\dfrac{1}{x+h} - \dfrac{1}{x}}{h} = \lim_{h \to 0} \frac{\dfrac{x - (x+h)}{x\,(x+h)}}{h} = \lim_{h \to 0} \frac{x - (x+h)}{hx\,(x+h)}$$

$$= \lim_{h \to 0} -\frac{1}{x\,(x+h)} = -\frac{1}{x^2}$$

▼ Group Work 1: Exploring Limits

Have students work on this exercise in groups. Problem 2 is more conceptual than Problem 1, but makes an important point about the sums and products of limits.

Answers:

1. **(a)** (i) Does not exist (ii) Does not exist (iii) 4 (iv) Does not exist

   (b) (i) Does not exist (ii) 1 **(c) (i)** 0 (ii) Does not exist

2. **(a)** Both quantities exist.

   (b) Each quantity may or may not exist.

▼ Group Work 2: Give Me Two Breaks

This exercise foreshadows concepts used later in the discussion of continuity, in addition to giving students practice in taking limits. After the exercise, point out that mathematicians use the word "puncture" as well as "hole".

Answers:

1. No, yes, yes, no
2. The holes are at $x = -1$ and $x = 2$. A "hole" is an x-value at which the function is not defined, yet the left- and right-hand limits exist (or an x-value where the function is undefined, yet the function is defined near x.)
3. Does not exist, $\frac{1}{3}$
4.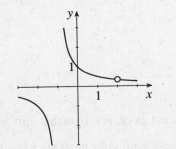

   Some holes can be "filled in" and some cannot.

5. This has the kind of hole that can be "filled in".

▼ Homework Problems

Core Exercises: 3, 12, 17, 23, 30, 35, 37

Sample Assignment: 3, 5, 12, 14, 17, 21, 23, 28, 30, 33, 35, 36, 37

1. Given the functions f and g (defined graphically below) and h and j (defined algebraically), compute each of the following limits, or state why they don't exist:

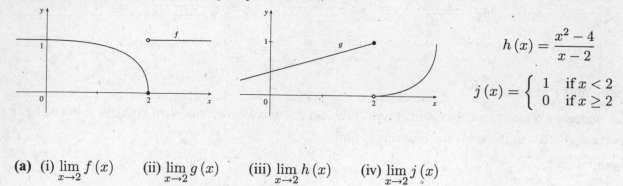

$$h(x) = \frac{x^2 - 4}{x - 2}$$

$$j(x) = \begin{cases} 1 & \text{if } x < 2 \\ 0 & \text{if } x \geq 2 \end{cases}$$

(a) (i) $\displaystyle\lim_{x \to 2} f(x)$ (ii) $\displaystyle\lim_{x \to 2} g(x)$ (iii) $\displaystyle\lim_{x \to 2} h(x)$ (iv) $\displaystyle\lim_{x \to 2} j(x)$

(b) (i) $\displaystyle\lim_{x \to 2} [g(x) + h(x)]$ (ii) $\displaystyle\lim_{x \to 2} [f(x) + j(x)]$

(c) (i) $\displaystyle\lim_{x \to 2} [f(x) g(x)]$ (ii) $\displaystyle\lim_{x \to 2} [f(x) j(x)]$

2. (a) In general, if $\displaystyle\lim_{x \to a} m(x)$ exists and $\displaystyle\lim_{x \to a} n(x)$ exists, is it true that $\displaystyle\lim_{x \to a} [m(x) + n(x)]$ exists? How about $\displaystyle\lim_{x \to a} [m(x) n(x)]$? Justify your answers.

(b) In general, if $\displaystyle\lim_{x \to a} m(x)$ does not exist and $\displaystyle\lim_{x \to a} n(x)$ does not exist, is it true that $\displaystyle\lim_{x \to a} [m(x) + n(x)]$ does not exist? How about $\displaystyle\lim_{x \to a} [m(x) n(x)]$? Compare these with your answers to part (a).

Give Me Two Breaks

Consider $f(x) = \dfrac{x-2}{x^2 - x - 2}$.

1. Is $f(x)$ defined for $x = -1$? For $x = 0$? For $x = 1$? For $x = 2$?

2. We say that $f(x)$ has two "holes" in it. Where do you think that the "holes" are in $f(x)$? Give your best definition of the word "hole".

3. Compute $\displaystyle\lim_{x \to -1} \dfrac{x-2}{x^2 - x - 2}$ and $\displaystyle\lim_{x \to 2} \dfrac{x-2}{x^2 - x - 2}$. Notice that one limit exists, and one does not.

4. Graph $y = \dfrac{x-2}{x^2 - x - 2}$. Geometrically, what is the difference between the two kinds of holes?

5. The function $g(x) = \dfrac{\sin x}{x}$ has one hole. Sketch this function. What kind of hole does it have?

13.3   TANGENT LINES AND DERIVATIVES

▼ Suggested Time and Emphasis

1–2 classes. Optional material.

▼ Points to Stress

1. Definition of a tangent line.
2. Definition of the slope of a curve.
3. Definition of the derivative.
4. The difference between average and instantaneous rates of change.

▼ Sample Questions

- **Text Question:** Geometrically, what is "the line tangent to a curve" at a particular point?

  Answer: There are different correct answers. Examples include the best linear approximation to a curve at a point, and the result of repeated "zooming in" on a curve.

- **Drill Question:** Draw the line tangent to the following curve at each of the indicated points:

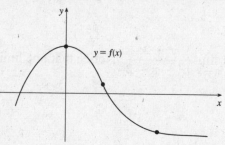

  Answer:

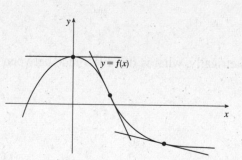

▼ In-Class Materials

- Point out that if a car is driving along a curve, the headlights will point along the direction of the tangent line.

- Illustrate that many functions such as x^2 and $x - 2\sin x$ look locally linear, and discuss the relationship of this property to the concept of the tangent line. Then pose the question, "What does a secant line to a linear function look like?"

- Show that the slope of the tangent line does not exist at $x = 0$ for either $f(x) = \sqrt[3]{x}$ or $g(x) = |x|$. Note that f has a tangent line (which is vertical), but g does not (it has a cusp).

- Discuss how physical situations can be translated into statements about derivatives. For example, the budget deficit can be viewed as the derivative of the national debt. Describe the units of derivatives in real world situations. The budget deficit, for example, is measured in trillions of dollars per year. Another example: if $s(d)$ represents the sales figures for a magazine given d dollars of advertising, where s is the number of magazines sold, then $s'(d)$ is in magazines per dollar spent. Describe enough examples to make the pattern evident.

- Show students how to estimate derivatives from tables of numbers. For example, one can estimate that if the following are position measurements versus time, the maximum velocity is achieved somewhere between $t = 2.9$ and $t = 3$.

t	2.8	2.9	3.0	3.1	3.2	3.3
$p(t)$	1.2	2.4	3.9	5.1	6.1	6.9

▼ Examples

- If $f(x) = 3x + 4$, then $f'(2) = 3$. In fact, $f'(k) = 3$.
- Let $f(x) = x^3$. Then an equation of the line tangent to this curve at $x = \frac{1}{2}$ is $y = \frac{3}{4}x - \frac{1}{4}$.

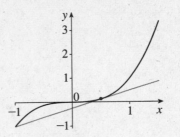

▼ Group Work 1: What's the Pattern?

Students will not be able to do Part 3 from the graph alone, although some will try. After a majority of them are working on Part 3, announce that they can do this numerically.

If they are unable to get Part 6, have them repeat Part 4 for $x = 15$, and again for $x = 0$.

Answers:

1., 2.

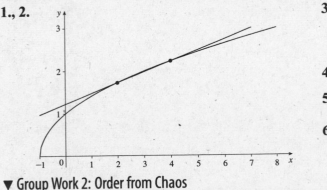

3. $2 - \sqrt{3} \approx 0.268$, $\sqrt{5} - 2 \approx 0.236$,

$\sqrt{4.5} - \sqrt{3.5} \approx 0.250$, $\dfrac{\sqrt{4.2} - \sqrt{3.8}}{0.4} \approx 0.250$

4. $\frac{1}{4}$ is a good estimate.

5. $\frac{1}{6}$ is a good estimate.

6. $\dfrac{1}{2\sqrt{a+1}}$

▼ Group Work 2: Order from Chaos

Have students work on this exercise in groups of three or four. Some groups may try to solve the problems by estimating the relevant quantities numerically, and others will use geometric arguments. For the purposes of this assignment, both approaches are equally valid.

Answers:

1. $f'(a) < m_{PQ} < \dfrac{f(c) - f(a)}{c - a} < m_{QR} < f'(b)$

2.
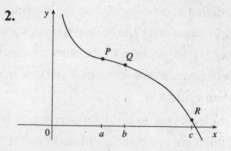

▼ Homework Problems

Core Exercises: 3, 6, 10, 15, 18, 22, 23, 27, 30

Sample Assignment: 3, 6, 8, 10, 12, 13, 15, 18, 19, 22, 23, 24, 25, 27, 29, 30

Consider the function $f(x) = \sqrt{1 + x}$.

1. Carefully sketch a graph of this function on the grid below.

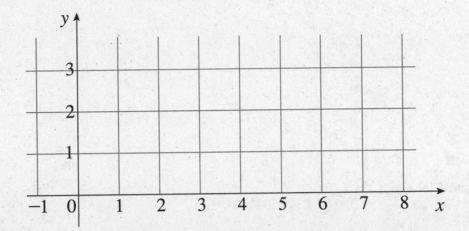

2. Sketch the secant line to f between the points with x-coordinates $x = 2$ and $x = 4$.

3. Sketch the secant lines to f between the pairs of points with the following x-coordinates, and compute their slopes:

   (a) $x = 2$ and $x = 3$ (b) $x = 3$ and $x = 4$ (c) $x = 2.5$ and $x = 3.5$ (d) $x = 2.8$ and $x = 3.2$

4. Using the slopes you've found so far, estimate the slope of the tangent line at $x = 3$.

5. Repeat Problem 4 for $x = 8$.

6. Based on Problems 4 and 5, guess the slope of the tangent line at any point $x = a$, for $a > -1$.

Below is the graph of the function $f(x)$.

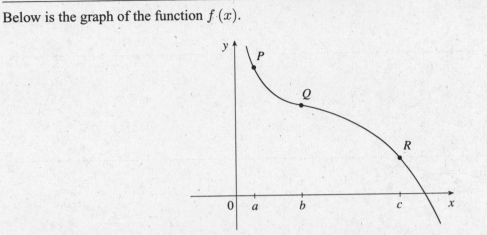

1. Place the following quantities in order, from lowest to highest: $f'(a)$, $f'(b)$, the slope m_{PQ} of the secant line PQ, the slope m_{QR} of the secant line QR, and $\dfrac{f(c) - f(a)}{c - a}$. Make sure to give justification for your answers.

2. Find points P, Q, and R as above such that $a < b < c$ and $f'(c) < m_{QR} < f'(b) < f'(a)$.

13.4 LIMITS AT INFINITY; LIMITS OF SEQUENCES

▼ Suggested Time and Emphasis

1 class. Optional material.

▼ Points to Stress

1. Limits at infinity.
2. Horizontal asymptotes
3. Limits of sequences.

▼ Sample Questions

- **Text Question:** Compute $\lim\limits_{x\to\infty} \dfrac{1}{x^2+2}$.

  Answer: 0
- **Drill Question:**

  (a) Give an example of a divergent sequence.

  (b) Give an example of a sequence whose limit is 2.

  Answers will vary

▼ In-Class Materials

- Note that sometimes we can approximate an infinite limit by shoving large numbers into a function. For example, let $f(x) = \dfrac{2x^2 + \sin x}{x^2 - 30x - 200}$. We can show that $\lim\limits_{x\to\infty} f(x) = 2$, and it is a fact that $f(10^6) \approx 2.00006$. This method doesn't always work, though. If $g(x) = \ln(\ln x)$, then $\lim\limits_{x\to\infty} g(x) = \infty$, that is, the limit does not exist. Yet $g(10^{99}) \approx 5.4291523$.

- Consider the motion on an object on a spring. In a frictionless world, it would oscillate forever. In the real world, the oscillations die out. We can model the height of the object versus time this way: $f(x) = e^{-x} \sin kx + H$ where H is the height of the object at rest.

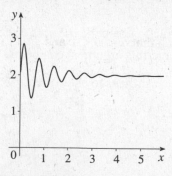

- Have the class come up with functions for which both $\lim\limits_{x\to\infty} f(x)$ and $\lim\limits_{n\to\infty} a_n$ exist, where $a_n = f(n)$. Then have them come up with functions for which they both do not exist. Then have them find one where $\lim\limits_{x\to\infty} f(x)$ does not exist and $\lim\limits_{n\to\infty} a_n$ does. One such case is $f(x) = \sin(2\pi x)$. Finally, have them try to find an example where $\lim\limits_{n\to\infty} a_n$ does not exist and $\lim\limits_{x\to\infty} f(x)$ does. They will fail. The text shows that this is impossible.

▼ Examples

- $\lim\limits_{x \to \infty} \dfrac{1}{1 - 2^{1/x}} = -\infty$

- $\lim\limits_{x \to -\infty} \dfrac{1}{1 - 2^{1/x}} = \infty$

- $\lim\limits_{x \to \infty} \dfrac{x^2 - 6x}{2x^2 + 2x} = \dfrac{1}{2}$

- If $a_n = \dfrac{n\,(n+1)\,(n+2)}{n^4}$, then $\lim\limits_{n \to \infty} a_n = 0$.

▼ Group Work 1: Recursive Roots

This problem gives the tools to show that if $x > 0$, then $\sqrt{x + \sqrt{x + \sqrt{x + \sqrt{x + \cdots}}}}$ exists and equals

$\dfrac{1 + \sqrt{1 + 4x}}{2}$. Students may find Questions 2 and 3 difficult. One hint to give them is that for a and $b > 0$,

$a < b \ \Rightarrow \ a^2 < b^2$. In a less rigorous class, it may be acceptable for students to notice that there is a trend (the terms are increasing, and approaching $1.6 < 2$) but they should also realize that noticing a trend isn't the same thing as proving that the trend will continue forever. This exercise can be done with less rigor by having students skip Questions 2 and 3 entirely.

Answers:

1. $a_1 = 0$
   $a_2 = \sqrt{1 + 0} = 1$
   $a_3 = \sqrt{1 + \sqrt{1 + 0}} = \sqrt{2} \approx 1.4142$
   $a_4 = \sqrt{1 + \sqrt{1 + \sqrt{1 + 0}}} \approx 1.5538$
   $a_5 = \sqrt{1 + \sqrt{1 + \sqrt{1 + \sqrt{1 + 0}}}} \approx 1.5981$

2. The easiest way to prove this is by induction. We want to show that if $a_n < 2$, then $\sqrt{1 + a_n} < 2$. The base case is trivial ($0 < 2$). The induction step: If $a_n < 2$, then $\sqrt{1 + a_n} < \sqrt{1 + 2} < 2$. If students haven't learned mathematical induction, this argument can be put into less formal language.

3. We now want to show $a_n < \sqrt{1 + a_n}$ It suffices to show that $(a_n)^2 < 1 + a_n$, or $(a_n)^2 - a_n - 1 < 0$. The quadratic formula, or a graph, can show that this is true if $x^2 - x - 1 = 0$ or if $0 < x < \frac{1+\sqrt{5}}{2} \approx 1.618$ (Actually, this is true for $\frac{1-\sqrt{5}}{2} < x < \frac{1+\sqrt{5}}{2}$). We can use an induction argument like the one in the previous part to show that if $a_n < \frac{1+\sqrt{5}}{2}$, then $a_{n+1} < \frac{1+\sqrt{5}}{2}$.

4. $a = \sqrt{1 + \sqrt{1 + \sqrt{1 + \sqrt{1 + \cdots}}}} = \sqrt{1 + \sqrt{1 + \sqrt{1 + \sqrt{1 + \sqrt{1 + \cdots}}}}}$. Therefore $a = \sqrt{1 + a}$.

5. Since $a = \sqrt{1 + a}$, we have $a^2 = 1 + a$ and $a = \frac{1+\sqrt{5}}{2}$.

6. 2, 3

▼ Group Work 2: Asymptotes Away

Answers:

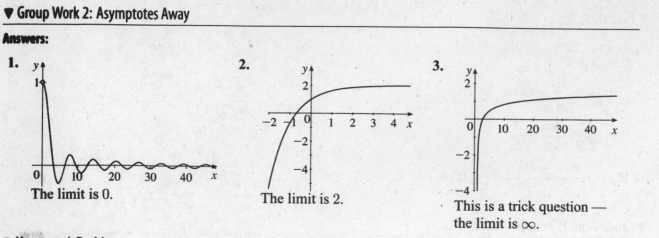

1.

The limit is 0.

2.

The limit is 2.

3.

This is a trick question — the limit is ∞.

▼ Homework Problems

Core Exercises: 3, 6, 12, 23, 28, 29, 32, 35

Sample Assignment: 3, 6, 9, 12, 15, 19, 23, 26, 28, 29, 30, 32, 34, 35

Recursive Roots

We want to find the value of

$$\sqrt{1+\sqrt{1+\sqrt{1+\sqrt{1+\cdots}}}}$$

1. Consider the recursive sequence $a_0 = 0$, $a_{n+1} = \sqrt{1+a_n}$. Compute the next five terms a_1, a_2, a_3, a_4, and a_5.

2. Show that $a_n < 2$ for all n.

3. Show that $a_{n+1} > a_n$.

4. If $\lim\limits_{n\to\infty} a_n = a$, show that $a = \sqrt{1+a}$.

5. What is the value of $\sqrt{1 + \sqrt{1 + \sqrt{1 + \sqrt{1 + \cdots}}}}$?

6. Using similar reasoning, try to compute $\sqrt{2 + \sqrt{2 + \sqrt{2 + \sqrt{2 + \cdots}}}}$ and $\sqrt{6 + \sqrt{6 + \sqrt{6 + \sqrt{6 + \cdots}}}}$.

Asymptotes Away

For each of the following functions, make a sketch and then compute $\lim\limits_{x \to \infty} f(x)$.

1. $f(x) = \dfrac{\sin(x)}{x}$

2. $f(x) = 2 - e^{-x}$

3. $f(x) = \ln(\ln x)$

13.5 AREAS

▼ Suggested Time and Emphasis

1 class. Optional material.

▼ Points to Stress

1. Estimation of areas using rectangles.

2. Calculation of areas as limits of Riemann sums.

▼ Sample Questions

- **Text Question:** In the formula $A = \lim\limits_{n\to\infty} \sum\limits_{k=1}^{n} f(x_k)\,\Delta x$, where does the Δx come from?

  Answer: It represents the width of each rectangle.

- **Drill Question:** Estimate the area under $y = x^2$ from $x = 1$ to $x = 3$ using two rectangles. Sketch the rectangles you use.

  Answer: Answers will vary depending on which rectangles are used.

▼ In-Class Materials

- **Start** by showing how the familiar equation $d = rt$ can be illustrated by a statement about the area of a rectangle (below left). Then argue intuitively that we can generalize this idea by finding the area under the velocity curve to get net distance traveled (below right).

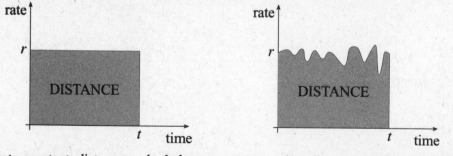

rate constant; distance = shaded area   rate varies; distance = shaded area (still)

- **Lead** students to discover that choosing left endpoints for a decreasing function always leads to an overestimate, whereas choosing right endpoints leads to an underestimate. They should check that the opposite trends hold for increasing functions. Challenge them to find a link between the midpoint estimate and the concavity of a graph.

- Look at the function $f(x) = \dfrac{6}{1 + x^2}$ from $x = 0$ to $x = 4$. Show that the obvious lower and upper bounds for the area under the curve are obtained as follows:

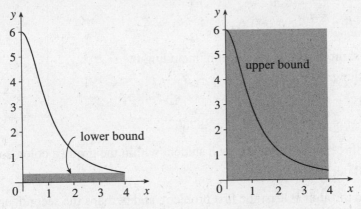

Obtain better lower and upper bounds by dividing the interval into 2 and then 4 subintervals. Finally, use the method of counting square units to estimate the area (between 7 and 8 square units).

▼ Examples

- Finding the area under $y = \sin x$ from $x = 0$ to $x = \pi$. Note that we get the same results using left endpoints as we do using right endpoints.

  With $n = 2$ rectangles, our estimate is $A \approx \dfrac{\pi}{2} \approx 1.5708$

  With $n = 4$: $A \approx \dfrac{\pi}{4}\left(1 + \sqrt{2}\right) = 1.8961$

  With $n = 10$: $A \approx 1.9835$

  With $n = 50$: $A \approx 1.9993$

- Finding the area under $y = e^x$ from $x = 0$ to $x = 2$:

n	Estimate using left endpoints	Estimate using right endpoints
2	3.7182	10.1073
4	4.9243	8.1189
10	5.7714	7.0492
50	6.2621	6.5177
1000	6.3827	6.3954

▼ Group Work 1: Position From Samples

Students are asked to gather velocity samples while driving, and then to try to recover their actual distance traveled by approximating the area under the velocity curve.

In class, have them plot their data points on graph paper, and try to draw a simple velocity curve that fits these points. Then have them approximate the area under the curve. (They should wind up using their data points as sample points.) They can see how close their approximations are by subtracting the initial odometer reading from the final odometer reading to get distance traveled. Note that most of this exercise will be done outside of class. It should be assigned a week or so before the in-class component.

Although it takes some time, this activity is an excellent way to make the abstract concrete.

▼ Group Work 2: Choose Your Weapon

Write the following on the board:

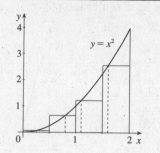

$$A = \lim_{n\to\infty} \sum_{i=1}^{n} f\left(x_i^*\right) \Delta x$$

Show students a simple example of a Riemann sum, including the geometric interpretation shown at right.

Compute

$$A \approx \tfrac{1}{2}\,(0.25)^2 + \tfrac{1}{2}\,(0.8)^2 + \tfrac{1}{2}\,(1.1)^2 + \tfrac{1}{2}\,(1.6)^2 = 2.23625.$$

Put students in groups of three or four. Assign each student within the group a color, so that each group has a Red, a Yellow, a Blue, and perhaps a Purple.

After they have all worked through at least the first problem, and perhaps the second, bring them together and ask them what happens to the distinction between the x_i^* as the number of intervals goes to infinity. Then discuss how we could get a more accurate estimate if we remove the restriction that the subintervals have to have equal width. Close by mentioning that soon they will be learning a way to find the exact answer to certain types of area problems.

Answers (will vary slightly):

	Red	Green	Blue	Purple
Two-interval approximation:	12.75	29.25	25.5	Answers will vary
Three-interval approximation:	17	28	25	Answers will vary
Six-interval approximation:	21	26.25	24.75	Answers will vary

	Red	Green	Blue	Purple
Two-interval approximation:	−0.15	−1.5	−0.9	Answers will vary
Three-interval approximation	0.5	−0.4	0.3	Answers will vary
Six-interval approximation	0.4	−0.05	−0.15	Answers will vary

Make sure to point out that when the function is not monotonic, the approximations still converge, but they may do so more erratically, getting first larger, then smaller.

▼ Homework Problems

Core Exercises: 1, 3, 6, 9, 14, 15, 18, 22

Sample Assignment: 1, 2, 3, 4, 6, 7, 9, 14, 15, 16, 18, 20, 22

GROUP WORK 1, SECTION 13.5

Position From Samples

This is an experiment to see if the techniques that we learn in our calculus classes actually work. We are going to try to test the notion that the area under a velocity curve gives the total distance traveled.

Conveniently, automobiles are equipped with instruments for measuring both velocity and position information. Recording mileage from the odometer gives position data, while the speedometer shows instantaneous velocity.

The idea of this experiment is to estimate change in position by working with some velocity data. Since we can use the odometer to determine the true distance traveled, we can determine the validity of our approximations.

Collecting Your Own Data

In groups of three or four people, arrange a time to go driving. Before you go, lay out a course. The choice of course is up to you, but it should be fixed before you begin to record data. If possible, you should traverse the course once before recording data, in case of unforeseen problems.

Each group must have a designated driver. *This person does nothing but drive.* The driver is in complete control of the experiment, and must abort it at any time traffic safety requires a change of plan.

One person in the car is responsible for calling out speedometer readings at intervals agreed upon by the group in advance. This person also is responsible for recording the odometer reading at the **start** and **finish** of the course.

The remaining person(s) in the car will record the time and velocity data according to the chosen method. Some suggestions:

1. Collect data once a minute.
2. Collect the first sample at 30 seconds, the second after an additional 90, the third after an additional 30, the fourth after an additional 90, etc.
3. Collect data every time you pass through an intersection or beneath a traffic light.
4. Collect data at every stop sign.
5. Collect data every time someone is annoyed by what they hear on the radio
6. Collect data at random times.

Your data collection methods and course layout should generate about 15–25 data points. Collect data using two methods. Traverse the course as many times as necessary to do this.

The following page is a sample form you may want to use. Be sure to make extra copies, since you will be using more than one data collection method. Summarize your findings in one or two paragraphs.

Acknowledgment: This workshop was developed at the NSF Geometry Center, University of Minnesota.

Velocity Data

Initial odometer reading:	

Sample	Time	Speed
1		
2		
3		
4		
5		
6		
7		
8		
9		
10		
11		
12		
13		
14		
15		
16		
17		
18		
19		
20		
21		
22		
23		
24		
25		
26		
27		
28		
29		
30		

Final odometer reading:	

Your group is going to attempt to approximate the area of the region below.

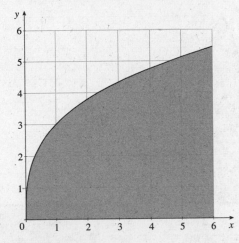

As you have seen, a good way to accomplish this task is to divide the interval up into equal segments, and approximate the area under the curve by vertical rectangles. We pick a point in each interval, x_i^*, and let the height of each interval be $f(x_i^*)$. Everyone in your group should have an assigned color (Red, Green, Blue, or Purple). Choose your x_i^* according to your color:

RED: You've landed a lucky load, because when you choose your x_i^*, you will, whatever the interval, have the labor-saving luxury of always looking to the point on the left of the interval. Approximate the area, using first two subintervals, then three subintervals, and finally six.

GREEN: Get ready for some really righteous rectangular rendering. When you choose your x_i^*, you are required to restrict yourself to the rightmost point on the interval. Approximate the area, first using two subintervals, then three subintervals, and finally six.

BLUE: Make merry, for your modeling method is magnificent. When you make your choice of x_i^*, you must always, whatever the interval, measure to the midpoint of that interval. Approximate the area, first using two subintervals, then three subintervals, and finally six.

PURPLE: Fun is forecast for your future, for you've found the most fanciful of the four colors. When you find your x_i^*, you are free to focus on your favorite point in the interval, any one you fancy. Approximate the area, first using two subintervals, then three subintervals, and finally six.

	Red	Green	Blue	Purple
Two-interval approximation:				
Three-interval approximation:				
Six-interval approximation:				

Now try to approximate the area of the region below using the same method. When you are done using your method, try to pick x_i^* to make your answer as big as possible, or as small as possible.

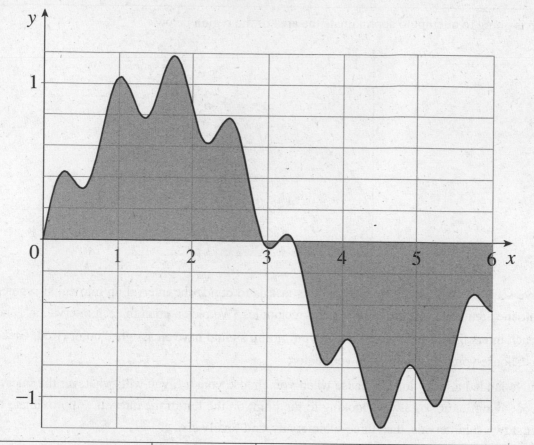

	Red	Green	Blue	Purple
Two-interval approximation:				
Three-interval approximation:				
Six-interval approximation:				